Internal Fire

"Every one knows that heat can produce motion. That it possesses vast motive-power no one can doubt, in these days when the steam-engine is everywhere so well known.

"To heat also are due the vast movements which take place on the earth. It causes the agitations of the atmosphere, the ascension of clouds, the fall of rain and of meteors, the currents of water which channel the surface of the globe, and of which man has thus far employed but a small portion. Even earthquakes and volcanic eruptions are the result of heat.

"From this immense reservoir we may draw the moving force necessary for our purposes. Nature, in providing us with combustibles on all sides, has given us the power to produce, at all times and in all places, heat and the impelling power which is the result of it. To develop this power, to appropriate it to our uses, is the object of heat engines.

"The study of these engines is of the greatest interest, their importance is enormous, their use is continually increasing, and they seem destined to produce a great revolution in the civilized world."

Sadi Carnot On Heat Engines – 1824

Internal Fire

C. Lyle Cummins, Jr.

Third Revised Edition

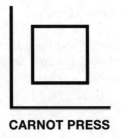

CARNOT PRESS

Wilsonville, Oregon

Library of Congress Cataloging-in-Publication Data

Cummins, C. Lyle, Jr.
  Internal fire.

  Bibliography: p.
  Includes Index
  1. Internal combustion engines – History.
1. Title.
TJ785.C85   2000   621.43'09   00-093588
ISBN 0-917308-05-0

Printed in the United States of America

Printed and Bound by
Paul O. Giesey/Adcrafters and Lincoln and Allen

Dedicated to

the Memory of my Father

CLESSIE LYLE CUMMINS

A later pioneer in the tradition

of those found between the covers of this book.

Acknowledgments

Those whom I acknowledged for their special help with my first edition twenty-five years ago again deserve recognition. This is so because I regard them as the mentors and facilitators who prepared me for a new and rewarding career. Beyond that, many of whom I met through my research have since become treasured friends.

A special few gave me the benefit of their wisdom at the outset. Lamont Eltinge, John L. Hummer and W. James King turned my initial doubts into firm determination about beginning the task that led to this book.

The exciting opportunity to do research in libraries and museum archives at home and abroad was an extra and ongoing dividend. My thanks to Hans-Ulrich Howe and Hans-Jurgen Reuss, at then Klöckner-Humboldt-Deutz AG, and Heinrich Lippenberger of Daimler-Benz AG, now retired. Irmgard Denkinger and Eduard Klein at the MAN AG Archives, both deceased, leave fond memories because of their help on this book and its sequel. Numerous others also extended hospitality and an opportunity to study the treasures under their care. I can not forget those experiences.

Deserving of particular recognition for this third edition is another dear friend who died unexpectedly earlier this year. He unearthed much new information on early engines and always took pains to ensure that his discoveries were passed on to me. Thankfully, before his death Dr.-Ing. Horst O. Hardenberg completed his own book, *The Middle Ages of the Internal-Combustion Engine 1794-1886,* which has great technical depth on pre-Otto engines, He was the motivating force that brought about this new edition of *Internal Fire.*

Lastly, I continue to express my debt of gratitude to an understanding wife. Without Jeanne's unceasing encouragement and enduring confidence in what I attempted with the first edition in 1975, and since, they would have remained unfulfilled dreams.

Lyle Cummins

Wilsonville, Oregon
November 9, 2000

Table of Contents

Preface

There is little that influences our everyday life more than the internal-combustion engine. Yet strangely enough, almost nothing of depth has been written about its early years. The automobile and the airplane are well chronicled, illustrating their changing styles and aerodynamic sleekness, but little is generally available to tell with accuracy the annals of the powerplants in these wonderful and often cursed machines.

The author sincerely hopes that this book will be enjoyed as a readable narrative, for it is more than an explanation of "how it worked." It is the story of creative people whose efforts interacted, often harshly, with economic realities, with available technology and with a limited knowledge of practical fuels. The role played by patents in directing steam and then internal-combustion engine development is not neglected. Finally, there is the engineer's growing understanding of the nature of heat itself and, in time, how this knowledge helped in the evolution of heat engines.

In the intervening years since the first edition of *Internal Fire* was published in 1976 the author has been grateful for the welcomed suggestions from its readers. Their feedback, combined with my own ongoing research, have made it possible to add new material and clarifying comments.

What has been truly rewarding are the many friends made through a sharing of common interests. It is hoped that readers of this third edition will continue to expand my circle of those traveling the same fascinating, historic path.

Wilsonville, Oregon   November 9, 2000

Introduction

The year 2001 marks the 125th birthday of the modern internal-combustion engine. We must say "modern" because virtually all of the basic elements of our present reciprocating four-stroke cycle engine were present in Nicolaus Otto's creation more than a century ago. While much occurred prior to his great accomplishment to make it possible, he set the course of future development in a direction which has seen few deviations.

Never was there a more appropriate time to pause and reflect on the train of events Otto and his struggling predecessors put into motion. Because, for better or worse, the internal-combustion engine changed human life. It freed us from many of the drudgeries enslaving us since the beginning of time. It gave us the personal freedom, regardless of station in life, to visit anywhere at any whim. It created industries which make possible the employment of our bursting population, and the engine provided the means to carry destruction to the entire world. Its insatiable appetite for our finite energy resources, along with its contribution to the degradation of our environment, are also part of its being. Have we created a slave who has become our master? The author is an optimist and thinks not. Recent advances in technology continue to decrease its thirst and pollution and will continue to do so. However, it must soon compete with even newer forms of energy transformers still in laboratories only a few decades ago.

Who were the dreamers and doers in the power parade? How did politics, finance and the law affect the rational and orderly development of an idea? These questions and others combine to form a story having a romance and excitement that too long has been stifled or overshadowed by the exterior trappings hiding the engine from its rightful view.

What is the mystique of such an inanimate assembly of iron, steel and. aluminum parts? Why does an engine man carry on a clandestine romance with his creation? A few suggestions might stimulate the imagination of the uninitiated or bring a recollection to the mind of the already succumbed. Cause this dormant mass to inhale air and energy. Then kindle a fire. Suddenly a silent, cold piece of machinery becomes a living, breathing, powerful being that responds to care and external stimuli just like its human counterpart, also a heat engine. Shut off its air supply and it suffocates. Remove its food and it starves. Abuse it and reduce its life expectancy. To all this throw in the excitement of a surge of power as a throttle is opened, with the pulsating din and the cherry glow of an exhaust manifold telling of the churning inferno within. Consider the oil, water, pressurized fire, air, explosive liquid, and spent gases coursing their way through the labyrinth of passages and chambers, their sole purpose being to convert within milliseconds a charge of energy into a pulse of power. We take so much for granted as we confidently turn a key to start our car, or as we relax in a plane while the ground falls away and we enter the realm of the eagle!

Our story cannot begin (nor end) with Otto. He only marks an important milestone. The vision of a power source independent from nature's forces of animal, wind and water was ages old. But it took an Event or great need, acting as a catalyst, to induce creative currents in the minds of a few determined geniuses.

The event was the Industrial Revolution of 18th century England. This was a powerful stimulant to the development of new technology for the production of new goods and services required more energy. A rapidly increasing population also demanded more fuel for its creature comforts. Water power was first harnessed to run the new textile mills, and even with the great strides made in perfecting quite efficient water-wheels, the available energy which could be extracted from the flat-profile streams of the English countryside soon reached a point of diminishing return. The need for more heating and industrial coal forced the miners to dig ever deeper, but subterranean water poured into these deeper mines faster than horse powered pumps could remove it. Mines were forced to close down. England faced an energy crisis.

England's solution to her problem was the steam engine. Thomas Newcomen's "fire" pumping engine saved the mines, and then later James Watt's improved steam engine powered the mills which water could not serve. The question not immediately considered was at what cost in fuel. Soon this question did become a focal point and of concern. The steam engine of Watt, the gas engine of Otto and the "Rational Heat Engine" of Rudolf Diesel marked the progress in the continuing search for efficiency.

Chapter 1

Gunpowder and Steam

The internal-combustion engine began with the invention of the cannon. As a domesticated machine it did have the serious drawback that it threw away the piston on each power stroke. However, the potential for more peaceful applications of that explosive power released in the cannon's breech was not overlooked. In the late 1600s there were several serious attempts, using gunpowder as a fuel, to raise a piston in a vertical cylinder and then to let gravity and atmospheric pressure return it. Abbe Jean de Hautefeuille (1647-1724) proposed raising water by setting off a gunpowder charge in a chamber, releasing the resultant pressure, and then when the residue air had cooled, the vacuum thus formed would lift a quantity of water; he did not consider using a cylinder-piston mechanism.[1] The power of a vacuum, along with the instruments to measure pressure in an evacuated chamber, had already been explained by the scientists Evangelista Torriceilli (1608-1647), Blaise Pascal (1623-1662) and Otto von Guericke (1602-1686).

A working piston in the cylinder of an engine employing heat was first constructed by Christiaan Huygens (1629-1695). In 1673 he wrote of his experiments with gunpowder, calculating from these experiments that the equivalent of a 3,000 pound weight could be raised at least thirty feet by burning only one pound of gunpowder.[2] A free hand sketch sent to his brother of the proposed machine (Fig. 1-1) shows a piston D in a cylinder AB having ports E,E at the outer end of the cylinder. Attached to the port exits were moist leather hoses F,F. With the piston in its upper position, a gunpowder charge was ignited in capsule C inserted in the bottom of the cylinder, and the expanding gases exited through the hoses until cylinder pressure equaled atmospheric. At this point the flexible valves closed. Then as the cylinder cooled, its pressure dropped below atmospheric so that the greater outside pressure pushed down the piston and lifted weight G. It was a "one shot" operation in that a fresh charge of gunpowder had to be added for each lifting cycle.

1

As late as 1729 there was a proposal for a jet propelled ship using a gunpowder engine. John Allen claimed in his patent:[3]

> For navigating a ship in a calm, my method will be effected by forcing water or some other fluid through the stern or hinder part of a ship at a convenient distance under the surface of the water, into the sea, by proper engines placed within the ship. Amongst the several and peculiar engines I have invented for this purpose is one of a very extraordinary nature, whose operation is owing to the explosion of gunpowder. I have found out a method of firing gunpowder *in clauso,* or in a confined place, whereby I can apply the whole force of it, which is inconceivably great, so as to communicate motion to a great variety of engines;... .

Over sixty years passed before there was any further recorded work on an internal-combustion engine. Our story, therefore, takes a detour down the road of steam or external-combustion progress. A look at the early evolution of steam power, while I-C development lay dormant,

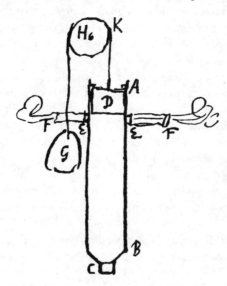

Fig. 1-1.   Huygen's gunpowder engine, 1673. From a freehand sketch to his brother dated Sept. 22, 1673. (Klemm, *A History of Technology,* 1964)

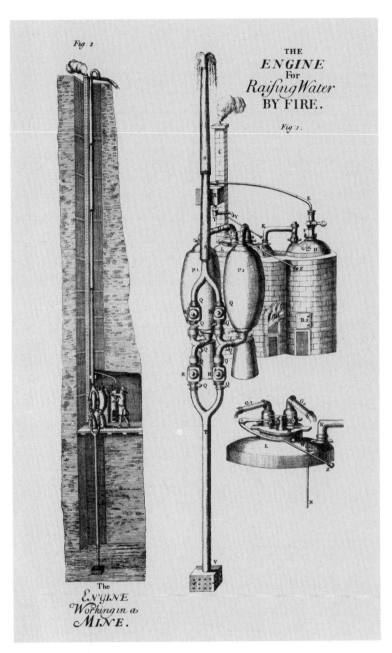

Fig. 1-3   Thomas Savery's "Miner's Friend." (The Science Museum, London)

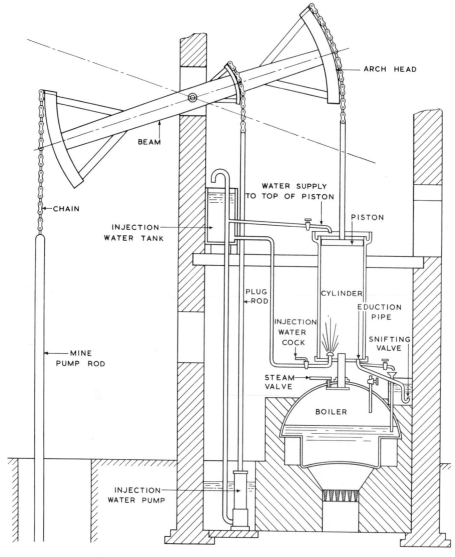

ARCH HEAD

BEAM

WATER SUPPLY
TO TOP OF PISTON

CHAIN

PISTON

INJECTION
WATER TANK

PLUG
ROD

CYLINDER

EDUCTION
PIPE

INJECTION
WATER
COCK

SNIFTING
VALVE

MINE
PUMP ROD

STEAM
VALVE

BOILER

INJECTION
WATER PUMP

Fig. 1-4   Schematic diagram of Newcomen pumping engine (The
          Science Museum, London)

Fig. 1-5   Newcomen mine pumping engine at Dudley Castle, near
Coventry, 1717. (The Science Museum, London)

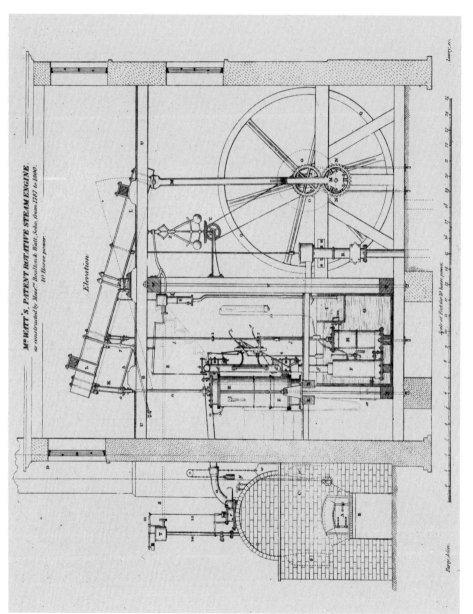

Fig. 1-8   Watt double-acting engine with sun and planet power
transmitting gears, 1787.. (The Science Museum, London)

will help in understanding why the later non-steam pioneers made some of their conclusions and decisions. The 18th century steam era was also a time for the building of technology in metallurgy, machine tools and practical mechanism.

Denis Papin (1647-1712?), Huygens' gifted assistant during the gunpowder tests, soon turned his thoughts to the potential of steam power. Insight as to why is revealed in a letter he wrote in 1695 to a prospective client. A modern translation from a portion of this letter reads:[4]

> As water has the property that it is converted by fire into steam ... and can then be easily condensed again by cold, I thought that it should not be difficult to build engines in which, by means of moderate heat and the use of only a little water, that complete vacuum could be produced which had been sought in vain by the use of gunpowder.

Papin's assumption that he could construct a working steam engine was based on a small model he had tested five years earlier. Here, a piston and rod were fitted in a two and a half inch diameter vertical tube. Steam generated by heating a little water in the closed tube raised the piston to the end of its stroke where it was latched. A vacuum was next formed by cooling the tube. When manually released, the piston was pushed downward by the atmosphere, as in Huygen's gunpowder engine. Unfortunately, the tube had to fulfill the triple function of boiler, power cylinder and condenser. The idea was, therefore, quite impractical, but Papin was the first to capture the power of steam in a cylinder to move a piston. (As early as 1606 Giovanni Battista della Porta (1538-1615) had discussed how, by condensing steam in a closed chamber, a suction could be created for lifting water.)

Other contributions to the introduction of steam power by this exiled French Huguenot were the "digester," a form of pressure cooker or boiler, and a subsequent safety valve. It would be difficult to conjure a better example of invention following necessity than the addition of a pop-off valve to his boiler!

Thomas Savery

The fruit of Papin's work carried over to England, where as a member of the prestigious London Royal Society, a scientific study group chartered by Charles II, his efforts most likely planted a seed of an idea in the mind of a fellow member and inventor. This colleague, Thomas

Savery (1650?-1715), subsequently developed and marketed about 1700 a steam-operated water pump called "The Miner's Friend."

Savery may also have been guided by Edward Somerset, the Marquis of Worcester (1601-1667), who in 1663 vaguely described a steam operated water pump: "An admirable and most forcible way to drive up water by fire, not by drawing or sucking it upwards... ."[5] Specific details are scanty, yet one contemporary of Savery inferred they were enough for him to build on Worcester. Little credence is given to this claim.

Savery's pistonless engine (Fig. 1-2; Fig. 1-3, Plate) drew water into a pipe as a result of a vacuum formed by condensing steam in a chamber separate from a boiler, the lifted volume of water being trapped above a one-way or check valve. (The chamber might be termed a cylinder without a piston.) Steam was then readmitted from the boiler into the chamber, and with pressure now behind the trapped water, forced it

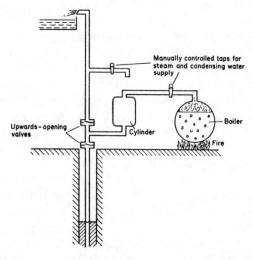

Fig. 1-2. Schematic diagram of Savery engine. (Cardwell, *From Watt to Clausius*, 1971)

upward past a second check valve into a discharge pipe. The condensing water and steam valves were hand-operated. In addition to the basic inefficiency of alternately heating and cooling the pumping cylinder, the height water could be lifted (up to an estimated 150 feet) was directly dependent on available steam pressure. Consequently, to achieve the required lifts, Savery was forced to employ pressures which often exceeded boiler, valve and joint capabilities. Imagine the Dantesque scene in a dark, hot mine shaft with the "Miner's Friend" hissing and leaking steam, the choking smoke from a firebox under the boiler, and a sweating, frightened attendant opening and closing valves. It was possible to operate the pump machinery up to five cycles per minute, but we have no reliable data on performance. Thermal efficiency is estimated to be much less than one-half percent.

Because of lift limitations and major safety problems, the Savery "fire engine" was soon relegated to the pumping of domestic water in a few of England's country houses and gardens. Here a lower steam pressure could be tolerated, and a servant could expect a longer life. Savery's concept had no lasting influence, even though it was a commercial success for a few years.

Savery's thinking was not confined to mines. He stated in his book extolling the virtues of the mine pumping engine: "I believe it may be very useful to Ships, but I dare not meddle with that matter; and leave it to the judgment of those who are the best judges of Maritain Affairs."[6] It is claimed in letters addressed to Leibniz that Denis Papin, in 1707, ran one of Savery's engines in a boat on the Fulda River in Germany. Propulsion is assumed to be by the jet of exiting water from the pump.

Savery also enjoyed the protection of a generous English patent granted to him in 1698. The language of its preamble was not overly modest and likely reflected the thinking of the inventor-entrepreneur. His patent was for a

> ... new invention of Raiseing of Water and occasioning Motion to all Sorts of Mill Work by the Impellent Force of Fire, which will be of great Vse and Advantage for Drayning Mines, Serveing Towns with Water, and for the Working of all Sorts of Mills where they have not the Benefitt of Water nor constant Windes.[7]

Originally issued for the normal period of fourteen years, the patent was extended by Parliament, for vague reasons today, an additional twenty-one years. (It is interesting to speculate as to the advantages of belonging to the London Royal Society at that time.) This patent was to assume far greater importance than just for Savery, as we shall see shortly.

Thomas Newcomen

Heat engine progress to 1700, Savery's work included, bordered on little more than novelty or scientific experimentation. Thomas

Newcomen (1663-1729) changed this, and in turn altered the course of history. His intuitive genius plus years of trial and error determination resulted in the first reliable and safe steam engine. An ironmonger from Devon who made and sold-to-order specialty foundry products, he had little or no exposure to the scientific work of the distant London Royal Society. He worked with the primitive technology available to him, and he did not have to wait for future discoveries to make his machine perform successfully. Newcomen "stayed within his time" even though his invention was visionary.

By 1712 Newcomen and his helper, John Calley, had progressed far enough to build their beam engine[8] for actual mine pumping at Dudley Castle near Coventry (Figs. 1-4 and 1-5, Plates). For safety, only low pressure steam (less than five pounds per square inch) was used to raise a vertically acting piston. When the piston had reached its maximum height the steam was condensed by spraying cold water into the cylinder. The vacuum formed caused atmospheric pressure to push the piston downward on the working stroke. (Fig. 1-6.) The most significant advances were a) not cooling the boiler with each stroke (Papin), and b) letting the atmosphere mechanically pump the water rather than making high pressure steam blow it out (Savery).

Newcomen's engines employed a rocking-beam with chains connected to each end, one to the vertical piston rod and the other to a pumping rod in the mine shaft. By traveling over ends formed as arcs of circles the chains imparted a vertical, linear motion to the piston and pump rods. The weight on the chains kept them taut. Two other major improvements by Newcomen were automatic valves controlled from the rocking beam and a "snifting valve" to blow out air trapped in the system, a Savery problem. Without the latter, air would gradually build up in the cylinder and greatly reduce the steam's effectiveness. A difficult problem for Newcomen to overcome was sealing the clearance between the irregular surfaces of the piston and cylinder. No boring machines were available to produce a round and and straight cylinder casting with any accuracy in the sizes needed. Newcomen's solution was to add a leather sealing flap to the top of the piston and there keep it flooded with water.

An average "speed" for these pumping machines was up to sixteen "draws" of water per minute. It was reported that the early Dudley Castle engine made twelve draws per minute and ten gallons of water were raised over 150 feet on each stroke. This required a little under six horsepower. Cylinder diameters of Newcomen engines ranged from ten inches up to a monster seventy-two inches. Thermal efficiency was not over one-half percent.

It is regrettable that so little is known of the man who truly started the heat-power industry or that his efforts were given so little recognition by his contemporaries. Coming mostly from the learned aristocracy, they generally refused to believe that a mere layman could create such a machine without help from the trained minds of the Natural Philosophers. Historians of the day attributed much of Newcomen's success to the direct help of Savery and Papin, which was not the case. The Newcomen Society, formed in 1920 "for the study of the History of Engineering and Technology," has served to change this lack of deserved recognition. Through their publications, not only Newcomen but many others have received their due and sometimes belated honor.

Newcomen was also deprived of any recognition he might have attained by being granted a patent. Even though his engine was unlike Savery's in concept and construction, the Savery patent was so broad that Newcomen either could not or chose not to test its validity and to file for his own. Thus his far-reaching invention was unprotected. Newcomen's idea was independently conceived about the same time as Savery's, but he delayed in applying for a patent until his experimental effort neared completion. Savery, on the other hand, did not wait, and being nearer to Court (in probably more ways than just proximity), effectively blocked Newcomen. However, Newcomen and Savery got together in 1712 and made a business arrangement which allowed all Newcomen engines to be built under the extended-life Savery patent. When Savery died in 1715 his patent rights were acquired by interests that apparently included Newcomen. To what extent Newcomen profited financially is unknown, although it was presumably minimal.[9] Newcomen died before the basic Savery patent expired in 1733, but he did live to see his engines operating in a number of European countries in addition to those at the mines of England.

James Watt

The brilliant Scotsman, James Watt (1736-1819), transformed the crude and wheezing mine pump into a truly versatile engine. Watt was a practical engineer as well as a dedicated scientist, and his name will always be synonymous with steam power. His contributions were to all phases of engine design, control and instrumentation. He also did much to advance the embryonic state of thermodynamics with his research into the nature of heat.

One of Watt's most famous inventions, his first, was the separate condenser. (Fig. 1-6) By condensing the steam in a chamber other than the engine cylinder, the reheating process for the cylinder on the next cycle was eliminated. The cylinder could now be maintained at a uniform high temperature. This saving in steam doubled Newcomen engine efficiency with almost no other changes. Watt was granted a patent in 1769 on his condenser,[10] and like Savery, had it extended by Parliament until 1800. The reason for the extension in 1775 was that, with almost half of its fourteen year life gone, Watt had yet to see any financial return because of business and developmental problems. The patent was entitled the "Method of Lessening the Consumption of Steam and Fuel in Fire Engines" and had no drawings. Two of the principles outlined in it were:

> First, that vessel in which the powers of steam are to be employed to work the engine, which is called the *Cylinder* in common fire engines, and which I call the *Steam Vessel,* must, during the whole time the engine is at work, be kept as hot as the steam that enters it; first, by enclosing it in a case of wood, or any other materials that transmit heat slowly; secondly, by surrounding it with steam or other heated bodies; and thirdly, by suffering neither water not any other substance colder than steam to enter or touch it during that time.

> Secondly, in Engines that are to be worked wholly or partially by condensation of steam, the steam is to be condensed in vessels distinct from the steam vessels or cylinders, although occasionally communicating with them: these vessels I call *Condensers;* and, whilst the engines are working, these condensers ought at least to be kept as cold as the air in the neighborhood of the engines, by application of water, or other cold bodies.[11]

A real stroke of fortune for Watt was his long association with Matthew Boulton (1728-1809), a prosperous manufacturer at Soho near Birmingham. Boulton and Watt launched their partnership in 1775 when Boulton bought the share of the condenser patent rights owned by a bankrupt partner of Watt. (In addition to financial problems caused by his business failure, Watt also suffered the tragedy of the loss of his first wife in 1773 and over the years five of his six children.) The firm of Boulton & Watt, at Soho, was responsible for all Watt steam engines. Between 1775 and 1800 almost 500 engines were placed in operation by the company.

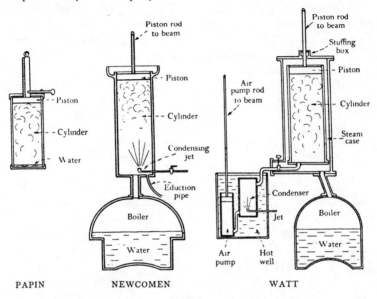

Fig. 1-6.   Papin, Newcomen and Watt operating principles compared. (Dickenson, *A Short History of the Steam Engine,* 1938)

The first double-acting steam engine was also built by Watt. Since there would now be an upward force exerted by the piston, chains linking the beam to the rods were no longer possible. By his "parallel motion linkage" the rod movement of the piston remained vertical while the beam end moved through its circular arc. (Fig. 1-7; Fig. 1-8, Plate.) Following this invention came his epicyclic, or sun and planet, gear mechanism which converted reciprocating into rotary motion. He had first devised the more simple rod and crankshaft approach, but the idea, based on a suggestion from his assistant William Murdock, was stolen and then patented by an ex-employee. Even though the rod and crank method was not new and Watt could have had his competitor's patent invalidated, he chose to avoid a court fight. When the crank patent expired in 1794 Boulton & Watt began to abandon the sun and planet mechanism. Murdock (1754-1839) went to work for Watt in

9

1773 and rose to be works manager. He invented and patented the slide valve and was the first to use an eccentric drive from a crankshaft. Murdock is equally remembered for his pioneering work in the production of coal gas for lighting.

Watt's patent for admitting steam into the cylinder during only the first part of the stroke and then letting it expand over the remainder was also a potential coal saver. This idea was never exploited because Watt refused to use a boiler pressure higher than four to five psi.

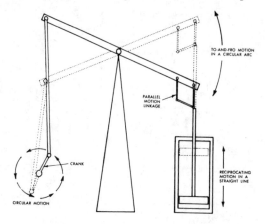

Fig. 1-7. Mechanical motions in a beam engine. (King, *Beam Engines,* 1972)

The Watt engine required a higher degree of precision in machining than did the Newcomen. Another bit of good luck and timing for Watt was the discovery of the talents of John Wilkinson (1728-1808), an ironmaster from Staffordshire. Wilkinson had just made and patented in 1774 a new cannon boring machine which was adaptable to the large cylinder diameters needed by Watt. Wilkinson's first job was to machine a thirty and a fifty inch diameter cylinder, both of which proved to work as advertised. The thirty inch cylinder was installed in Wilkinson's own foundry where it was used in an engine to provide power for blowing air into his furnaces.

Watt is also famous for his more precise definition and standardization of a unit of power than was being used at the time. It became almost a matter of necessity to accurately define the output of an engine because he had to prove, sometimes literally, how many strong horses his engines could replace. The measure he finally decided on for the horsepower unit (33,000 pounds lifted one foot in one minute) was conservative by fifty percent, but he wanted no dissatisfied customers. Boulton and Watt were paid a royalty on each engine sold, the amount being one-third of the fuel saving over what a Newcomen-type engine used, or would use, if one were to be installed instead. Even though Watt adamantly refused to allow a high steam pressure in his engines, the refinements he added raised the thermal efficiency of the steam engine to over four percent by the year 1800. Another contribution by Watt was the use of pressure gauges to give maximum and minimum cylinder pressure as an indicator of performance. John Southern, Watt's assistant, invented in 1796 an instrument to record visually the cylinder pressure throughout the entire expansion-exhaust cycle. He called this an "indicator diagram." Watt also adapted from water wheels to steam engines the flyball governor for speed control.

By the close of the 18th century a new form of power had been given to both the mine and factory. Even though the steam engine was only beginning to make a major impact on industrial life, its limitations and disadvantages were coming into focus. The steam engine was to reign supreme and set the standard for a hundred more years, but the science and technology pouring from it were to provide the seeds of its own demise.

Sir Walter Scott wrote of a meeting in Edinburgh with James Watt after he had passed his eightieth birthday:

> Amidst this company stood Mr. Watt, the man whose genius discovered the means of multiplying our national resources to a degree perhaps even beyond his own stupendous powers of calculation and combination.... This potent commander of the elements — this abridger of time and space — this magician, whose cloudy machinery has produced a change on the world, the effects of which, extraordinary as they are, are perhaps only now beginning to be felt — was not only the most profound man of science, the most successful combiner of powers and calculator of numbers as adapted to practical purposes — was not only one of the most generally well-formed but one of the best and kindest of human beings.[12]

11

NOTES

1. Friedrich Sass, *Geschichte des deutschen Verbrennungsmotoren-baues von 1860 bis 1918,* (Berlin, 1962), p. 3.
2. Friedrich Klemm, *A History of Western Technology,* (Cambridge, 1964), p. 215.
3. From Allen's English patent No. 513 of August 7, 1729.
4. Klemm, *op. cit.,* p. 221.
5. Dionysius Lardner, *The Steam Engine,* (London, 1840), pp. 23-4. See also H. W. Dickinson, *A Short History of the Steam Engine,* Cambridge, 1838), pp. 13-16, 21-22, for comments on Worcester's ideas and on Savery vs. Worcester.
6. Thomas Savery, *The Miner's Friend; or an Engine to Raise Water by Fire,* (London, 1702), p. 32.
7. English patent No. 356 of July 25, 1698. There is no description in the patent. The Royal Society's *Philosophical Trans.,* No. 253, June 1699, p. 228, contains a drawing and a short description.
8. One of the best beam engine collections is located at the Henry Ford Museum, Dearborn, Michigan. The exhibits include a Newcomen engine ca. 1760 erected in its entirety. See: W. J. King, *Beam Engines,* a Museum booklet describing its collection of this engine type.
9. Alan Smith, "Steam and the City: The Committee of Proprietors of the Invention for Raising Water by Fire, 1715-1735", *Trans., The Newcomen Soc.,* vol. 49, 1977-78, pp. 5-20. Smith details the company formed after Savery's death and all that is known of Newcomen's share in it.
10. English patent No. 913 of January 5, 1769.
11. *Ibid.,* p. 2. (Watt's entire patent is quoted in Klemm, *op. cit.,* pp. 256-59.)
12. Sir Walter Scott, *The Monastery,* from the Waverley Novels, (Chicago, n.d.), pp. 35-36.

Chapter 2

Air Engines

The first voice in the wilderness calling for another power than steam was Henry Wood (1715-1795). Wood, who later became the vicar of High Ercall, lived in an area of coal pits, iron foundries and forges using Newcomen engines. His British patent of 1759,[1] did not describe a mechanism or give specific details. He proposed to pump heated air directly from a furnace into a "great cylinder," cool the air, and then as in the Newcomen engine, let the atmosphere do the work on the inward stroke. The great significance of Wood's intuitive thought was not to go through the steam phase when air alone was a capable gaseous medium. His concept did not surface again for over thirty years.

Wood called his invention a means for "...Working a Fire Engine upon a New Principle different to any Method heretofore used, and at less than Half the Expence of Coals any Method now used requires... ." How he arrived at his figure of one-half the fuel cost is an unsolved mystery. The patent, granted by "His most Excellent Majesty King George the Second..., in the thirty-second year of His reign... ." says that Wood's invention

> is to work a fire engine on the principle of hot or rarified
> air, produced by the air passing through fire, or through red
> hot pipes, or through boiling water, or by any other way
> heated or rarified.[2]

The remainder of Wood's disclosure tells of an air pump. This pump would be required after the piston had completed its inward, working stroke, to force hot air into the cylinder for the next expansion stroke. Wood assumed the cylinder pressure containing the residue cooled air remained above atmospheric. He said this was necessary to "drive out the condensed air through what is now called the snifting pipe." The air pump later came to light during an infringement suit brought by

Boulton and Watt against Jonathan Hornblower (1753-1815), one of the bothersome Cornish competitors. They claimed that Hornblower, who had developed and patented in 1781 a rudimentary form of compound engine[3] infringed the Watt 1769 condenser patent. (A compound engine exhausts the steam from a primary or high pressure cylinder into a second cylinder where it is further expanded to a lower pressure before exhausting to the air. Triple and even quadruple expansion engines were successfully built prior to acceptance of the steam turbine.) Hornblower's attorney referred to "Mr. Watt, with all his retinue of Doctors, Professors, Philosophers, Mathematicians and Mechanics"[4] in somewhat derogatory terms and cited the Wood patent because his air pump anticipated by ten years the "Third Principle" claimed in the Watt patent. Watt's great prestige tended to prevail, and the decision ultimately went against Hornblower just a year before the expiration of the Watt patent.

The "hot-air" or "Caloric" concept proposed by Wood became an accomplished fact by the early 1800s. These external-combustion air engines evolved from a flash of then-unappreciated inspiration and bounced along a road involving ingenious mechanism, and unfortunately, thermodynamic ignorance. Their full potential was not attained; nevertheless, thousands of these air engines were produced by 1870. Generally of very low output (one-twelfth hp or less up to two hp), they were safe, fairly reliable, simple to operate, and the better ones consumed less fuel than a comparable steam engine. They did suffer from excessive weight and too often from heat-caused piston cracking and burning. They served to provide a highly visible target for the gas fueled internal-combustion engine to shoot at when it finally came on the scene, and they were soon made obsolete by its rapid progress.

As our area of interest is directed to internal-combustion engine history, we regretfully will only touch on a few highlights in the fascinating story of air engines. Numerous variations and combinations of air engine theory and design resulted in a stable full of hybrid (and mongrel) editions by the close of their era. Our brief glimpse will be confined to the pioneering examples of three basic classifications.[5] Each of these three was the brainchild of a man whose inventive genius was in no way limited to the air engine.

Cayley Engine

Sir George Cayley (1773-1857) was in 1807 the first to build a working model of Wood's earlier air engine proposal.[6] Thirty years later

14

Cayley patented an improved design which was then built by the Caloric Engine Company. These "furnace gas" engines (Type 1, Fig. 2-1) drew a fresh air charge on each cycle into an enclosed, usually pressurized (by an air pump), coal fired furnace chamber. The heated air, mixed with combustion products, then passed through a working cylinder and was exhausted. A serious disadvantage was the scouring of piston and cylinder walls by ashes and cinders from the furnace. Engines of this general type were produced in the United States by the Roper Caloric Engine Company beginning in the early 1860s (Fig. 2-2, Plate),[7] and in England in 1880 by the same company which built Cayley's 1837 engine, but from a design by Buckett. (Fig. 2-3, Plate)

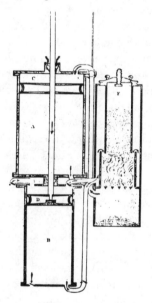

Fig. 2-1.   Cayley's hot-air engine of 1807. (*Nicholson's Philosophical Jour.*, 1807)

Cayley is most remembered for his far reaching and revolutionary work in the field of aerodynamics and not for hot-air engines. The London Science Museum contains a small silver disc inscribed with his initials, the date 1799, and a force diagram showing lift and drag components acting on a bird wing. He referred to these components as "useful resistance" and "resistance proper." Cayley's work with fixed wing theory was a milestone in the history of mechanical flight because he

15

defined the problem as one of having a surface support a weight by applying power to overcome air resistance. He later invented the dihedral or flat vee wing concept for aerodynamic stability.[8] Who is to say what Cayley might have accomplished a century before the Wright brothers if he had had available a lightweight powerplant?

Stirling Engine

The heat regenerator and air engine patented in 1816 by the Reverend Robert Stirling, D.D. (1790-1878) ranks as one of the unique and amazing inventions in the entire heat-power history. His idea becomes all the more remarkable when considering the limited understanding at that time on the nature of heat and its relationship to work. The Stirling engine theory of operation was misunderstood and a source for argument until the late 1800s, and even with our modern thermodynamic tools its explanation is still not simple. A description of the Stirling engine may be likened to a running commentary of the concurrent happenings taking place in a busy three ring circus.

Robert Stirling was ordained to his first parish and was granted his first patent at the age of twenty-six. He is remembered not only as a minister and an inventor, but also as a classical scholar and scientist; before his death he was prominent in the Church of Scotland. Stirling's later air engine effort was in collaboration with his younger brother, James, a respected civil engineer from Edinburgh. Four of his sons became engineers, all making their mark in the engineering world.

An aura of mystery surrounds Stirling's first patent since its contents remained unknown for almost one hundred years. For an unexplained reason the specifications, i.e. the written disclosure, and the drawings did not become an officially completed document. The patent, No. 4,081 of 1816, was, therefore, treated as a lapsed application without a specification and did not appear in the official public list. (Fig. 2-4) The conjecture is that the five pounds "Enrolling" fee to complete the legal requirements for final issuance was more than Stirling could afford in time and money, considering his recent arrival at his first parish. (Official bureaucracy and expensive procedures were major reasons for the British Patent Office reform in 1851.) Sometime during 1917 an original specification in Stirling's own handwriting found its way into the library of the British Patent Office.[9] Because of this omission, textbooks written prior to the finding refer to the second Stirling engine as the first and the third and last as the second. The two later patents of 1827 and 1840 were also listed in this way.

A.D. 1816 . . . . N° 4081.

Steam Engine and Saving Fuel.

LETTERS PATENT to Robert Stirling, of Edinburgh, Clerk, for his
invented " IMPROVEMENTS FOR DIMINISHING THE CONSUMPTION OF FUEL, AND IN
PARTICULAR AN ENGINE CAPABLE OF BEING APPLIED TO THE MOVING MACHINERY ON A
PRINCIPLE ENTIRELY NEW."   6 months.

Dated 16th November 1816.

(No Specification enrolled.)

Fig. 2-4.   Title page of Robert Stirling's first English patent.

Stirling's own words, as quoted from his 1816 patent, give a clear
description of his objectives and theory of operation. The regenerator,
the basis for his patent, was given as applicable to "... diminishing
the consumption of fuel in Glass houses and other furnaces wherever a
high degree of heat is required... [and] ... in Breweries, Distilleries,
Dye Works and other Manufacturers, by transferring heat from one
portion of liquid, air or vapour to another." He says of the regenerator
specifically:

> When the width of the passage cannot be sufficiently
> diminished I encrease its length in order to attain the same
> end. The form and construction of the tubes, passages and
> plates in both the modifications of my general Contrivance
> or Arrangement may be varied according to circumstances;
> but the benefit to be derived from this contrivance arises
> from the fluids and other bodies to be heated and those to
> be cooled being made to move in opposite directions and it
> is for the invention or improvement of this arrangement
> that I have applied for and obtained His Majesty's Letters
> Patent.

Showing a rudimentary knowledge of heat transfer characteristics he goes on to state:

> ... the quantity of fluids which is allowed to run through the respective passages must be inversely proportional to the specific heat of the respective fluids which may be learned from books or from observing the degree to which they are heated or cooled in their passage.

Stirling gives a general theory of his engine which is told with such clarity that there is no room left for doubt as to his thinking:

> I employ the Expansion and Contraction (or either) of atmospheric air or any of the permanent gases by heat and cold to communicate motion to a piston or other similar contrivance. In order to produce this expansion and contraction I cause the air to pass from a cold to a hot part of the engine and the contrary alternately either in the same passage ... or in different passages. ... I apply fire to the warmest part of the engine, in order to supply the waste of heat occasioned by its transmission from the hot to the cold parts by the radiating and conducting power of the materials of which they are formed, by the change of the capacity for heat which the air suffers from condensation and rarefaction, and by the impossibility of transferring the whole of the heat from the air to the passages and the contrary and I apply a stream of cold air or water to the coldest part of the engine to carry off said waste heat. The passages are of course Hot at the one extremity and Cold at the other, and in passing through them the air is alternately heated and cooled or expanded and contracted.

The Stirling regenerative air engines[10] employed a closed cycle with external-combustion. (Type II, Fig. 2-5) Air was contained within a cylinder closed at one end by a rigid plate and at the other by a piston whose small clearance from the cylinder wall was sealed by a ring of oil. (Fig. 2-6) The cylinder diameter was about two feet and the length about ten feet. An engine as described in the patent was built to pump water from an Ayrshire, Scotland, quarry in 1818. It reportedly ran for two years, producing an estimated two hp, but its operation ceased

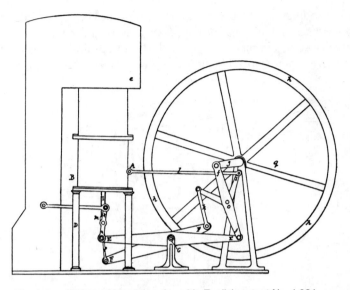

Fig. 2-5.   Stirling 1816 engine, from his English patent No. 4,081
of November 16, 1816.

when the closed end of the cylinder became overheated and either
cracked or was badly distorted. The sealing piston acted as the power
piston and was connected by conventional Watt "straight line mechanism" linkage to a crankshaft. Also in the cylinder above the power
piston was a thin-walled displacer piston. (Stirling called it a plunger.)
It was hollow, closed on both ends and airtight. The walls had a brass
or silver sheathing "to reduce waste heat from radiation," and the inside
was compartmentalized to prevent the air in contact with the hot end
from conducting heat to the cooler end and vice versa (a dubious addition). Stirling wanted as great a temperature extreme between each end
of the displacer as possible. The motion of the displacer was designed to
be out of phase with and lead that of the power piston. A rod passed
through a stuffing box seal in the lower piston and was connected to the
crank throw by linkage similar to what was used for the power piston.
Rollers placed halfway along the length of the displacer guided it in the
cylinder. The regenerator was formed by diagonally wrapping several
layers of fine wire at right angles to each other around the outer, cylindrical surface of the displacer. According to the patent, the clearance
between the cylinder wall and the displacer was slightly less than one-
half inch on a side. This clearance was partially filled by regenerator

wire windings. An air bleed valve located in the cooled portion of the cylinder above top-center of the power piston regulated power output by exhausting and then sucking in a little outside air during operation. The engine was stopped by fully opening the valve.

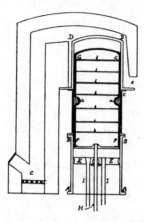

Fig. 2-6. Cross-section view of cylinder, Stirling 1816 engine.
(From the patent drawing)

We can begin the cycle when the power piston is at the bottom of its stroke and the displacer piston is at its top-center. (Position 1, Fig. 2-7) All of the air is now contained in the colder chamber A between the two pistons. The air has been cooled to allow the pressure to drop to near or to slightly below atmospheric.

Flywheel inertia carries the lower piston upward (Position 2), and the air in chamber A is compressed. This forces the cooled air past the regenerator surface of the momentarily stationary displacer. The air warmed by passing through the regenerator enters upper chamber B and has its temperature further raised by heat added from the upper cylinder walls and end which are exposed to the furnace flue. The effectiveness of the regenerator determines the additional heat needed from the external heat source and thus has a direct bearing on the engine's overall thermal efficiency. This vital point was either lost or never fully understood by Stirling's successors.

Further expansion of the hot air in chamber B forces down the displacer; chamber B continues to receive more preheated air forced upward past the regenerator by the still rising power piston. The lower piston and the displacer come together while the lower piston is at its

20

top-center. (Position 3) With all of the air now contained in the hot chamber B, further expansion pushes down both pistons as a unit to their bottom-center position. (Position 4) The displacer is raised by fly-wheel inertia while the lower piston is momentarily at rest. The regenerator, cooled by air passing upward during Positions 1-3, now begins to absorb heat once more as the expanded air in chamber B is forced past when the displacer rises. This action removes heat from the air to the regenerator so that the passing air is cooled by the time it enters chamber A, ready to begin anew the cycle at Position 1.

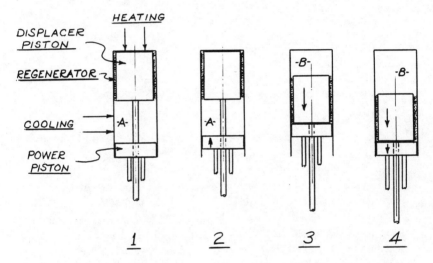

Fig. 2-7. Power and displacer piston operation, Stirling 1816 engine.

Although the regenerator is no longer an integral part of the displacer, the basic cycle of operation described above is very similar to that used in modern Stirling engines.

Robert and James Stirling were granted two patents, No. 5,456 of 1827 and No. 8,652 of 1840, disclosing further air engine improvements. These included a double-acting engine, engines with pistons in separate cylinders, and regenerators in ducts outside of and connecting the cylinders. Some of their improvements did not work out well in practice. In 1843 a double-acting engine was installed in a Dundee foundry; this last engine effort by the Stirling brothers developed forty-five hp at thirty rpm and was in operation for several years.

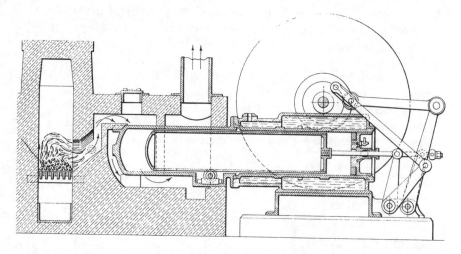

Fig. 2-8.   Lehmann hot-air engine, cross section view. *(The Engineer,* 1959)

Modified Stirling engines designed by Wilhelm Lehmann were pro-
duced in Germany beginning in the 1860s. The Deutsches Museum,
Munich, has a well preserved example built by Maschinenfabrik J.
Arndt, Dessau. The Lehmann engine, closed cycle but without a regen-
erator, was made in England by Sir W. H. Bailey & Co., Ltd.,
Manchester. (Fig. 2-8) A.E. & H. Robinson & Co., and its licensees L.
Gardner & Sons, Ltd. and Pearce & Co., all of Manchester, manufac-
tured a line of small, closed cycle air engines between 1895 and 1920.
(Fig. 2-9) The Lehmann and Robinson as shown had no regenerator,
but later models of the Robinson did.

The only closed cycle air engine to take advantage of a regenerator
was one patented in 1876 and built by Alexander K. Rider of
Philadelphia. (Fig. 2-10, Plate) This design was an outgrowth of his earlier air engine work to improve on the Ericsson engine. Rider positioned the displacer and power pistons in separate, parallel cylinders
which were connected by a regenerator composed of a stack of slightly
separated thin plates. (Fig. 2-11, Plate) These one-fourth to one hp air
and water pumping motors were very reliable. A number were used to
provide the air supply for church organs. Hayward Tyler and Co., Ltd.,
London, the sole English licensee, alone sold almost a thousand of this
design between 1877 and 1895. Several Rider and Hayward Tyler
engines are in the collection of the Henry Ford Museum, Dearborn.

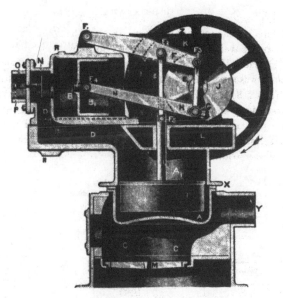

Fig. 2-9. Robinson (Gardner) hot-air engine, coke fired version.
(L. Gardner & Son, Manchester)

Ericsson Engine

John Ericsson (1803-1889), a Swedish engineer and prolific inventor, came to the United States after a thirteen year stopover in England. Most tend to associate Ericsson with his design for the Civil War ironclad, *U.S.S. Monitor,* the ship which changed the concept of naval warfare. While not first invented by him, the screw propeller finally received general acceptance through his many years of effort, beginning in the 1830s. Not the least of his other engineering contributions was his own brand of air engine, an open-cycle, external-combustion type and the third significant category to be covered.

Evidence of Ericsson's interest in air engines begins with an 1826 British patent and continues on through his U.S. Patent No. 226,052 of 1880. In 1857 he was encouraged enough to begin production of a relatively compact engine made by his newly established Massachusetts Caloric Engine Co. By 1860 over 3,000 of these engines had been sold in the U.S. and Europe. The successful design, based on his U.S. Patent No. 22,281 of 1858, had a large horizontal cylinder containing the displacer and power pistons; the hot end was set in a furnace. There was no regenerator as such, but a small regenerative effect was obtained

23

from a long piston skirt on the displacer which slid between furnace walls in the shape of concentric rings, (Figs. 2-12; 2-13 Plate) Since the air charge was used only once, fresh air was introduced into the chamber on the instroke of the displacer via one-way valves in the top of the power piston. Air was exhausted through a similar one-way valve in the cylinder wall at the furnace flue.

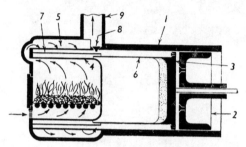

Fig. 2-12.   Ericsson engine of 1858; furnace and piston cross-section view (*The Engineer,* 1959)

Ericsson built to numerous designs of air engines. Although ineffi-cient and noisy as compared with closed-cycle engines (and the newly introduced Otto internal-combustion engine), they were still reliable and simple to operate. Ericsson's successors recognized the potential of Rider's 1876 development and in 1898 joined with him to form the Rider-Ericsson Engine Co. This firm continued to build the Rider engine described above and also further evolutions of the Ericsson line. The last of these was a closed cycle Stirling-type with its genesis in the 1880 Ericsson patent. (Figs. 2-14; 2-15, Plate) Though a good engi-neer, Ericsson unfortunately had little knowledge of thermodynamics and appeared to cling to the outmoded and generally disproved "caloric" theory of heat. This theory, which will be discussed shortly, led a few air engine experimenters to pursue the trail of perpetual motion machines.

Ericsson was an able promoter who had the ability to bounce back from engineering disaster. After a few promising experiments with smaller engines of similar variety, he fell into the trap of scaling up beyond what available technology would allow. (Fig. 2-16, Plate) Obtaining financial backing from business associates, he constructed a 2,200 ton ship, the *U.S.S. Ericsson.* The ship had four "caloric" engines, each with a cylinder fourteen feet in diameter and with a pis-ton stroke of six feet. Using four regenerator assemblies containing a total network of wire almost fifty miles long, the engine was designed to produce 600 hp. (Ericsson's early efforts, including his 1855 patent, made use of regenerators. In 1833, while still in England, he unsuccessfully fought to have Stirling's 1826 patent declared invalid. Ericsson was probably unaware of the 1816 Stirling patent.[11]) Because of the very high mechanical losses and air losses past loose piston fits, the estimated actual output was only 300 hp at nine rpm. On the ship's maiden voyage from New York to Washington, D.C. in February 1853 paddle wheels thirty-two feet in diameter drove it through the water at eight knots. Fuel consumption was about double that predicted but was still less than that of a comparable power steam engine. Improvements, including forced draft blowers, were added, but before any conclusive tests could be made with the new modifications, the ship sank in a sudden squall just outside of New York harbor. (Engine room ports had been left open when the storm hit, and the ship took on too much water.) The Ericsson was later refloated and the engines replaced by steam.[12] The air engine became almost extinct by the early 1900s, and the story about these intriguing "dinosaurs" would normally end there.[13] However, the possibilities created by recent advances in metallurgy and heat transfer technology have revitalized one of the old air engine concepts. The quiet, low emission Stirling engine may yet provide a viable long range alternative in the energy vs. environment dilemma and once again may prove to be a worthy competitor to the internal-combustion engine in the twenty-first century. The final chapter is yet to be written.

NOTES
1. English patent No. 739 of May 25, 1759.
2. Wood's patent No. 739, p. 1.
3. English patent No. 1,298 of 1781.
4. Anon., "Invention of the Hot-Air Engine and the Engine Driven Air Pump," *The Engineer,* August 13, 1948, pp. 168-69.
5. Prof. Adolf Slaby, "Beiträge zur Theorle der Geschlossenen, Luftmaschinen," *Verh. Ver. Gew. Fleiess., Berlin,* (Berlin, 1878). Slaby's contributions to theory and his tests of the "early" engines were numerous.
6. *Nicholson's Journal,* November 1807, pp. 260-62.
7. The Henry Ford Museum, Dearborn, Michigan, has a representative collection of hot-air engines, including the Roper.

8. See: M.J.B. Davy, *Interpretive History of Flight*, Science Museum, (London, 1937), for a comprehensive story on Cayley.

9. Anon., "The Centenary of the Heat Regenerator and the Stirling Air Engine," *The Engineer*, December 14, 1917.

10. The reader interested in the thermodynamic analysis of the Stirling or "regenerative" cycle is referred to Edward F. Obert, *Internal Combustion Engines*, 3rd ed., (Scranton, 1968), pp. 175-77.

11. William C. Church, *The Life of John Ericsson*, (New York, 1911), v. 1, p. 72.

12. *Ibid.*, pp. 189-98, for more on the *SS Ericsson*.

13. A short, comprehensive history of hot-air engines, including more recent developments, was written by T. Finkelstein in a series in *The Engineer*, 1959, pp. 492-97, 522-27, 568-71 and 720-73. He includes a lengthy bibliography. Finkelstein is an engineer with an historical sense for his product.

Chapter 3

Thermodynamics:
Carnot Charts a Course

Steam power was like the heady taste of new wine to the early nineteenth century world. Its possibilities seemed limitless. The Stephenson locomotives, engineering masterpieces in themselves, thrilled the railroad passenger as well as the stockholder. The *S.S. Savannah* and *S.S. Cleremont* offered mariners for the first time the potential freedom from the vagaries of wind and current. Even the limited successes of hot-air engines fired the imagination of a power craving people. Yet, remarkably, all of these accomplishments were achieved without understanding that heat was a form of energy and that work was its mechanical equivalent. ("Work," as an engineering term, may be defined as the product of a Force times a Distance.) The steam and hot-air technologists did not wait for help from this yet to be born science of heat energy, so vital to the coming internal-combustion engine. But a separate group, drawing from the practical knowledge offered by steam, conceived fundamental and revolutionary ideas that were to have ramifications far beyond the heat engine. Let us briefly look at these mental giants involved in creating the new science Thermodynamics and the cornerstones they so solidly placed.

Joseph Black, M.D. (1728-1799) was a professor of medicine, a chemist and a respected teacher at the University of Glasgow when James Watt worked there as an instrument maker. About 1760 Black's meticulous experimentation with heated bodies resulted in the discoveries (never published by him) of what we call specific heat or heat capacity. He also discovered and explained the phenomenon of latent heat, both of vaporization (boiling) and fusion (freezing). He and his scientific contemporaries made lasting contributions toward an understanding of the effects of heat, but still fully embraced the prevailing theory of the nature of heat. (Watt independently discovered the effect of the latent heat of vaporization during his early work with steam engines and went to Black for an explanation. However, legend has it that first Black explained this phenomenon to Watt, who thereupon realizing the reason for the great waste of steam in the Newcomen engine, proceeded to invent the condenser.)[1]

The caloric, or material, theory of heat said that heat (caloric) is a material substance, an elastic fluid, whose particles strongly repel one another. The fluid is one of those imponderable substances like electricity, magnetism and light which is not subject to gravitational attraction. Caloric has little or no weight (there was doubt as to which) and is squeezed out by friction or flows out of a body by the application of fire to produce the sensation of warmth. Caloric particles are attracted to ordinary matter, the attraction depending on the kind of matter, and flows into atomic or molecular voids within the host substance.

According to the theory, "caloric" or heat could be neither created nor destroyed. A major implication of this theory for the heat engine (steam or otherwise) was that no foundation existed for an energy bridge to span the chasm between heat and work. It is difficult from our perspective to realize that such a belief could exist so late in scientific thinking. (The 1856 edition of the *Encyclopedia Britannica* still gave credence to the caloric over the energy theory.) Yet this idea was useful in its day because it allowed a non-contradictory explanation of the known thermal phenomena — something extremely difficult to explain by the still undeveloped "particle motion" concept first considered by Francis Bacon in 1620. Even though we have refuted the old caloric notion, do we not continue to talk of heat "flowing" from one body to another or of a body "soaking up" heat?

The first major attack on the caloric theory came from an American, Benjamin Thompson, alias Count Rumford (1753-1814), whose life was filled with an almost unbelievable series of events.[2] At the age of twenty, after an advantageous marriage to a wealthy widow, he was commissioned a major in the New Hampshire Militia. He was a Tory spy during the Revolutionary War, a Lt. Colonel in the British Army, a Bavarian Count who saved Munich from being a battleground for the French and Austrians, a prolific inventor (fireplaces, lamps, the drip coffeepot, etc.) and an experimenter of note. A supreme egotist, he raised money to found the Royal Institution of Great Britain, primarily as a museum to show off his inventions and deeds. He ended his days in Paris after marrying in 1805 (but not for long) the widow of Lavoisier, the French "father of chemistry" and one of the strongest advocates of the caloric theory.

Rumford's famous cannon boring experiment in 1798, when he was superintendent of the Munich arsenal, convinced him that heat was not a substance. He showed that no matter how long a dulled boring tool was worked against the sides of a cannon bore the cannon would keep producing heat, even though hot metal chips were also removed from their parent body. The caloric proponents said, somewhat justifiably, that he did not turn the cannon long enough to remove all the caloric. Rumford stopped short of concluding that his generated heat was equivalent in some quantitative way to mechanical work, although he indicated the "heat evolved was directly proportional to the time during which the horse [turning the cannon] acted."[3] As D.S.L. Cardwell wrote, Rumford was "the false dawn of the kinetic theory."[4]

Humphry Davy (1778-1829), whose friction experiments with ice were published a year after Rumford's cannon boring work, cast a further doubt on the validity of the caloric theory. Davy, only nineteen at the time, supposedly generated heat by rubbing together two pieces of ice. His reasoning brought him to the conclusion that "Heat... is to be regarded as a peculiar motion, probably a vibration of the particles ... ."[5] Davy later acknowledged that the test procedure used was scientifically unsound, but we cannot fault his intuitive logic.

British ingenuity produced the steam engine, but it was a son of France who provided the true measure of its limitations, and more importantly, the rationale to develop a new, more efficient power source. Nicholas Leonard Sadi Carnot (1796-1832) was a unique happening. He was a genius who had wisdom without age, and insight without experience. His life was tragically brief, but in only one short published treatise he gave form and substance to a new science. If we could rate earthly minds in astronomical terms, Carnot's must be that of a "super-nova."

Sadi Carnot was not born into obscure surroundings; his father, Lazare, was then one of the five Directors of France. Lazare Carnot was a military engineer, poet, and respected mathematician. He organized the twelve armies which repelled the foreign invasion after the Revolution, appointing Napoleon to head one of the armies and his first independent command. From then on, Carnot's life was intimately involved with that of Napoleon, including acting as Minister of War when Napoleon was First Consul.

The unique environment provided by his father could not help but act as a powerful catalyst to Sadi's inquiring mind. Until he entered the École Polytechnique at sixteen his father had directed his education.

The years from 1812 to 1815 were a private and public turmoil; Sadi, a student as well as a junior engineer officer, saw some military action during Napoleon's closing days. In and out of the army as a result of changing political climates, he ultimately resigned his commission and retired from the army in 1828. His most productive years began in 1820 when he devoted himself to intensive study, primarily in physics and economics. During this period he had occasion to visit numerous factories both in and out of France to observe their operation and organization. Sadi's exposure to the steam engine on these study tours gave him an accurate knowledge of how it worked and aroused his curiosity about its potential efficiency.

In 1824 Sadi Carnot published his solitary work, *Reflections on the Motive Power of Fire and on Machines Fitted to Develop that Power.*[6] It was written in lucid and almost layman-like language. Sadi used his lawyer brother, Hippolyte, as his literary critic to ensure that his theories were clearly presented. (Hippolyte Carnot played an important part in drafting the constitution of 1875, and his son, Sadi, named after his uncle, became the third president of the Third Republic in 1887.)[7] The paper received one good review, sold a few copies, and then dropped into obscurity. Fortunately, Carnot's ideas were kept alive through the writings of a contemporary, Emile Clapeyron (1799-1864).[8]

At the age of thirty-six Carnot contracted a severe case of scarlet fever. While convalescing at his country home a cholera epidemic struck that area, and because of his weakened condition the onslaught of the new disease caused his death within a few hours.

Just what were the contributions of Sadi Carnot, a man whose total professional work is contained within a small book and a few notes? Cardwell, an authority on the history of thermodynamics, made the comment:

> Perhaps one of the truest indicators of Carnot's greatness is the unerring skill with which he abstracted, from the highly complicated mechanical contrivance that was the steam engine (even as early as 1824), the essentials, and the essentials alone, of the argument. Nothing unnecessary is included and nothing essential is missed out. It is, in fact, very difficult to think of a more efficient piece of abstraction in the history of science since Galileo taught men the basis of the procedures.[9]

Carnot invented a method by which all heat-engines, as well as refrigerating machines, can be investigated for their efficiency and power. This was the "closed cycle" analysis whereby the working fluid returns to its initial state after proceeding through intermediate states. He also defined a "reversible" and an "irreversible" cycle and demonstrated the impossibility of a reversible cycle. Professor Keenan in a modern definition says, "A process is called reversible if the system and all elements of its environment can be completely restored to their respective initial states after the process has occurred."[10]

As his father before him had disproved the possibility of perpetual motion in machines,[11] thus Sadi did the same for heat engines. Using a hydraulic analogy, he explained:

> In accordance with the principles we have now established, we can reasonably compare the motive power of heat with that of a head of water: for both of them there is a maximum which cannot be exceeded, whatever the type of hydraulic machine and whatever the type of heat-engine employed.[12]

He said that the maximum efficiency of a heat-engine is based on the temperature difference between the beginning and end of an expansion (power) stroke in an engine.

> The motive power of heat is independent of the agents employed to realize it; its quantity is fixed solely by the temperatures of the bodies between which is effected, finally the transfer of the caloric.[13]

As corollaries to the importance of the temperature difference, he analyzed the reasons for the basic inefficiency of a steam engine:

> ... The employment of very strong vessels to contain the gas at a very high temperature and under very heavy pressure [and] ... the use of vessels of large dimensions ... are, in a word, the principal obstacles which prevent the utilization in steam-engines of a great part of the motive power of heat. We are obliged to limit ourselves to the use of a slight fall of caloric, while the combustion of the coal furnishes the means of procuring a very great one.[14]

Thus we can only take advantage of the small steam temperature drop during the expansion stroke and not the drop from the combustion temperature heating the water in the boiler. With this in mind, he suggested using air as the gaseous medium:

> The use of atmospheric air for the development of the motive power of heat presents in practice very great, but perhaps not insurmountable, difficulties. If we should succeed in overcoming them, it would doubtless offer a notable advantage over vapor of water. As to other gases, they should be absolutely rejected. They have all the inconveniences of atmospheric air, with none of the advantages.[15]

The need for compressing the air to be burned prior to actual combustion of the air was also indicated:

> In order to give air great increase of volume, and by that expansion to produce a great change of temperature, it must first be taken under a sufficiently high pressure; then it must be compressed with a pump or by some other means before heating it. This operation would require a special apparatus, an apparatus not found in steam engines. [It] ... requires but a small pump.[16]

It appears that Carnot did not consider compressing the air in the same cylinder where combustion and expansion take place. This was to be the great invention fifty years later by Nicolaus Otto. (See Chapter 9)

Carnot's teachings were to have a strong influence on Rudolf Diesel, whose engine was based on an expansion cycle advocated by Carnot:

> We can easily conceive a multitude of machines fitted to develop the motive power of heat through the use of elastic fluids; but in what ever way we look at it, we should not lose sight of the following principles:
>
> (1) The temperature of the fluid should be as high as possible, in order to obtain a great fall of caloric, and consequently a large production of motive power.

32

(2) For the same reason the cooling should be carried as far as possible.

(3) It should be so arranged that the passage of the elastic fluid from the highest to the lowest temperature should be due to increase of volume; that is, it should be so arranged that the cooling of the gas should occur spontaneously as the effect of rarefaction.[17]

This was the original "diesel cycle" with its maximum temperature differential and its attempt to achieve "adiabatic" expansion, i.e., no heat loss to the cylinder walls during the power stroke.

Carnot's treatise still talked of heat in terms of the caloric theory as we have just seen. Although he may have had his doubts regarding the soundness of this theory while writing *Réflexions*, he did not so indicate. However, his later unpublished notes show its repudiation: "When a hypothesis no longer suffices to explain phenomena, it should be abandoned. This is the case with the hypothesis which regards caloric a matter, as a subtle fluid."[18]

Finally, Carnot stated for the first time in reasoned manner the all important energy relationship of heat to work and what later came to be known as the "First Law of Thermodynamics:"

> Heat is simply motive power, or rather motion which has changed its form. It is a movement among the particles of bodies. Wherever there is destruction of motive power, there is at the same time production of heat in quantity exactly proportional to the quantity of motive power destroyed. Reciprocally, whenever there is destruction of heat, there is production of motive power.

> We can establish the general proposition that motive power is, in quantity, invariable in nature; that it is, correctly speaking, never either produced or destroyed. It is true that it changes its form — that is, it produces sometimes one sort of motion, sometimes another — but it is never annihilated.[19]

A common restatement of the First Law is: energy can be neither created nor destroyed, but only converted from one form to another.

With a message of advice and caution to future generations of engineers, Carnot concluded his great essay:

> We should not expect ever to realize in practice all the motive power of combustibles. The attempts made to attain this result would be far more hurtful than useful if they caused other important considerations to be neglected. The economy of the combustible is only one of the conditions to be fulfilled in heat-engines. In many cases it is only secondary. It should often give precedence to safety, to strength, to the durability of the engine, to the small space which it must occupy, to the small cost of installation, etc. To know how to appreciate in each case, at their true value, the considerations of convenience and economy which may present themselves; to know how to discern the more important of those which are only secondary, in order to attain the best results by the simplest means: such should be the leading characteristics of the man called to direct, to coordinate the labors of his fellow men, to make them cooperate towards a useful end, whatsoever it may be.[20]

The revealing observation of Cardwell sums up the impact of Sadi Carnot:

> Everything that has happened since 1824 has confirmed Carnot's judgment, and we must therefore divide the history of the heat-engine into two very distinct periods: *before Carnot and after Carnot.*[21]

Julius Robert Mayer (1814-1878) and James Prescott Joule (1818-1889) were, unknowingly to each other, to expand on the heat-work relationship theory proposed in Carnot's notes. Mayer from Heilbronn in 1842 and Joule from Manchester in 1843 independently published their initial papers on the "First Law."[22] By 1850 Joule's famous paddle-wheel experiments on the conversion of work to "heat" had produced a number (772) which was within one percent of the accepted equivalence value today of 778.2 ft. lb. per Btu.* Mayer, a medical doctor whose more physiologically oriented writings slightly preceded Joule,

*A Btu (British thermal unit) being the heat required to raise one pound of water one degree Fahrenheit.

34

A WEEKLY JOURNAL OF PRACTICAL INFORMATION IN ART, SCIENCE, MECHANICS, CHEMISTRY AND MANUFACTURES

VOL. VIII.—NO. 7.
(NEW SERIES.)

NEW YORK, FEBRUARY 14, 1863.

SINGLE COPIES SIX CENTS.
$3 PER ANNUM—IN ADVANCE

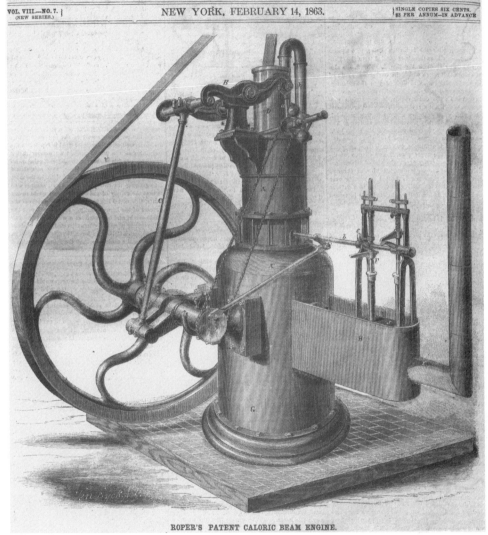

ROPER'S PATENT CALORIC BEAM ENGINE.

Fig. 2 2   Roper hot-air engine of 1863. (*Scientific American,* 1863)

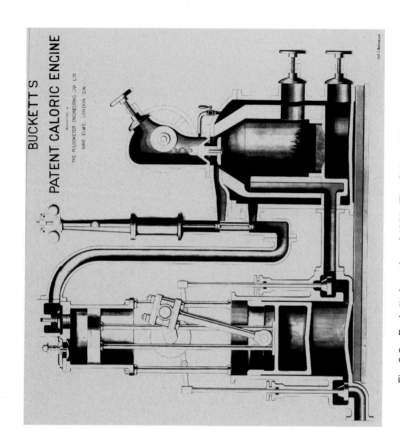

Fig. 2-3   Buckett air engine of 1880. (The Science Museum, London)

Fig. 2-10   Rider hot-air pumping engine with regenerator, ca. 1900. (Collection of Greenfield Village and the Henry Ford Museum, Dearborn, Mich.)

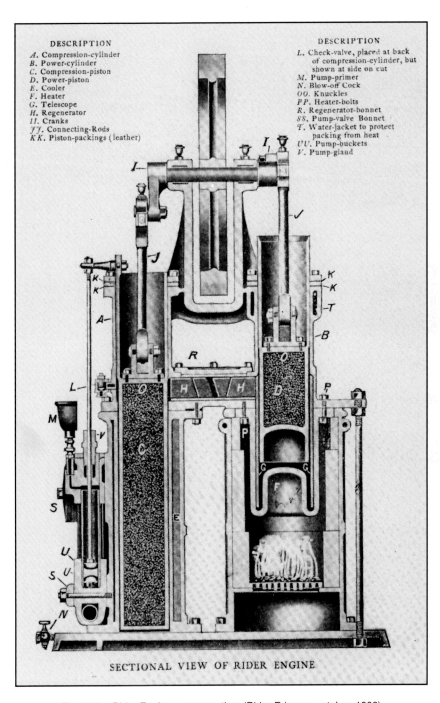

DESCRIPTION

A. Compression-cylinder
B. Power-cylinder
C. Compression-piston
D. Power-piston
E. Cooler
F. Heater
G. Telescope
H. Regenerator
II. Cranks
JJ. Connecting-Rods
KK. Piston-packings (leather)

DESCRIPTION

L. Check-valve, placed at back
   of compression-cylinder, but
   shown at side on cut
M. Pump-primer
N. Blow-off Cock
OO. Knuckles
PP. Heater-bolts
R. Regenerator-bonnet
SS. Pump-valve Bonnet
T. Water-jacket to protect
   packing from heat
UU. Pump-buckets
V. Pump-gland

SECTIONAL VIEW OF RIDER ENGINE

Fig. 2-11   Rider Engine, cross-section. (Rider-Ericsson catalog, 1906)

Fig. 2-13   Ericsson 1858 engine in the Deutsches Museum, Munich. (Author photos)

FOR successful operation the RIDER and the ERICSSON engines require but a live brisk fire in the furnace. Any one able to make a fire can operate them satisfactorily; there are no magnetos, spark plugs, ignition systems, connections, gauges, valves or anything of the kind to take care of. Light the fire and keep it up, THAT IS ALL.

The operation is very simple. A cylinder contains the air which, when heated, expands and acts on a piston; the hot air is then cooled by the water that is being pumped, and the cycle is repeated.

This is a single acting engine of very LOW SPEED, little lubrication is required and the wear is negligible. This is the main reason, besides its rugged construction, why the average life of the RIDER and the ERICSSON engines is over 30 years, and why replacement parts are so seldom needed.

* * *

THE speeds at which RIDER and ERICSSON Engines operate are as follows:

Engine	Revolutions per Minute
Ericsson 5	110-130
Ericsson 6	110-130
Ericsson 8	100-120
Ericsson 10	100-120
Rider 6	100-120
Rider 8	100-120
Rider 10	80-110

* * *

THESE engines have operated successfully in all climates and under all conditions. As with other engines, altitude above sea level affects the efficiency of this pump in the ratio of 5% less for every 1,500 feet above sea level.

Fig. 1   Fig. 2

Ericsson Type
Deep Well Pumper Installation.
For Depths of Over 21 Feet Up To 135 Feet.
FIGURE ONE
View of the Installation.
FIGURE TWO
Detail of Engine and Deep Well Cylinder.

Fig. 2-14   Ericsson pumping engine, ca. 1900. (The Smithsonian Institution)

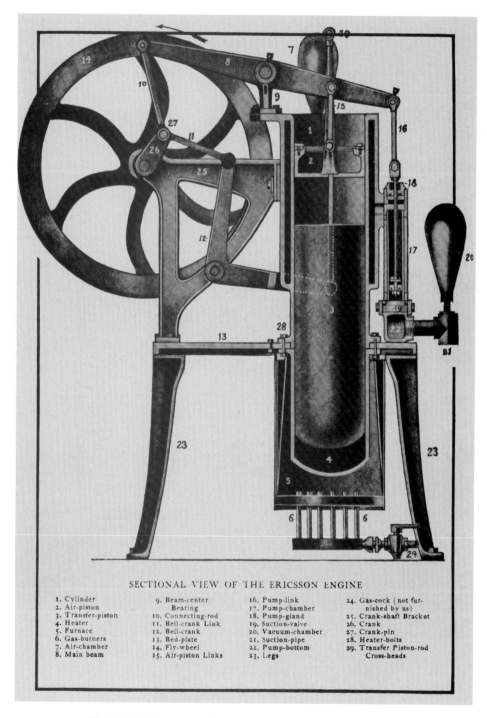

SECTIONAL VIEW OF THE ERICSSON ENGINE

1. Cylinder	9. Beam-center Bearing	16. Pump-link	24. Gas-cock (not furnished by us)
2. Air-piston	10. Connecting-rod	17. Pump-chamber	25. Crank-shaft Bracket
3. Transfer-piston	11. Bell-crank Link	18. Pump-gland	26. Crank
4. Heater	12. Bell-crank	19. Suction-valve	27. Crank-pin
5. Furnace	13. Bed-plate	20. Vacuum-chamber	28. Heater-bolts
6. Gas-burners	14. Fly-wheel	21. Suction-pipe	29. Transfer Piston-rod
7. Air-chamber	15. Air-piston Links	22. Pump-bottom	Cross-heads
8. Main beam		23. Legs	

Fig. 2-15   Ericsson pumping engine, cross-section view. (Rider-Ericsson catalog, 1906)

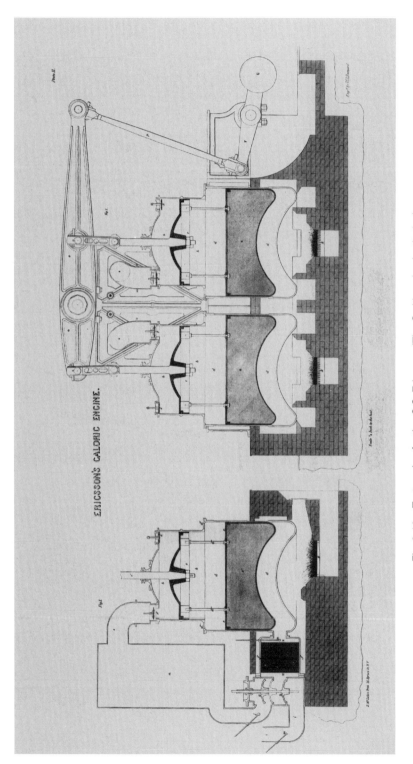

Fig. 2-16   Test engine for the *S.S. Ericsson*. (The Smithsonian Institution)

Fig. 5-5   Model of Rivaz 1805 engine-powered wagon. (Swiss
Museum of Transport and Communication, Lucerne)

struggled alone for years in the battle for acceptance of the theory and ultimately suffered a nervous breakdown because of the frustration. Joule was more fortunate. He gained the endorsement of Rudolf J.E. Clausius (1822-1888), the great German physicist who, in the 1850s, helped complete the foundations of classical thermodynamics with an expression of the "Second Law" and his invention of the concept of entropy.

While a discussion of entropy is beyond the scope of this book, we can say that it is another expression of thermodynamic irreversibility. Joule's own countryman, William Thomson, later Lord Kelvin (1824-1907), quested along a path similar to Clausius. Joule's writings caught Kelvin's attention, and the two men soon became friends. Kelvin ultimately put his influential blessing on Joule's theory which, along with that of Clausius, officially buried the caloric theory. With the general acceptance of a "dynamical" theory of heat, it no longer was heresy to say that heat could be created and destroyed.

The First Law — the Law of Conservation of Energy — left a thermodynamic loophole which needed to be closed. Professor Bent aptly explains the situation:

> It has been suggested that mechanical energy might be delivered more economically by drawing upon the thermal energy of the surroundings (that is the energy it has in excess of what it would have at absolute zero). Why not operate an oceangoing vessel, for example, off the virtually inexhaustible supply of thermal energy in the oceans? Pump aboard warm water, extract energy from it to operate the ship's mechanical machinery, and when finished eject the cold water, or icebergs overboard. There being no violation of the First Law, who, except the Coast Guard, could possibly object? As it turns out, this is rather like asking a cold man to warm himself on the energy of an icicle. Nothing in the First Law prohibits the transaction *icicle colder-man warmer;* nonetheless, it is well known that energy transfers of this kind never occur. Similarly, processes whose net effects are equivalent to the cooling of a body and the raising of a weight (or the performance of some other kind of useful mechanical work, as, for example, the operation of an oceangoing vessel) have never been observed.[23]

35

The Second Law of Thermodynamics, as postulated by Clausius and Kelvin neatly remedied this omission. In essence, the Second Law placed limits on the efficiency of any engine which converts heat energy into useful work, whether it be a human or a mechanical machine. Clausius' statement of the Second Law (1850) went: "Heat cannot of itself pass from a colder to a hotter body." Kelvin (1851) was less bold when he said: "It is impossible, by means of inanimate material agency, to derive mechanical effect from any portion of matter by cooling it below the temperature of the coldest of the surrounding objects." The question of why the conversion of heat energy into work was subject to restrictions finally had an answer.

The King is Dead! Long Live the King!

The caloric theory was gone, but what was its ultimate replacement? The dynamical theory was only a temporary solution holding interim regnancy; within a few years another new and daring proposal was made. Out of the classical thermodynamics begun by Carnot came a kinetic-molecular theory based on an atomic hypothesis. Karl Krönig (1822-1879), a German chemist, is usually credited with the revival of a kinetic theory first suggested by Robert Boyle (1660) and later by Daniel Bernoulli (1738). However, it was Clausius to a large degree, who began the bridge which was to span the gap between atomic theory and thermodynamics. Because of the unknown territory he was exploring, Clausius was very careful to separate thermodynamic from kinetic theory. He did not want both discarded if the latter should ultimately be disproved:

> Before writing my first memoir on heat, which was published in 1850, and in which heat is assumed to be a motion, I had already formed for myself a distinct conception of the nature of this motion, and had even employed the same in several investigations and calculations. In my former memoir I intentionally avoided mentioning this conception, because I wished to separate the conclusions which are deducible from certain general principles from those which presuppose a particular kind of motion and to the special conclusions which flow therefrom.[24]

He went on to propose an even further extension to his basic atomic ideas:

I may also remark, that by thus ascribing a movement to the atomic masses themselves, we do not exclude the hypothesis that each atomic mass may be provided with a quantity of finer matter, which without separating from the atom, may still be moveable in its vicinity.[25]

The concurrent work of James Clerk Maxwell (1831-1879) and others lent reinforcement to Clausius; the concept that heat was merely the kinetic energy derived from molecular movement gained grudging, but steady, acceptance. Ludwig Boltzmann (1844-1906) added a new dimension with his statistical thermodynamics and his relationship of the Second Law to the theory of probabilities. Boltzmann, who bore the brunt of attacks on the kinetic theory of gases, offered a philosophical reason for the difficulty of others to accept these revolutionary ideas: "And how awkward is the human mind in divining the nature of things, when forsaken by the analogy of what we see and touch directly."[26] He was to commit suicide in a fit of despondency only a few years before his greatest detractor fully embraced his teachings.

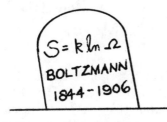

Boltzmann's famous "bridging equation" between classical thermodynamics and molecular statistics is inscribed on his tombstone in Vienna

The reader may rightly question the relevance of the above to engine history, but he should be aware that, as a direct outgrowth of the scientific investigations made on the steam engine, came thermodynamics which, in turn, played a major role in the evolution of present day atomic theory.

Internal Energy

With heat recognized as a form of energy convertible into work, a thermodynamic process can be analyzed wholly on an energy basis. A body, or a system, no longer contains a quantity of "heat" but of "internal energy." Raising or lowering the temperature of the body either increases or decreases its internal, or stored, energy. An energy balance, functioning as an accountant's ledger balance, becomes possible: the energy added to a system equals the internal energy already within the system plus the energy leaving the system. (Fig. 3-1). The supplied energy may be in the form of heat, chemical, electrical or a work equivalent. The departing energy, likewise, can take the various forms just mentioned or simply as non-recoverable losses. In terms of an engine, the fuel energy supplied is converted into, or must balance with, the useful work plus the losses to the exhaust, cooling water, heat radiation, etc. The energy balance proved to be a valuable analytical tool.

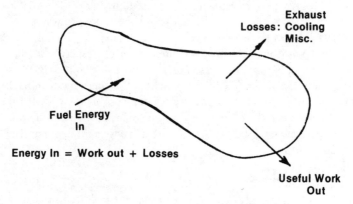

Fig. 3-1.   An Engine "Energy Balance"

The new thinking caused a shift in emphasis from the economy to the thermal efficiency of an engine. This new criterion of engine capability created a dichotomy which sometimes plagues us today in our era of more costly energy. An engine in a vehicle, for example, does not necessarily operate at its most *efficient* point to deliver the *greatest economy*. To phrase it another way, the point of lowest fuel consumption for a specified power output of an engine may not provide the minimum fuel consumption when that engine performs a given task.

There was the inevitable time lag between an understanding and acceptance of the new energy theories and their application. By the 1860s engineering students were beginning to be exposed to a formalized treatment of the endeavors by the thermodynamic pioneers; William J.M. Rankine (1820-1872) wrote the first textbook on the subject in 1859. The internal-combustion engine industry was to have a powerful investigational means at its command when it came into existence.

NOTES

1. D.S.L. Cardwell, *From Watt to Clausius*, (Ithaca, 1971), pp. 40-42. The author effectively refutes this story started by Prof. Robinson, a colleague of Watt's and the publisher of Black's lectures shortly after his death.

2. Sanborn C. Brown, *Count Rumford, Physicist Extraordinary*, (Garden City, 1962). A very readable biography.

3. Duane Roller, *The Early Development of the Concepts of Temperature and Heat*, (Cambridge, 1950), p. 9 1.

4. Cardwell, *op. cit.*, p. 95.

5. Roller, *op. cit.*, p. 89, as quoted from Davy's essay of 1799, "On the Production of Heat by Friction."

6. Sadi Carnot, *Réflexions sur la puissance motrice du feu*, edited by E. Mendoza, (New York, 1960). This is a reissue of R.H. Thurston's translation of 1890. Prof. Mendoza has included important works of Clapeyron and Clausius along with a biographical and explanatory introduction.

7. S.J. Watson, *Carnot*, (London, 1954). A biography of Lazare Carnot.

8. Emile Clapeyron, "Memoir on the Motive Power of Heat," *Journal de L'École Polytechnique*, 1834. An analytical approach to verify Carnot's results, the derivations were explained by indicator diagrams.

9. Cardwell, *op. cit.*, p. 201.

10. Joseph H. Keenan, *Thermodynamics*, (New York, 1941), p. 67.

11. Watson, *op. cit.*, p. 25. (L. Carnot, *Essal sur les machines*, 1783.)

12. Cardwell, *op. cit.*, p. 196, as quoted from Sadi Carnot.

13. Sadi Carnot, *Réflexions . . .*, p. 20 of Mendoza edition.

14. *Ibid.*, p. 49.

15. *Ibid.*, p. 55.

16. *Ibid.*, p. 55.

17. *Ibid.*, p. 48.

18 *Ibid.*, p. 68, "Selections from Posthumous Manuscripts of Sadi Carnot."

19. *Ibid.*, p. 67.

20. *Ibid.*, p. 59.

21. Cardwell, *op. cit.*, p. 208.

22. Julius R. Mayer, "Remarks on the Forces of Inorganic Nature," Liebig's *Annalen der Chemie* (1842), and James P. Joule, "On the Caloric Effects of Magneto-Electricity, and on the Mechanical Value of Heat," *The Philosophical Magazine* (1843), xxiii.
23. Henry A. Bent, *The Second Law,* (New York, 1965), p. 25.
24. Stephen G. Brush, *Kinetic Theory,* (New York, 1965), p. 112. Quoted from "The Nature of the Motion which we call Heat." English trans. in *The Philosophical Magazine* (1857), pp. 108-27.
25. *Ibid.,* p. 113.
26. Ludwig Boltzmann, *Lectures on Gas Theory,* trans. S.G. Brush, (Berkeley, 1964), p. 17. The quotation is from a letter written in English to *Nature,* Feb. 28, 1895.

Chapter 4

Patents: Origin and Influence

The protection given an inventor by a patent grant can be a vital factor leading to the commercial success of his idea. We have already seen this with Newcomen and Watt. Most of the major engine ideas were patented, and in turn, were affected by those patents. The record of technology growth through the teachings of patents is also invaluable. A digression may be in order, therefore, to provide background and insight into the evolution of patents, patent law and their relevance to the subject of engine history.

The dictionary has no trouble providing us with a definition of the word "invention." However, in a legal sense, the highest tribunals to this day have not rendered a clear guideline as to what constitutes invention. Most often they define what it is not. One legal interpretation said:

> "Invention" for patent purposes, has been difficult to define. Efforts to cage the concept in words have proved almost as unsuccessful as attempts verbally to imprison the concept "beautiful." Indeed, when one reads most discussions of "invention" one recalls Kipling's, "It's pretty, but is it Art?" and the aphorism that there is no sense in disputes about matters of taste. Anatole France once said that literary criticism is the adventure of the critic's soul among masterpieces. To the casual observer, judicial patent decisions are the adventures of judges' souls among inventions. For a decision as to whether or not a thing is an invention is a "value" judgment. So are many other judicial judgments in other legal provinces, but "invention" is a particularly elusive standard.[1]

Another provides additional insight:

41

Invention is not always the offspring of genius; for frequently it is the product of plain hard work; not infrequently it arises from accident or carelessness; occasionally it is a happy thought of an ordinary mind; and there have been instances where it is the result of sheer stupidity. It is with the inventive concept, the things achieved, not with the manner of its achievement or the quality of the mind which gave it birth, that the patent law concerns itself.[2]

But points of law and semantics which now worry patent lawyers and judges caused no problem to the dispensers and receivers of patents long ago. In studying the history of patents we must be careful to distinguish between a "true and first patent of invention" and that of "true and first importers" into a country.[3] Many early patents were actually nothing more than an importation franchise. (It is still possible in England, for example, to have a patent issued in the name of a resident agent representing the inventor who may be a "communicant from abroad." This piece of information was not always specified before 1852.) Our brief discussion of patent history will only pertain to patents of "true invention."

Although the concept of a "charter" or what came to be called a "letters patent" (from *littorae patentes*) originated in the clouds of antiquity, we do find the source of a rudimentary patent grant for true invention beginning in the city states of Italy. The Republic of Florence issued such a grant in June of 1421 to the architect Filippo Brunelleschi. He "invented some machine or kind of ship, by means of which he thinks he can easily, at any time, bring in any merchandise and load on the river Arno and on any other river or water, for less money than usual... ."[4] He was given three years protection from competitors whose boats "would be burned."

British Patent Practice

Patents or charters were granted for exploration and industry by most European countries, but the growth of a patent system for invention, as we know it, began in England. It was to spread to the American Colonies 150 years before the founding of the United States patent system.[5] The codifying of patent law was an outgrowth of the conflict between the English Crown and Parliament. Royal prerogative was considered a cherished right by the Monarch whereby he could grant a monopoly to an individual or company in return for financial and political support. Abuses were flagrant, and the rising free enterprise advocates objected. After years of wrangling, Parliament finally passed the Statute of Monopolies in 1624 under James I, thirteen years after the "new" authorized translation of the Bible. This statute was an outgrowth of a concession made by Elizabeth I in 1601 when she said that no future patents or monopolies would be granted without "first hav[ing] a Tryal according to the Law for the good of the people."[6] The statute also cleared up an impossible situation, as no body of law existed in this area. Monopolies were now prohibited except for patents of invention, but no distinction was yet made between true invention and importation of an idea. New patents of invention were issued for a fourteen year term which was equal to two seven-year apprenticeships and which was deemed sufficient to train workmen in the manufacture of the invention.

There was little change in English patent law from the Statute of Monopolies until the 1852 Patents Act. However, patent form and style were evolving. By 1755 patents were required to have a specification describing the invention. The major problem in obtaining a patent was the cost. For United Kingdom protection, which included England, Scotland and Ireland, the total fees were about £300 and £100 in England alone.[7] Fig. 4-1 shows estimates of official patent fees in England in 1829.

Few services were performed for the inventor during his application's wandering through the government channels. Records were poorly kept and specifications sometimes lost. (This may explain the disappearance and mysterious reappearance of Robert Stirling's 1816 patent 100 years later.) It was almost a disincentive to apply for a patent. Charles Dickens, in his *Poor Man's Tale of a patent* (1825), summarized a frustrated inventor's marathon effort to gain a patent:

> Look at the Home Secretary, the Attorney-General, the Patent Office, the Engrossing Clerk, the Lord Chancellor, the Privy Seal, the Clerk of the Hanaper, the Deputy Clerk of the Hanaper, the Clerk of Patents, the Lord Chancellor's Purse-bearer, the Deputy Sealer, and the Deputy Chaff-wax. No man in England could get a patent for an Indian-rubber band or an iron hoop, without feeing all of them. Some of them, over and over again. I went through thirty-five stages. I began with the Queen upon the Throne. I ended with the Deputy Chaff-wax. Is it a man, or what is it?[8]

			£ s. d.	£ s. d.
	Secretary of State	Reference	2 2 6	
		Warrant	7 13 6	
		Bill	7 13 6	
Stamps			———	17 9 6
£ s. d.	Mr Attorney General	Report	4 4 0	
6 0 0		Bill	15 16 0	
			———	20 0 0
	Signet Office	Fees	3 1 0	
		Gratuity	1 1 0	
		Office-keeper	5 0	
			———	4 7 0
	Privy Seal	Fees	2 16 0	
		Gratuity	1 1 0	
		Office-keeper	5 0	
			———	4 2 0
30 2 0	Great Seal Office	Fees	5 17 8	
		Boxes	9 6	
		Gratuity	2 2 0	
		Hanaper	7 13 6	
		Deputy	10 6	
		Recipi	1 11 6	
		Sealers	10 6	
		Office-keeper	5 0	
			———	19 0 2
		Passing the Patent		10 10 0
		Letters,		1 1 0
5 0 0		Specification according to its length		
				———
41 2 0				76 9 8
			Stamps	41 2 0
			Total	117 11 8

Fig. 4-1. Estimate of English patent fees in 1829. (Boehm, *The British Patent System,* 1967)

Dickens referred to the English Patent Office as the "Office of Circumlocution."

The hue and cry became so great that the 1852 Patents Act was passed as a general reform measure. But the original intent of the Statute of Monopolies was unchanged. The cost of a patent was reduced to thirty pounds for the first three years, and it now was good throughout the United Kingdom. An official Patent Office also was established.

It was not until the 1883 Patents Act that an application was examined for "novelty," i.e., to see if it was inventively new. Before that time patent claims were registered with only a formalities check to determine if the subject of the patent warranted protection. After 1852, however, an issued patent was published for a three month public inspection and only then became effective if no opposition was filed. The minimum fee was further reduced to three pounds for the first four years of protection. The fee was only to cover costs and was not a bureaucratic moneymaking endeavor. The fourteen year patent life was kept until 1919 when it was changed to the current sixteen years. Not until 1902 was there an official requirement to investigate for "prior art," i.e., to see if a previously issued patent or publication "anticipated" the application under examination. The above is worth remembering as, in light of current practice, we would well wonder how an English inventor in the period prior to 1852 was granted such broad claims.

In addition to the expense of a patent, litigation was also prohibitive with an average trial running £600. The fortunate patent owner had less worry about a competitor trying to have the patent declared invalid (Newcomen's patent frustration by Savery and Watt's "stolen" crankshaft idea). It also worked the other way, too, in that a poor patent holder could not afford to sue an infringer.

United States Practice

United States patent law, as set out under the Constitution,[9] was borrowed from the English system to that time but was tempered with a uniqueness of its own. From the inception, an inventor was not granted "property" (as with the Statute of Monopolies) but a "sole and exclusive right and liberty" to make and sell his invention. Another important difference was that a patent was issued only for true invention and not for an import franchise. Over the next one hundred years the concept of a patent being property, albeit an intellectual property, was gradually introduced through court decisions. Thus U.S. philosophy veered slightly toward the British who had always equated a patent with property. However, within the last sixty years the doctrine of "public interest" has come to be dominant. Justice Douglas said in 1944 "It is a mistake ... to conceive of a patent as but another form of private property. The patent is a privilege 'conditioned by a public charter.'"[10] Also contrary to the British, the U.S. has refrained from classifying a patent as an outright monopoly. This distinction is an important one and deserves the careful reading of a 1933 Supreme Court decision:

> Though often so characterized a patent is not, accurately speaking, a monopoly, for it is not created by the executive authority at the expense and to the prejudice of all the community except the grantee of the patent. The term

monopoly connotes the giving of an exclusive privilege for buying, selling, working or using a thing which the public freely enjoyed prior to the grant. Thus a monopoly takes something from the people. An inventor deprives the public of nothing which it enjoyed before his discovery, but gives something of value to the community by adding to the sum of human knowledge. He may keep his invention secret and reap its fruits indefinitely. In consideration of its disclosure and the consequent benefit to the community, the patent is granted.[11]

The establishment of the United States patent system in 1790 generated new practices which also differed from the English. (The bill creating the legal system for U.S. patents, H.R. Bill No. 41, was signed into law on April 10, 1790, just three days after passage in Congress.) The examination for novelty, along with a description of the invention, was a specified requirement. And since the stated constitutional objective of a patent was to promote industry, the incentive to file for an application was enhanced by keeping fees very low. After 1836 the application fee was thirty dollars for U.S. citizens but was 500 dollars for Britishers, by way of "reciprocity."[12] A consecutive numbering system began with a general reorganization in 1836. Prior to this time a patent was assigned no number. (1836 Was also the year of the "Great Patent Office Fire" which destroyed almost all of the drawings, models and documents. The building had been spared this fate by the British in 1812 upon the persuasion of its head, Dr. William Thornton.) A patent was now issued for fourteen years with the possibility of an extension to twenty-one years; in 1861 this was changed to a compromise term of seventeen years where it has remained.

German Practice

Germany is the third industrial country whose patent system exerted a strong influence over the course of engine development. Patent grants were first issued by the German states as far back as the 16th century, but formalized laws by these states did not begin until the first half of the 19th (Prussia, for example in 1815, and Bavaria in 1825). A unified German patent law went into effect July 1, 1877 — six years after the founding of the Second Empire. It combined the examination procedure of the United States with the publishing for "opposition proceedings" introduced by Great Britain in 1852; the life of a patent was for eighteen years. This so-called German System was later adopted by Austria, Denmark, Finland, Norway, Sweden and The Netherlands. (The Netherlands had abolished their patent system between 1869 and 1910.)

Since industry stimulation is an intention of a patent, the events taking place after a patent issues are worth consideration. The owner of a patent can exploit the covered invention either by retaining complete control or by licensing others. If he remains the sole producer, a widespread use of that invention may not be as rapid as if he had allowed others to share with him in the production. Boulton and Watt granted no licenses under the Watt patents, and although they prospered, the growth of steam technology was stifled. Their philosophy was one of slow, evolutionary development; and with no venturesome licensees to push along their product, the steam engine failed to progress as fast as it might have during that period. With the expiration of Watt's condenser patent in 1800 the steam engine blossomed forth in many new directions. Conversely to the above, an obstructing patent will stimulate the ingenuity of others (if there is a profitable need for the invention) to discover new ideas yet avoid infringement.

From the historical viewpoint, a patent is an available document which should most accurately describe what the inventor really had in mind. The specification and drawings fully disclose the construction and operation as well as the touted advantages of the new device or process. The claims perform their legal function of defining the limits of invention and tell what is new and novel in the invention. Advantage can also be taken of the court proceedings which possibly arise later from an infringement or a validity suit after the patent issues. Trial testimony may uncover new information as to the background of the inventor and the invention.

The United States judicial system has added over the years new interpretations as to what a patent is, its limits of protection and its worth to society. In view of this, the opinion of Mr. Chief Justice John Marshall in 1832 offers a fitting close to this brief look at the patent. His fundamental philosophy is worth recalling in a day of confusion by the Government over patent reform and by the courts over patent validity:

> ... and it cannot be doubted that the settled purpose of the United States has ever been, and continues to be, to confer on the authors of useful inventions an exclusive right in their inventions for the time mentioned in their patent. It is the reward stipulated for the advantages derived by the

public for the exertions of the individual, and is intended as a stimulus to those exertions. The laws which are passed to give effect to this purpose ought, we think, to be construed in the spirit in which they have been made; and to execute the contract fairly on the part of the United States, where the full benefit has been actually received: if this can be done without transcending the statute, or countenancing acts which are fraudulent or may prove mischievous. The public yields nothing which it has not agreed to yield; it receives all which it has contracted to receive. The full benefit of the discovery, after its enjoyment by the discoverer for fourteen years, is preserved; and for his exclusive enjoyment of it during that time the public faith is pledged... .[13]

NOTES

1. Harold G. Fox, *Monopolies and Patents*, (Toronto, 1947), p. 243. As quoted from Circuit Court Judge Frank, *Picard v. United Aircraft Corporation*, (1942) 53 USPQ 563 at 569.
2. *Ibid.*, p. 246. *Radiator Specialty Co. v. Buhot*, (1930) 39F 2d 376.
3. Douglas Falconer, et al., *Terrell on the Law of Patents*, 12th ed., (London, 1971), p. 25.
4. Bruce W. Bugbee, *The Genesis of American Patent and Copyright Law*, (Washington, D.C., 1967), p. 17. Quoted from Frank D. Prager, "Brunelleschi's patent," JPOS, February 1946.
5. *Ibid.*, p. 60. A patent of invention in America was granted to one Samuel Winslow from the Massachusetts Colony in 1641 for processing salt.
6. E. Burke Inlow, *The Patent Grant*, (Baltimore, 1950), p. 24. As quoted from Sir Simonds D'Ewes, *Journals of all the Parliaments during the Reign of Queen Elizabeth* (London, 1682), p. 652.
7. Klaus Boehm, *The British Patent System, I Administration*, (Cambridge, 1967), p. 19.
8. *Ibid.*, p. 21.
9. U.S. Constitution, Art. 1, Sect. 8, Cl. 8: "The Congress shall have Power: ... to promote the Progress of Science and Useful Arts, by securing for limited Times to Authors and Inventors the exclusive Right to their respective Writings and Discoveries;"
10. Inlow, *op. cit.*, p. 132. Special Equipment Co. v. Coe., (1944) 324 US 370, 382.

11. Bugbee, *op. cit.,* as quoted from *U.S. v. Dubilier,* (1932), 289 US 178.
12. Bugbee, *op. cit.,* p. 201.
13. C.D. Tuska, *An Introduction to Patents for Inventors and Engineers,* (New York, 1964) p. xii. As quoted from *Grant v. Raymond,* 31 US 218, 241, 242.

INTERNAL FIRE

Chapter 5

Internal-Combustion Engines: 1791-1813

While James Watt defended his steam engine against Hornblower and other Cornish competitors*, a new breed of experimenters began to research another power form. Part of their concept involved a "reversion" to the repetitive explosions of the old gunpowder engines. Fortunately, more hospitable fuels were considered. Unlike steam and yet similar to the forthcoming hot-air engines, this new internal-combustion engine utilized the expansive force from air heated during a combustion process. But unlike the external-combustion hot-air engine, inflammable gas and air were mixed and ignited anew within the engine cylinder for each expansion portion of the cycle.

It took almost ninety years for the internal-combustion or I-C engine to suffer through its often traumatic gestation period. During this trial and error interim, reciprocating steam power approached a development zenith; and the hot-air engine also attained a relatively brief flash of acceptance.

John Barber: 1791

A gas turbine patented in 1791? The thought is not only humbling but true. John Barber disclosed in that year[2] an internal-combustion engine having all of the elements of a modern gas turbine. In addition, he was the first to consider using manufactured coal gas as a fuel, which by itself was a significant contribution to engine technology. The fuel was burned as it was made: "I make use of two ... Retorts in order to keep the Engine working with one of them whilst the other is cleansed of the Coaks and Ashes of the Materials used for procuring Inflammable Air."[3] Barber directed the expanding combustion gases

---

*Watt, writing to Boulton in 1796 said of Cornishmen: "The rascals seem to have been going on as if the patent were their own. We have tried every lenient means with them in vain; and since the fear of God has no effect upon them, we must try what the fear of the Devil can do."[1]

exiting from a nozzle to impinge "with amazing force and velocity"[4] on an impulse-type turbine wheel geared to an output shaft. He built on Giovanni Branca (1571-1645) who had described a steam operated impulse-type turbine in 1629; it was to power a "Pounding-mill" through wood tooth reduction gears.

John Barber
Pat. No. 1833 of 1791
"Gas Turbine"

"A Specification of an Engine for using inflammable AIr for the purpose of procuring Motion and facilitating Metallurgical Operations and which may be applied to the grinding of Corn, Flint, Manganesse or other Matter, also for rolling, slitting forging and battering Iron and other Metals, turning of Mills for spinning and Engines for turning up Coals, Minerals from Mines of all sorts, stamping of Ores, raising Water, and any other Motion that may be required."

  1 – Retort
  2 – Gas Condenser
  4 – Air Compressor
  6 – Stop Cocks (Throttle)
  7 – Exploder
  8 – Flywheel (Impulse Turbine)
10 – Speed Reduction Gears

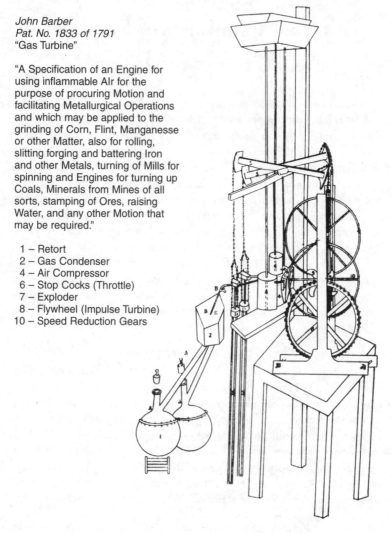

Fig. 5-1. John Barber's gas turbine. (From his 1791 English patent drawing)

Air and gas for combustion were pressurized (to an unknown extent) by reciprocating piston pumps driven from the turbine reduction gears. (Fig. 5-1) Again Barber was ahead of his time since he wanted to compress the combustible mixture prior to ignition.

A very schematic patent drawing, our only record, looks quite unlike the modern conception of a geared turbine. The drawing shows a gas producer ("retort"), compressor, a combustion chamber ("exploder"), a turbine wheel ("flywheel") and reduction gears.

It is not known if Barber built a workable engine, since his design requirements were far ahead of available materials technology. Yet he did show an auxiliary pump for injecting a small stream of water into the burning gases leaving the combustion chamber. This was "to prevent the inward pipes and mouth of the exploder from melting by the intenseness of the issuing flame."[5] He had either intuitively recognized a heat problem would exist or added the water cooling to attempt to improve engine life as a result of an actual bitter experience.

Another intriguing application is suggested for Barber's engine. The patent says that:

> the fluid stream may be ... passed out at the stern of any ship, boat, barge, or other vessel, so as by an opposing and impelling power directed against the water carrying such vessel, the vessel with its contents may be driven in any direction whatsoever.[6]

Thus while his reaction mechanics were in error, he predicted the pure jet engine to come 140 years later.

Robert Street: 1794

A patent issuing three years after Barber's gives the first record of a reciprocating I-C engine burning a gaseous fuel and air mixture.[7] Robert Street, a varnish maker, explains in the patent his idea for a pumping engine to run on vaporized turpentine. Considering the man's trade this was a quite logical fuel. He says of the combustible mixture:

> The quantity of spirits of tar or turpentine to be made use of is always proportioned to the confined space, in general about ten drops to a cubic foot. This process will produce an inflammable vapour force.[8]

The schematic patent drawing (Fig. 5-2) and his own words, as quoted from the specification, describe the engine's operation:

> A, an iron cylinder; B, a solid iron piston, made to fit the cylinder; D, a strong frame in which the cylinder is suspended; E, a stove to keep the bottom of the cylinder hot; F, a counter sink touch hole; and near the bottom of the cylinder, as soon as the bottom is heated sufficiently, pour a small quantity of spirits of tar or turpentine into the funnel, which falls on the hot part of the cylinder, and instantly the liquid is converted into an inflammable vapour; at the same moment raise the piston by means of the lever G, which sucks in the external condensed air and also raises a light to the touch hole; the confined vapour takes fire similar to gunpowder, and, by the combined power of the inflammable and rarified air thus incorporated together, forces the piston B up the frame, and also raises with it the long shaft K, which descends with the piston to the bottom and works the pump or other machinery at the opposite end at L. The two sides of the frame, Figure 1st and 2d, are made hollow like a groove, to guide the piston in his [*sic*] return into the cylinder; the same operation continued, a constant motion is communicated.

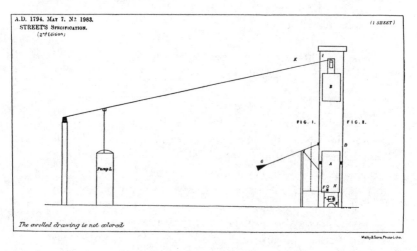

Fig. 5-2.   Robert Street's turpentine-fueled engine. (From his 1794 English patent drawing)

There was no compression of the fuel-air charge prior to ignition. This proved to be a fundamental deficiency in the thinking of almost all the early I-C experimenters, and the benefits to be derived from a compressed charge were denied or ignored for too long.

Street's engine was a hand operated, power assisted water pump. Like Savery's pump 100 years earlier, the engine could not sustain continuous running by itself. Pumping work was derived from the weight of a falling piston which acted through a long lever arm. Street makes no reference to the downward piston stroke being aided by atmospheric pressure. An explosion threw up the piston, and gravity returned it. He must have built an engine as described in his patent, but unfortunately no record exists which gives construction or performance details.

Philippe Lebon: 1801

Fuel is the final determinant of engine design; never did an engine for general usage have its development proceed independently of an available energy source. A designer must be assured his creation will have a compatible and an adequate fuel supply when it breathes into life. The contributions of Philippe Lebon (1769-1804) are a good illustration of this vital interrelationship between an engine and its fuel.

Lebon is most remembered for his original and prophetic work with coal gas and its great lighting potential. A well-educated engineer and chemist, he was able to draw upon published theory and experiments with inflammable gases. Lebon also described[9] an engine that could use the gas made in his gas generator. (Fig. 5-3)

Long before the end of the eighteenth century it was known that highly heating a charge of coal or wood in a retort or a furnace having no incoming air supply resulted in the distillation of a very flammable gas. Stephen Hales (1677-1761) had reported on this phenomenon in 1727. The process was referred to for a long time as the "destructive distillation of coal." As seen earlier, John Barber was also aware of this. A valuable characteristic of the gas was that it burned with a luminous yellow flame. The volume and composition of the generated gas was a function of the coal's temperature and the length of time it was exposed to that temperature. Before the gas from the furnace could be efficiently burned it had to be cooled and "washed" or "scrubbed" of the tars and sulfur impurities. A useful byproduct was the coke remaining in the closed furnace at the end of the "cooking" cycle. Later, when the demand for coke increased, the roles reversed. New plants were built to obtain mainly coke, and "coke oven gas" became the saleable byproduct.

Coal gas, also known as town gas (in England) and illuminating gas, was very rich in hydrogen and methane or marsh gas (approximately thirty five to forty five percent each) and low in carbon monoxide (three to six percent). Its heating value of 500 to 600 Btu per cubic foot of gas was slightly over half that of today's commercially obtainable natural gas, giving it the highest heating value of early manufactured gases. Gas making processes introduced in the latter part of the 1800s as a result of changing industry and gas engine needs had quite different compositions. (A few of the significant newer processes and their implications to the I-C engine are discussed in Chapter 12.)

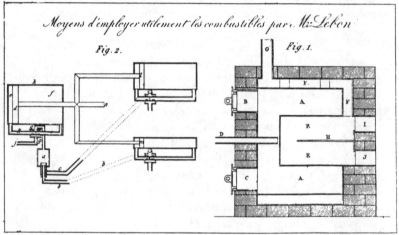

Engine
a. Air-gas mixing & ignition chamber.
b. Gas supply pipe.
c. Air supply pipe.
d. Double-acting power piston.
e. Combustion &
f. expansion chambers.
g. Box containing engine actuated supply & exhaust valves.
h. Power cylinder.
i. Pipe for incoming burning & then exhaust gases.

j. Exhaust pipe.
k. Same as I. but serving opposite cylinder chamber.
l. Air supply pump piston.
m. Gas supply pump piston.
n. Connecting rod.

Gas Generator
A. Sealed gas generator box.
B. Closable ports for adding coal and
C. removing coke at end of distillation cycle.

D. Gas outlet to engine or lamps.
E. Furnace to heat the closed chamber A.
F. Circulating flue to pass hot furnace gases around A.
G. Furnace chimney.
H. Platform to hold second coal bed.
I. Combustion air supply and
J. openings for charging and cleanout.

Fig. 5-3.   Phillippe Lebon coal-gas producer and double-acting engine. (From his French patent of addition – 1801)

Lebon in France and William Murdock with Boulton and Watt in England are credited with launching the gas lighting industry. Lebon's progress was greatly hindered by a lack of interest; there was a concurrent national diversion involving the Revolution. His career also was tragically cut short when he died from a complication of gout.[10]

One witness to a Lebon promotional stunt in 1801 that lit a Paris hotel was James Watt's second son, Gregory. His favorable report to the Soho management on Lebon's practical demonstration gave them encouragement to continue funding Murdock's paralleling efforts, whose first experimental gas lighting system was tested in 1792. Boulton and Watt went on to sell their, and the world's, first commercial lighting plant in 1806. It had a fifty lamp capacity. (The customer was the then famous Philips and Lee cotton spinning mill at Salford. One of the partners, George Lee, was a friend of James Watt and had acted as a stimulus to Watt in the development of the engine indicator in the early 1790s.) Because their primary interest was the building of steam engines, Boulton and Watt failed to keep up with the rapid advances occurring in manufactured gas technology. As a consequence of having lost their gas plant-making leadership they abandoned this activity in 1814. Others had already picked up the baton. In 1812 the London "National Light and Heat Co." was chartered, and by 1815 with its new name of "The Gas Light and Coke Co.", had laid almost fifteen miles of gas pipe. The United States was not far behind with the formation of a gas lighting company in Baltimore in 1816 and then New York in 1823. It is a paradox that the company which did the most to bring the steam engine to the world also introduced a product which later sowed the seeds of destruction for that engine. What might it have been if Boulton and Watt had viewed themselves as an "energy conversion company" rather than only steam engine builders?

The double-acting engine described by Lebon (Fig. 5-3) leaves little doubt that he understood the essentials of internal-combustion power. He analyzed the factors peculiar to such an engine and then outlined means to implement them. The Lebon proposal was not one of an inventive mechanic but of a practical engineer using known scientific principles. The aspects he considered included:

— Control over the gas-air ratio.
— Pumping gas and air into a combustion chamber under pressure.
— The use of a closed combustion chamber.
— The possibility of electric spark ignition.
— The expansion factor of the combustion gases.
— Actuating all the valves in an I-C engine mechanically.

It is not known if Lebon ever built an engine to put this advanced thinking into practice, and it is assumed he never did.

The Lebon engine had limitations, but no more than many of the designs by others over the next sixty years. He failed to utilize the advantage of compressing a fuel-air charge prior to combustion, although he did pump the gas and air through separate pipes into an external mixing and ignition chamber. Since the strokes of the double-acting, auxiliary pump pistons were identical to that of the power piston, gas and air were forced continuously into the external ignition chamber throughout an entire power stroke. With each stroke a new ignition took place and a power impulse was produced. After initiating combustion by an electric spark the expanding gases were alternately valved to a main chamber on each side of the power piston on alternate strokes of the piston. Lebon says of the ignition means:

> Assuming that the ignition of the gas has once begun: we know that, by the electric spark, we can bring it about in closed vessels. We can use an electric machine which can be driven by the gas one, in such a manner as to repeat the detonations, the timing of which can be regulated and determined: ...[11]

Lebon's calculations for the expansion of the burning gases assured him that after deducting pumping and friction losses the engine could still produce useful work. As the piston moved on a power stroke, spent gases from the previous stroke in the opposite chamber were pushed out of that chamber through an exhaust valve and into the atmosphere.

Isaac de Rivaz: 1802-1813

The ambitious programs of a fourth man during this period carried I-C engine progress into the field testing stage with actual hardware. Isaac de Rivaz (1752-1828) was not interested in pumping or station-ary engines; his lifelong dream was to build a self-propelled wagon. He was not unsuccessful. The efforts of this Swiss engineer and government official resulted in the first vehicle powered by an internal-combustion engine. His work, generally unknown outside of Switzerland until recently,[12] has been documented through his notes and records of cor-roborating witnesses, all of which testify to his perseverance and resourcefulness. Rivaz began his vehicular work in the early 1780s using steam power, and not until almost 1800 did he seriously consider the potential of an I-C engine, a little over ten years after Nicolas Joseph Cugnot (1725-1804) tested his ill-fated, three wheeled steam wagon for the French army. From 1802 to 1813 he dropped steam in favor of what he thought was a more promising form of prime mover.

A new development caused Rivaz to switch to an "explosion" motor, even though some earlier attempts to use grains of gunpowder for ignition with such an engine forced quick abandonment. Allesandro Volta (1745-1827) had made a basic discovery for a spark-generating condenser that was adaptable to an engine. Volta's "electric pistol," a glass bottle blown in the shape of a hand gun, generated a spark by inductance and ignited marsh gas (methane) contained in a sealed chamber to fire out a stopper cork. This dramatic experiment, first performed in 1776, was later written about and demonstrated before a number of Europe's most learned scientific fraternity. Volta himself traveled extensively and exhibited the "pistol" and his more famous "Voltaic cell" or battery. The quotation from Lebon's patent on the possibility of igniting gas by an electric spark in a closed combustion chamber was a reference to the pistol. Volta had been elected to the French Royal Academy of Sciences in 1783, and his discoveries received great publicity in France. Napoleon, one of his admirers, made him a Count. In 1777 Volta had proposed a crude form of telegraph using his pistol. He suggested a one-wire system with the ground itself completing the circuit. The pistol was at the receiving end of the signal. At the sending end was a Leyden jar. Closing the circuit would cause an electric impulse to explode the gas in the pistol and herald that an expected event had occurred. Iron wire was to be strung over insulators on wooden poles.[13]

The Rivaz engines used atmospheric pressure to create the working stroke. A piston in a long vertical cylinder was forced upward by electrically ignited combustion gases. Through expansion and piston inertia a partial vacuum was formed in the cylinder. During the upward stroke the piston remained disconnected from the power train. Conversion to rotary from reciprocating motion was by means of a chain or rope fastened at each end to a long vertical rod extending from the piston. The chain made a tight loop around a pulley or drum so that as the rod moved up and down the chain caused the pulley to rotate. The chain served the function of a rack gear on the piston rod and a pinion gear on the pulley. (Fig. 5-4) On the chain driven drum was a pawl which, when the piston moved up, was free to pass over teeth on a ratchet wheel integral with and driving a second pulley. This second pulley drove a rope running down to a third pulley on the vehicle axle. Thus only when the piston was forced inward by atmospheric pressure and by its own weight could the pawl engage a tooth of the ratchet and transmit power to the wheels. The general concept was used on his vehicles built in 1805 and 1813 and is the basis of the 1807 patent.

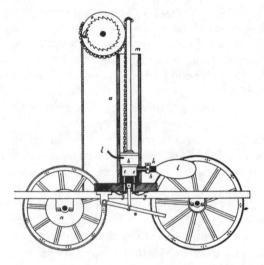

Fig. 5-4.   Isaac de Rivaz engine and carriage of 1805. (Michelet, *L'inventeur Isaac de Rivaz,* 1965)

When the physical dimensions of the "chariot" are considered, the 1813 *gran char mechanique* earned its title. (Fig. 5-5, Plate) It was 5.2 meters long by 2.1 meters wide. Total weight including passengers was about 2,100 pounds. The cylinder had a bore of 36.5 cm and the piston, weighing in at 160 pounds, had a travel of 97 cm. Each working stroke of the piston propelled the wagon about sixteen to twenty feet, and it was possible to repeat the power cycle at five second intervals. This resulted in a maximum possible average speed of about three miles per hour. Although the wagon reportedly was able to sustain a continuous speed on level ground, without a flywheel it tended to come to a stop between each power pulse on an incline. The steepest grade it supposedly negotiated was nine percent. The above performance data was recorded from a test run made near Vevey, Switzerland, on October 18, 1813.[14]

Rivaz did not merely content himself with engine developments alone. He foresaw a need for a fuel distribution network if mobile power was to be successful. He therefore proposed placing coal gas generators every two miles along roadways to serve as filling stations. His 1813 engine was fed gas to a "mixer" (Fig. 5-6) from a 0.4 cubic meter, leather skin bag (what apparently determined the two mile interval). He said that one pound of coal was required for each tank of gas.

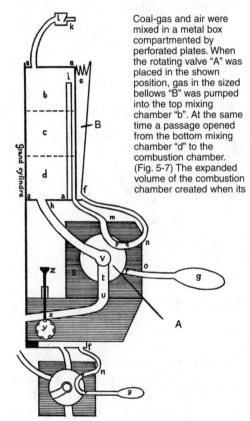

Coal-gas and air were mixed in a metal box compartmented by perforated plates. When the rotating valve "A" was placed in the shown position, gas in the sized bellows "B" was pumped into the top mixing chamber "b". At the same time a passage opened from the bottom mixing chamber "d" to the combustion chamber. (Fig. 5-7) The expanded volume of the combustion chamber created when its lower piston was pulled down by the hand lever, in conjunction with the volume of gas contained in the bellows, determined the fuel-air ratio. A check valve "L" in the air inlet permitted fresh air to be sucked into the mixing chamber "b" but prevented gas coming from the bellows to escape. The reported volumes of coal gas and air burned per expansion cycle were 100-200 cu. in. and 500-700 cu. in. respectively. This gave a gas-air ratio of about 1 to 6.

When valve "A" was rotated to its other position after combustion was initiated, the passage between the combustion and mixing chambers was broken. Also, the bellows "B" was no longer connected to the mixing chamber, but to the gas "tank." Expanding the bellows sucked in the next measured volume of gas from the collapsible leather tank.

Fig. 5-6.   Rivaz carburetor – 1813. (Michelet, *L'inventeur Issac de Rivaz*, 1965)

Operation of the engine was initiated by movement of a hand-controlled lever (Fig. 5-7) which in turn performed three simultaneous functions:

a) a lower piston was pulled down and away from the power piston, creating a vacuum in the combustion chamber to suck in a combustible mixture;

b) a valve opened to allow the premeasured and mixed charge of gas and air to flow into the combustion chamber; and

c) contacts in an electric circuit closed, causing a spark to jump a gap between two wire terminals in the combustion chamber (Volta's electric "pistol" and battery ideas).

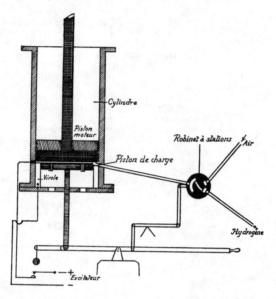

Fig. 5-7.   Schematic of Rivaz 1805 engine. (Michelet, *L'inventeur Isaac de Rivaz,* 1965)

It appears that the pressure operated exhaust valves allowed part of the burning gases to escape during the expansion process, but were closed when cylinder pressure dropped below atmospheric as the piston continued to travel upward. They remained closed until the internal pressure once again reached atmospheric toward the end of the inward working stroke. The power piston's down stroke was limited by a fixed stop in the cylinder. By making the two pistons come close to each other at the end of the working stroke residual exhaust gases were almost completely purged from the cylinder.

The work of Rivaz is worth noting for several reasons. Not only did he build an operable electric ignition system for an engine having a portable gas supply, he was also the precursor of future engines of similar concept. Eugenio Barsanti and Felice Matteucci, to the south in Florence built a more advanced Rivaz design about forty years later.

Ten years after that, Otto and Langen would introduce the first commercially successful atmospheric I-C engine using the same broad ideas. Thus the lineal descent from Rivaz to the Otto and Langen engine could be more than coincidence. This is not meant to detract from the contributions and original thinking of the later Italian and the German designers, but as engineers and inventors will confirm, germs of ideas grow out of chance encounters and remarks when there is common interest.

Claude and Joseph-Nicephore Niepce: 1806

Sadi Carnot briefly described the Niepce I-C engine in a footnote of his 1824 treatise.[15] Joseph Claude Niepce (1763-1828) of Chalon-sur-Saône and his younger brother Joseph-Niciphore Niepce (1765-1833) built a one cylinder model of about twenty-two cubic inches displacement (Fig. 5-8). More than a laboratory curiosity, it was reported that the 300 pound engine propelled a 2.5 meter long boat upstream on the Saône River.[16] The bore and stroke of the working piston was 24 x 48.7 cm.

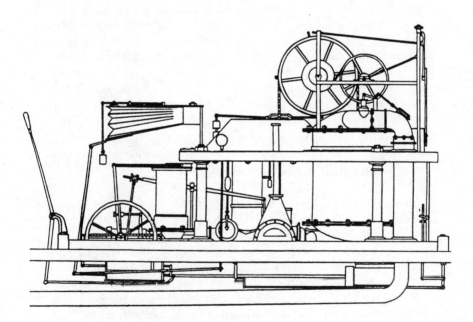

Fig. 5-8   Side view of the Niepce engine (1806/1807). (Niepce 1807 patent)

The piston alternately drew in water from the side of the boat and then expelled it to provide a cyclic jet pump. Lazare Carnot, Sadi's mathematician father, and chemist Claude-Louis Berthollet later saw it run at a cyclic rate of 12 or 13 piston strokes per minute.

The Niepce *pyréolophore* engine was said to have burned an expensive powdered fuel and that was one of the main reasons why the invention was abandoned.[17] This was low soot-forming lycopodium, a powder from the spores of what is more commonly known as club moss. Highly inflammable, it was used in fireworks and later for flash photography. The 1806 engine ran mostly on a blend of coal dust mixed with 20 percent rosin. A later version in 1817 used only petroleum.

A small diameter pipe was placed between the cylinder and the outlet of a bellows which supplied combustion air. Two ports were located along the pipe, one for injecting the powder and the other open to a glowing wick which was introduced into the combustion chamber for a brief moment. The wick would then be reheated by a flame burning outside the engine.

With each timed blast of the bellows, a timed injection of fuel (powder or?) was ignited as it was blown past the flame port on the way to the cylinder. In one test, the reported force acting on the piston could counteract a weight of over a hundred pounds. Cylinder scavenging after each stroke was by means of valves; an auxiliary piston served as an air pump to scavenge the cylinder.

Claude Niepce's continued obsession with the engine sapped his resources and later his sanity. Brother Joseph pursued another dream. In 1822 he made the first known positive image on a photographic plate. Seven years later he agreed to cooperate with Louis J.M. Daguerre who, after Niepce's death, went on to perfect the photographic process bearing his name.

John Cox Stevens: 1798

A recently discovered I-C engine development in the United States predates Lebon's 1801 efforts[18] and serves as an appropriate close to this chapter. It comes from John Cox Stevens (1749-1838) who is well known for his pioneering work with steam engines for boats and locomotives. Of interest also is the man who made and tested the Stevens I-C engine. Marc Isambard Brunel (1769-1849), the father in the famous British father and son engineering family,[19] spent from 1793 to 1798 in New York City as a city engineer. His interlude in America was a way station between France, where he had found his royalist leanings

64

would lead him to the guillotine, and England where he was to make engineering fame. Brunel correspondence to Stevens gives operation details. An unfiled patent application by Stevens provides some design information.[20] No sketches or drawings have been found.

Stevens first engine was conceived as the power plant for an oared paddle boat. Of the engine he says:[21]

> A piston ... put in motion by the explosion of inflammable gas ... is reacted upon by the pressure ... of the air in the cylinder above the piston. This air, as the piston rises, becomes more and more compressed... . By this means, the motion of the piston is gradually retarded ... . The explosion is instantly succeeded by a vacuum under the piston, and the condensed air acting above the piston, presses it down again. Thus a reciprocating motion is established ... which may be applied to any mechanical purpose.

From this it can be deduced that the vertical cylinder engine was similar to Street and Rivaz on its lower end, but the upper end now needed a cover. A piston rod passed through the upper cylinder "head" using a suitable stuffing box seal to let pressure build up between the piston and the upper end as it rose. "Some spirit" (ethyl alcohol) was injected by a "syringe" into a "heated brass cup" in the base of the lower cylinder. A candle by the fuel supply hole began the ignition process. Combustion air was supplied from an external bellows. Brunel reported to Stevens that after two firing cycles the cylinder air became so polluted with burned gases that the hole size of the port leading from the bellows into the cylinder would need to be increased for better scavenging of the gases.

Stevens also described a double-acting gas engine which would anticipate the later Lenoir engine (Chapter 7), i.e. having a power impulse on every stroke of the piston. Fuel and air were introduced as the piston began moving down the cylinder, and the charge was then ignited after it had traveled part way down its stroke. Ignition and valving methods were not disclosed.

These six pioneers revealed through their disclosures and hardware the two directions future I-C engine design would take — both turbine and reciprocating. After Barber, gas turbines submerged again into daydreams and awaited engineering advancements of the twentieth century.

The reciprocating I-C engine had at least a modest chance for success by borrowing known "tools" from existing and emerging technology.

Machine design, metallurgy and manufacturing techniques were still in somewhat primitive states, but so were engine builder's objectives. Technology spilled over from steam developments; however, the fundamental requirements of commercially practical I-C engines were more demanding. A steam engine had an inherent forgiveness factor unlike that of the still embryonic I-C engine. Even with unrefined design and fabrication or limited maintenance, a steam engine usually ran with passable performance. The problems of fuel chemistry, mixture control, timed ignition and cooling of areas exposed to high combustion chamber temperatures were design considerations not faced by steam engineers. Higher efficiency had to be paid for with a greater understanding of yet to come technologies.

NOTES
1. Francis Trevithick, *Life of Richard Trevithick, v. 1,* (London, 1872), p. 39.
2. English patent No. 1,833 of October 31, 1791.
3. *Ibid.,* Fig. 7.
4. *Ibid.,* Fig. 1.
5. *Ibid,* p. 3.
6. *Ibid.*
7. English patent No. 1,983 of May 7, 1794.
8. *Ibid.,* p. 2.
9. French patent No. 356 of 1799 describes Lebon's means to produce coal gas. His "patent of addition" dated August 25, 1801, gives the engine details.
10. The more widely known version of his death was that he was stabbed to death and robbed on a Paris street. The true record of his death is found in the French Archives Nationales: F14 2259.
11. Lebon patent of addition.
12. None of the comprehensive books on early engine history by the English and German writers at the turn of this century mention Rivaz. As late as the 1950s reference was made only to an engine as described in his French patent of January 30, 1807. Henry Michelet in his book *L'inventeur Isaac de Rivaz,* (Martigny, 1965), opened the door to the story of the man and his achievements.
13. Bern Dibner, *Alessandro Volta and the Electric Battery,* (New York, 1964), p. 31.

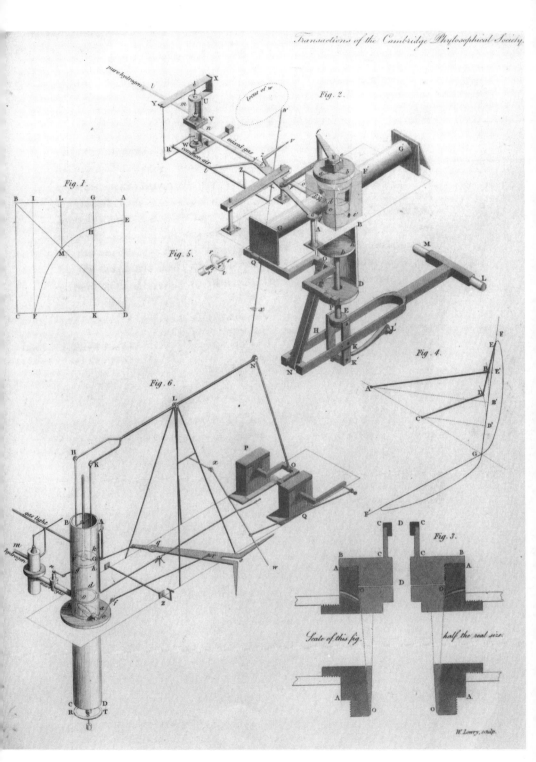

Fig. 6-1   William Cecil hydrogen-fueled engine – 1820. (*Trans. Cambridge Philosophical Soc.*, 1820)

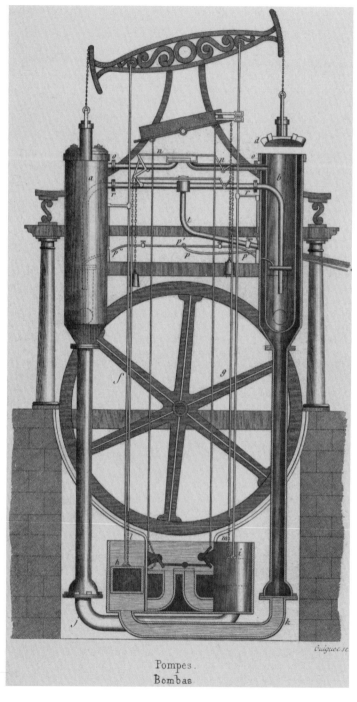

Pompes.
Bombas

Fig. 6-4   Samuel Brown vacuum pumping engine – 1824. (From a
contemporary engraving)

Fig. 6-8   Model of Samuel Morey 1826 atmospheric engine in the
Museum of History and Technology, Washington, D.C.
(The Smithsonian Institution)

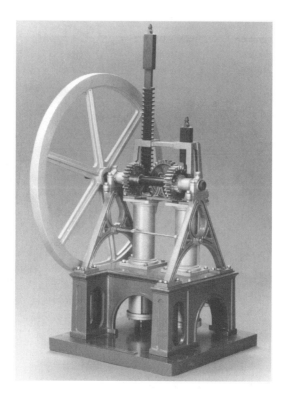

Fig. 6-24   Replica of Barsanti and Matteucci 1856 two cylinder
atmospheric engine in the FIAT Centro Storico, Turin.
(Author photo)

Fig. 6-28   Barsanti, Matteucci and Babacci opposed-piston
atmospheric engine of 1858. (Museo dell'Automobile,
Turin)

14. Michelet, *op. cit.*, pp. 222-27. Michelet has converted the length measures in use at the time of Rivaz into metric units, the ones given. He leaves the weights in livres or pounds. However, this pound is equivalent to 1.1 lb. avoirdupois. To be strictly correct, therefore, the weights in the Rivaz data should be multiplied by this factor. It will be the practice throughout the book to list data in their first published units unless otherwise noted.

15. Sadi Carnot, *Réflexions sur la Puissance Motrice du Feu,* (Paris, 1824), pp. 110-11, fn. He no doubt learned of the engine through his father. Lazare Carnot and chemist Claude Berthollet had been commissioned by the Institut de France, Académie des sciences, to study the engine. Their report of 15 December 1806 was reprinted in Hachette, *Traité Elémentaire des Machines,* (Paris, 1811), pp. 144-49.

16. Charles C. Gillispie, *Lazare Carnot Savant,* (Princeton, 1971), p. 28, fn.

17. Sadi Carnot misinterpreted his father's reference to lycopodium being the primary fuel.

18. Hardenberg to the author, September 1995, wrote of finding primary sources containing factual information on the Stevens engines. He graciously shared these and his analysis of how the engines functioned. This material later was incorporated into his *The Middle Ages of the Internal-Combustion Engine* 1794-1886, SAE, 1999.

19. The son, Isambard Kingdom Brunel (1806-1859), is famed for his leviathan steamships, suspension bridges and wide (7 feet) gage railways.

20. Marc I. Brunel to Stevens, undated letter and "Draft of a Patent Application." Both documents are at the New Jersey Historical Soc., Newark.

21. A document containing the engine's description was witnessed by Brunel on Jan. 30, 1798, to provide a record of invention. New Jersey Historical Soc.

INTERNAL FIRE

Chapter 6

Searching and Perfecting:
1820-1860

Not until 1860, almost three generations after its arrival, did a fledgling internal-combustion engine leave its nest and enter into the commercial world. The interim years of probing and experimenting were not sterile of new ideas nor void of achievement. All areas of design were touched upon, and the resulting efforts included carburetion and ignition systems ultimately adapted to production engines. There were also those visionary "might have beens" who almost, but not quite, founded a new industry.

Two schools of thought, atmospheric and non-compression, prevailed during this era. The former utilized our earthly location under a sea of air and followed a path similar to Newcomen and the first engines of Watt. The other borrowed from second generation, double-acting steam engines whose power stroke came not from the weight of the atmosphere but a force generated within the cylinder itself. Proponents of each concept won later battles in the marketplace, yet both quickly lost out to Otto when he introduced the four-stroke cycle engine.

Achievements by William Cecil, Samuel Brown and Samuel Morey in the 1820s and then thirty years later by Eugenio Barsanti and Felice Matteucci chronologically straddled the non-compression designs of Lemuel Wright, Stuart Perry and Alfred Drake. William Barnett falls partly in this latter group, but he is better remembered for an engine proposal having a degree of mixture compression prior to ignition, the key to an efficient I-C engine.

William Cecil: 1820

In 1820 the Rev. William Cecil (1792-1882) read a paper before the Cambridge Philosophical Society[1], detailing his work on a hydrogen fueled atmospheric engine. (Fig. 6-1, Plate) The engine, a laboratory model also demonstrated to the Society, is believed to have been the first self operating internal-combustion gas engine. Its performance was analyzed, and new information was provided about gas-air mixtures and their combustion characteristics.

Cecil, the son of an Anglican priest, was admitted to Magdalene College, Cambridge, in 1810, and four years later was elected a Fellow.[2] He was only twenty-six when he began building the engine. Cecil was ordained in 1820 and, except for one other technical paper "on an apparatus for grinding telescopes" in 1822, devoted the rest of his life to the Church of England.

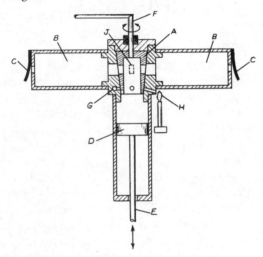

A – Conical plug valve rotatable through 90 degrees.
B – Horizontal expansion cylinders.
C – Outward opening flexible flapper valves.
D – Power piston.
E – Ventically acting connecting rod. It acted through a parallel-motion mechanism to a crankshaft.
F – Engine actuated lever to rotate plug valve.
G – Gas mixture supply pipe. Closed by valve when horizontal cylinders were interconnected to working cylinder.
H – Continuous gas flame for ignition.
J – Air supply groove on outer valve surface.

Fig. 6-2   Cecil engine, cross-section view.

The heart of Cecil's engine was a vertical "working" cylinder and two horizontal expansion cylinders, each fastened to a block containing a rotatable plug valve. (Fig. 6-2) A charge of air and hydrogen was drawn into the vertical cylinder as its piston was carried downward by flywheel inertia. Partial mixing occurred in a pipe connecting an external gas metering device to the cylinder. (Fig. 6-3) During the intake stroke the plug valve was positioned so that the horizontal cylinders were isolated from the vertical cylinder but were connected by passages in the valve to the atmosphere. Near the end of the intake stroke the plug valve was rotated quickly, through one quarter turn, to a momentarily held position. At this point a small valve port indexed with a "touch hole" at a continuously burning small flame. The flame passage into the cylinder was timed to remain open only long enough for the cylinder charge to ignite. After ignition this passage was closed by rotating the valve back a few degrees. Large ports in the plug valve now inter-connected all three cylinders (the position shown in Fig. 6-2). As the mixture burned and expanded, air and residual gases from the previous cycle in the identical horizontal cylinders were pushed out past one-way flapper valves. (Spring-loaded sliding valves were also described.) The rapidly cooling gases entering from the combustion chamber created a vacuum and caused the flapper valves to close. Atmospheric pressure acting on the under side of the piston pushed it up for the power stroke. When the piston reached inner dead center the plug valve was rotated back to its intake position for the next cycle to begin.

Water accelerated the cooling of the expanding gases. It came from the excess used to assist conventional packing in a stuffing box seat at

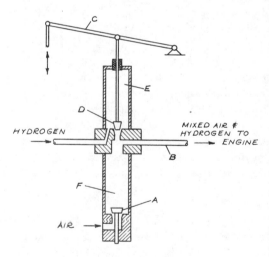

Operation Sequence:
As the engine piston begins its intake stroke, air is pulled past inlet valve (A) and into pipe (B) leading to the engine. Part way down, the stroke lever (C) lifts the slightly pressurized hydrogen metering valve (D) allowing hydrogen to flow from cylinder (E) into the pipe (B). Pressure in the cylinder (F) raises and valve (A) closes. When the lever (C) is pulled down by the engine mechanism to close the metering valve (D) the pressure once again falls in chamber (F) and valve (A) opens to let air enter. Hydrogen admission is thus sandwiched between air charges.

Fig. 6-3   Cecil hydrogen and air metering control.

the plug valve operating shaft. A combination of water and packing, rather than packing alone, reduced the shaft friction. Water sucked into the cylinders past the seal was blown out the flapper valves on the following power stroke.

Information was given about the vacuum formed in the engine. Cecil said that the maximum atmospheric pressure acting on the piston at the beginning of the power stroke was about 12.5 psi and was reduced to about 11.25 psi at the end. He indicated this assumed no seal leakage and no resistance to the air exhausting from the horizontal expansion cylinders.[3]

The engine could run smoothly at sixty rpm on a hydrogen consumption of 15.6 cubic feet per hour, or a gas-air ratio of 1:3. The ignition flame burned an additional two cu ft per hour. The leanest mixture allowable for stable running was 1:4 of hydrogen and air, and the "best power" ratio was 1:2.5. Maximum speed was limited by the length of time the ignition flame passage was open. If speed increased much beyond sixty rpm the time interval became too short for ignition to occur. Manual throttling was by means of a stop cock in the hydrogen supply line. The combustion cylinder had a volume of about thirty cubic inches, and the fifty pound flywheel was three feet in diameter. Unfortunately, because no power output was given, the thermal efficiency cannot be calculated.

Substitute fuels for hydrogen included "carbureted hydrogen, coal gas, vapour of oil turpentine, or any ardent spirit."[4] None were tried by Cecil, but he said he did not expect them to prove as effective as his first choice of pure hydrogen. One hundred and fifty years later hydrogen is once again under active study as a fuel to replace or to enrich gasoline and gas turbine fuel. Cecil's thinking was not limited to atmospheric engines. He recognized the power of his engine was derived from a pressure differential between the atmosphere and the cylinder vacuum and that it was independent of the force created by the combustion process. "But," he stated, "an engine might be constructed to work by the exploding force only; or by the exploding force and the pressure of the atmosphere jointly."[5]

Samuel Brown: 1823-1833

The cloistered environment of a laboratory held no interest for Samuel Brown (1788-1849?). This one-time cooper[6] was a bold experimenter and entrepreneur who believed in the public forum as a stage for his "vacuum engine" demonstrations. Within the span of a few years he was able to lay claim to a number of firsts. If his engine had been shown to a world not already reaping the benefits resulting from steam power, Brown might have been hailed as the Newcomen of the I-C engine. But it was to take more than "just a little bit better" to unseat an accepted and entrenched leader.

In 1824 he built a full scale model of his patented[7] pumping engine. This one and a half horsepower engine could raise 300 gallons of water

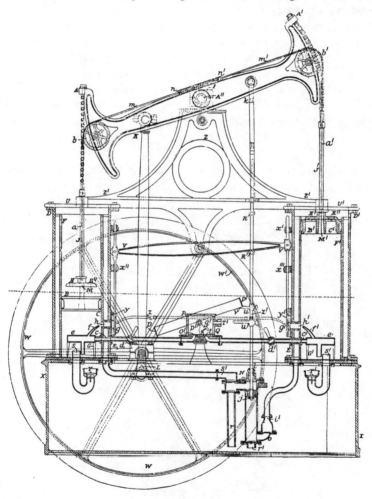

Fig. 6-5   Piston version of Brown pumping engine. (From his
English patent of 1823)

about fifteen feet for each cubic foot of coal gas consumed.[8] (Fig. 6-4, Plate) Both the pumper and a piston version (Fig. 6-5) were in reality atmospheric engines with the unique feature being the means for creating a vacuum.

Brown formed a company in 1825 to build "gas vacuum engines" for powering boats and barges."[9] (He is not to be confused with another Samuel Brown who received a patent that same year for a new method of ship propulsion.[10])

He later patented an improved design of vacuum engine[11] and tested the general concept in a four wheeled vehicle during May 1826. (Fig. 6-6) A report stated the carriage "was successfully tried on the steepest part of Shooter's hill [Kent]" where the grade was about nine percent.[12] The engine had a cylinder bore of twelve inches with a piston stroke of twenty-four inches. The wagon wheels were five feet in diameter on a wheelbase of over six feet. Total weight including gas and water was over 2,200 pounds.[13] All dimensions are approximate and are scaled from a drawing.

The company that was to produce marine engines held one memorable public demonstration of their product on the Thames River at

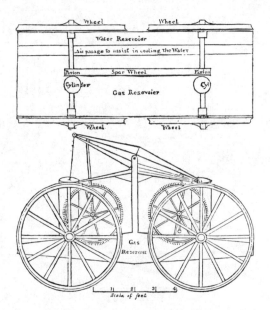

Fig. 6-6   Brown's vacuum engine-powered carriage – 1826.
(*Mechanic's Magazine*, 1826)

London in January of 1827. An engine weighing about 600 pounds was installed in a thirty-six foot boat and was coupled to a Brown-designed screw-type propeller mounted in the bow of the boat.[14] The test, supposedly witnessed by the Lords of the Admiralty, showed the boat capable of making seven to eight miles per hour upstream "as long as the gas was supplied." Although Brown himself considered the run to be a success, a majority of the directors thought differently since the company was dissolved a few weeks later.[15] It was also conjectured that the adoption of screw propellers by the British navy may have received a setback of several years because of the experience.[16]

A modest success was achieved with the pumping engine, and several were in operation as late as 1832. One, for raising water in a canal at Croydon, was reported on after eighteen months service.[17] It had a power cylinder forty-two inches in diameter by twenty-two feet high. A slightly larger engine demonstrated in Brown's shops at Eagle Lodge, Brompton, lifted 750 gallons per stroke against a twelve foot head at a rate of four strokes per minute. Brown claimed that on an annual basis the profit from the sale of coke formed in the gas making process, after deducting the running expenses of coal, wages, and depreciation, was £102. This was against a cost of £275 for a comparable steam engine. It is not known how long these pumping engines remained in service.[18]

The operating cycle for the pumping engine begins with coal gas being fed through a timed valve into one of two combustion cylinders (Fig. 6-4, Plate); identical events occur in the other cylinder one-half cycle later. Concurrently with gas admission, a cover is lifted off the top end of the cylinder. After sufficient gas has entered, a second valve, located at a continuous gas flame, opens a passage into the cylinder and ignites the gas-air charge. When the resultant fire has sufficiently heated the cylinder contents the cover is dropped; the gas and flame valves also close at the same time. A vacuum begins to form with the commencement of cooling.

The combustion cylinder is set in an outer casing, and the annular space between the two concentric cylinders is filled with water. The raisable lid over the cylinders seals only the outer casing against the atmosphere. There is a clearance under the lid for water from the annulus to pour into the combustion cylinder as the vacuum increases. The added cooling from the addition of water accelerates the generation as well as the degree of vacuum. The vacuum in turn "lifts" water up a pipe from a tank under the engine base; a check valve prevents a back flow of water from the annulus when no vacuum is present. With the opening

75

of a third valve the vacuum in the cylinder is broken and the water therein is allowed to drain. The exiting water passes through an outward opening check valve, into a collecting trough, onto an overshot water wheel (whose axle is the power output shaft) and back to a holding reservoir at the base. The cylinder does not completely empty of water; the level only lowers to the height of the surface in the collecting trough. The next pumping cycle is ready to begin.

The mechanism to effect engine operation is unique to Brown. Two tanks in the base alternately refill with water by the opening of timed valves submerged in the small holding reservoir located between the tanks. A float in each tank is connected by a long rod to an end of an overhead beam and causes the beam to rock as the water levels in the float tanks alternately rise and fall. The beam lifts and lowers the cylinder covers. Trip arms on one of the long rods tip a small pivoted tank back and forth. The tank is partially filled with mercury and tips with a quick "snap" action to open and close the gas and air valves. (The original mercury switch!) Chains hanging from the ends of the "tipping tank" are connected to the float tank water supply valves in the holding reservoir. Other trip arms, one on each beam lifting rod, operate the flame ignition valves.

Water thus serves as a condensing fluid in the cylinder to increase the vacuum, a power transmitting and engine valve control means.

By eliminating the water wheel and merely dumping the raised water at a higher level, the engine becomes a vacuum operated pumper. It is only necessary to locate the desired water surface in the holding reservoir at the same level as that of the body of water to be lifted.

The 1823 piston version (Fig. 6-5) works on the same general idea but now the beam transmits power directly into a crankshaft. Water serves only for cylinder cooling since the beam directly or indirectly controls all valve action.

Brown's Thames boat engine was described in the April 5, 1826, patent. The combustion cylinder design was borrowed from the earlier engines, but a new feature was the addition of a separate power cylinder containing a double-acting piston. The vacuum generated in the combustion cylinder was valved first to one side of the piston and then the other. The patent drawings (Fig. 6-7) show an engine with three power cylinders, each having a mated combustion cylinder. Depending on the required power output, the ratio of combustion cylinder to power cylinder volume should be between twelve and eighteen to one. This ratio permitted twelve power strokes (six up and six down) of the piston for each vacuum generating cycle in the combustion cylinder.

A, Cover raised, vessel filling with flame.   B and C, Covers down, vessels vacuous.

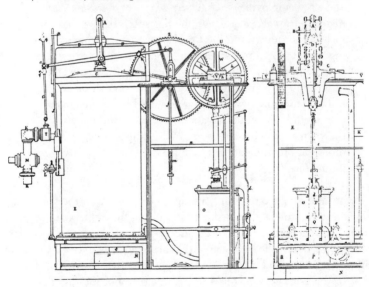

Fig. 6-7   Brown three cylinder vacuum engine. (From his English
patent of 1826 and Clerk, *The Gas and Oil Engine,* 1896)

Cooling water was drawn from and returned to a "cistern" under the engine. Brown said that it was important not to let the water temperature rise too high, and that for locomotive service hot water should be dumped frequently and replenished with cold.

Power was transmitted to a three-throw crankshaft by a connecting rod which passed through a stuffing box seal. The rod remained parallel and axial to the cylinder bore, and angular movement was accommodated by allowing the whole cylinder assembly to pivot about gimbals. Flexible hoses carried the vacuum from the combustion cylinders to three-way slide valves at the power cylinders. These valves alternately directed atmospheric air to one side of the piston while the opposite side was under a vacuum. All valve action was timed by levers controlled from the crankshaft.

A correspondent for *Mechanic's Magazine* was quite enthusiastic about Brown's first engines and compared his results with those of his predecessors. It appeared that the earlier engines could not get the gas to ignite or the engine blew up. Further comments were:

> Mr. Brown has tried gas for the production of a vacuum; and, by employing the *extinction of a peaceable flame,* instead of a *violent explosion,* he has succeeded — has furnished his country and the world with a power which, judging from the *first* machine, (and what would have been the judgment from *the first* steam-engine?) will be convenient in its application, and cheap and safe beyond all precedent. ... Mr. Brown has worked long and hard but there are none who would not think the labour well paid in the reward — the thanks of a benefitted and admiring public, and that more solid remuneration which Britain secures for her ingenious sons.[19]

Praise later changed to doubt, and just a few years later the same magazine joined a growing list of skeptics resulting from the boat company failure. It then referred to the engine as "one of the many nine-day-wonders for which the public are periodically indebted to the Office of Patents."[20] Brown did not take criticisms quietly, as evidenced by a letter to the London *Times* in 1827: "...there is not the slightest foundation, my persevering and constant attention having enabled me to bring my engine to a state of perfection, nearly if not quite, equal to the most sanguine expectations which have been formed regarding it.[21]

Footnotes to the Brown story in America are found in the 1828 *Journal of the Franklin Institute.*[22] The editor tells of an engine based on the Brown principle which was "placed in his hands" in 1814 and, when tested, "appeared 'to work with considerable power." He said he then moved away and the engine was returned to the inventor. No name is mentioned. Reference was also made to Samuel Brown's son being invited to Philadelphia in 1828 by one of the city's "most respected fellow citizens" in order to build one of his father's engines. The editor said the engine was under construction and had not yet been tested.

Samuel Morey: 1826-1829

Concurrently with Brown's work in England, Samuel Morey (1762-1843) was experimenting with an atmospheric engine at Orford, New Hampshire, a small town on the Connecticut River. The first publicly authenticated I-C development in America, it advanced the state of the art with such mechanical features as cam-actuated poppet valves and a base mounted crankshaft. (Figs. 6-8, Plate and 6-9) Morey could draw upon his years of steam engine experience in his endeavors with the new power form; his designs were practical and good examples of so-called Yankee ingenuity. He was granted eighteen United States patents prior

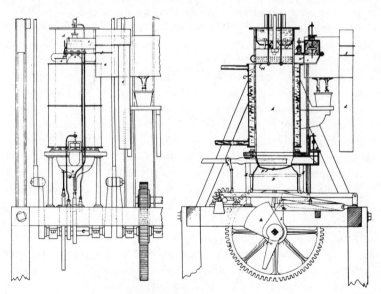

Fig. 6-9   Morey engine from drawings in his patent of 1826. (From the English patent in Hazard's name)

to the one for a gas engine on April 1, 1826.[23] These included steam engines and pumps, lamps, fireplaces and gas producing apparatus. His first patent for a steam powered fireplace spit issued in 1793. Much of his early steam work was based on boat engines, and an admiring biographer makes a case for Morey as the rightful inventor of the paddle-wheel steam boat.[24] Regrettably, little is generally known about this prolific contributor to early American technology.

There is only one known surviving copy of Morey's gas engine patent, the Patent Office copy being destroyed in the 1836 fire.[25] The invention was protected also in England under the name of Erskine Hazard, an American engineer friend living in London. The English patent, although omitting details of Morey's numerous experiments, follows closely the engine description as stated in his United States patent.[26] Morey had demonstrated his engine (Fig. 6-10) in New York City after securing the U.S. patent, and it was at that time Hazard most likely became involved in Morey's behalf.[27]

Morey broke new ground with his concept of fuel preparation. He recognized that it was impractical in portable engine applications to produce or to carry a tank of pre-made gas on the conveyance. The solution was to vaporize, as required by engine need, a liquid fuel of alcohol or turpentine right at the engine. Morey's "preparation vessel" thus became the earliest liquid fuel carburetor for an I-C engine. The carburetor contained no moving parts (Fig. 6-11) and consisted simply of a box compartmented into a labyrinth of half inch square passages. Air first coursed through vapor rising off warmed fuel in the base, and the turbulence created by the passage design served to combine the two components into a homogeneous mixture. With a sufficiently large vaporizing area the fuel had to be heated only to a "blood warm" temperature. Below eighty degrees Fahrenheit the volatility of turpentine was too low to sustain engine operation. Morey claimed that by adding heat from a small lamp the generated vapor from the box was enough to supply two eight inch diameter by twenty-four inch stroke cylinders with up to 100 charges per minute. This gave a crank speed of 50 rpm and a geared-up flywheel speed of as high as 150 to 200 rpm (if it is safe to assume, which it is not, the gear ratio is accurately depicted by the patent drawing). Morey indicated the rate of vaporization was speed responsive in that a higher air velocity produced more combustible mixture.

A seemingly insignificant detail, yet vital to safe operation, was the addition of wire screen or "gauze" fire barriers (Fig. 6-9) between the "inflaming valve" and the carburetor. These were added "to prevent

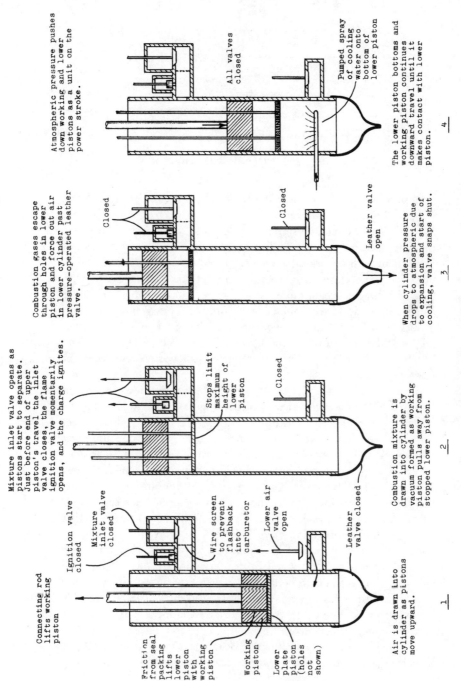

Connecting rod lifts working piston

Mixture inlet valve opens as pistons start to separate. Just before end of upper piston's travel the inlet valve closes, the flame ignition valve momentarily opens, and the charge ignites.

Ignition valve closed

Mixture inlet valve closed

Wire screen to prevent flashback into carburetor

Lower air valve open

Stops limit maximum height of lower piston

Closed

Friction from seal packing lifts lower piston with working piston

Working piston

Lower plate piston (holes not shown)

Leather valve closed

1

Air is drawn into cylinder as pistons move upward.

2

Combustion mixture is drawn into cylinder by vacuum formed as working piston pulls away from stopped lower piston.

Combustion gases escape through holes in lower piston and force out air in lower cylinder past pressure-operated leather valve.

Closed

Closed

Leather valve open

3

When cylinder pressure drops to atmospheric due to expansion and start of cooling, valve snaps shut.

Atmospheric pressure pushes down working and lower pistons as a unit on the power stroke.

All valves closed

Pumped spray of cooling water onto bottom of lower piston

4

The lower piston bottoms and working piston continues downward travel until it makes contact with lower piston.

Fig. 6-10 Operation of 1826 Morey engine

81

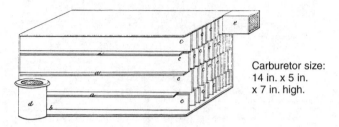

Carburetor size:
14 in. x 5 in.
x 7 in. high.

Fig. 6-11   Morey carburetor. (Hazard's patent drawing)

explosion in the box, should the vapour valve not close in time."[28] The value of this idea for an engine was later confirmed by George Brayton (Chapter 10) who faced a similar problem and solved it by reinventing the same method. Brayton said in his 1872 patent, "Many months of experiment with a working engine subjected to every variety of conditions likely to occur in daily use have proved to me that a series of wire-gauze diaphragms (six or more) perfectly intercept the flame and render danger from accident impossible."[29] Brayton was granted a claim including in combination a "perforated partition whose office is to ... prevent the back action of the ignited charge."[30] He was a fortunate beneficiary of the Patent Office fire which destroyed Morey's record of prior invention.

A September 1829 letter Morey wrote to business friends in Philadelphia[31] gave a few details of the engine's performance. He reported it had propelled a boat, nineteen feet long by five and a half feet wide, at speeds up to eight miles per hour and that the operation was economical and "as regular as any that are driven with steam." The stern mounted engine occupied only eighteen inches of hull length. Morey closed with thoughts about his future plans: "I can but hope and trust that the ensuing winter will see the engine well applied to a carriage on a railroad." The letter was written only four months after America's first steam locomotive arrived in New York from England.

Proceeds from the sale of his steam related patents, combined with business interests at Orford and Fairlee, Vermont (he owned a sawmill and a large acreage of timberland near there), provided him with the funds to continue his experimentation. He had earlier been responsible for the design and construction of the canals and locks at Bellows Falls on the Connecticut River.[32]

Morey diligently pursued the sale of the gas engine until 1830 but was never able to find a buyer. Nevertheless, he had that gift of imagination, coupled with the conviction of the rightness of his ideas, to make some prophetic comments. These visions were recorded in one of his unpublished papers. For farmers he said, "There will be little use of horses" after his engine was perfected. Also, "I see no reason why it [the gas engine] may not, in addition to the uses to which steam is applied, be applied with the greatest advantage in drawing carriages on good roads and railways and particularly for giving what seems to be much wanted direction and velocity to Balloons."[33]

Lemuel Wright: 1833

While Morey's engine cooled down for the last time, a new design was on the drawing board of Lemuel Wellman Wright.[34] This engineer from a London suburb patented his non-compression engine in 1835 and pointed to yet another direction for I-C development to take.

A logical question for those who sought alternatives to steam power was: if steam engines did not need the atmosphere to move pistons, why should a gas engine? Let the power stroke come from the combustion expansion force acting on the piston. Return the piston by flywheel inertia, or better yet, make the engine double-acting like most steam engines and have every stroke be a power stroke. (Lebon had shown one way, but his scheme was too ambitious for the technology of the times.) This concept of continuous power strokes was to act as a mental block until Otto proved his own revolutionary one power stroke for every two shaft turns.

The non-compression* engine grew to resemble its steam counterpart in both appearance and operation. Thermal efficiency was never but little better than that of contemporary high pressure steam engines. Expansion possibilities were very limited (the key to its gross inefficiency), and cooling of the combustion chamber was a paramount problem.

Wright may have recognized these inherent expansion and cooling difficulties, but his solution made the design overly complex. An air and coal gas mixture was ignited in a small antechamber connected to the cylinder, and burning gases could expand over most of the piston stroke. (Fig. 6-12) Later engines of this type had expansion over only one-half of the total stroke. In addition to large water jackets around the cylinder, the piston was cooled by pouring water into a hollow piston rod. Wright's patent was the first to specify cylinder cooling as a necessary means for protecting engine parts. This was distinct from the water

---

*No compression of the combustible mixture prior to ignition.

jackets on atmospheric engines where cooling was thought to be desirable only to promote higher cylinder vacuums. The Wright configuration, resembling a small "table pattern" steam engine popular at the time, incorporated a flyball governor for speed control. This was also

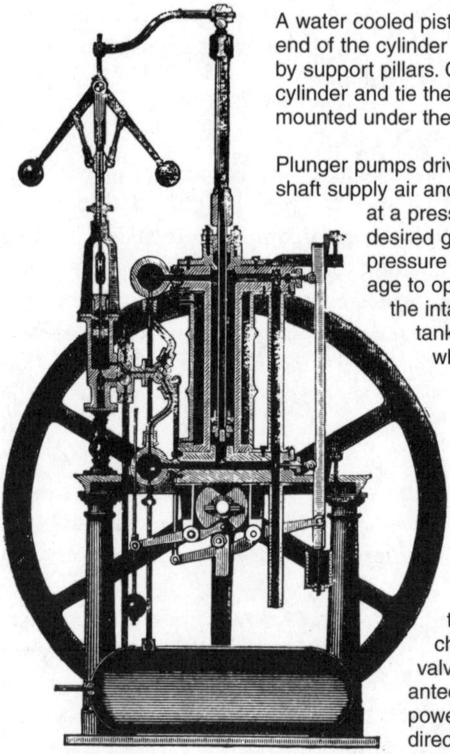

A water cooled piston rod coming out at the top end of the cylinder is linked to a crosshead guided by support pillars. Connecting rods straddle the cylinder and tie the crosshead to a crankshaft mounted under the cylinder.

Plunger pumps driven by eccentrics on the crankshaft supply air and coal gas to tanks maintained at a pressure of one to two psi. If the desired gas pressure is exceeded, a pressure operated plunger moves linkage to open a valve and spill gas back to the intake side of the pump. The air tank bleeds to the atmosphere when its pressure limit is reached.

Gas and air are separately piped through rotary valves into metering chambers under the flyball governor. If speed increases a larger air charge is measured and, with the resultant leaner mixture, power is reduced. The cam controlled rotary valves are timed to allow the gas-air charges to pass back through the valves and mix on their way to an antechamber connected to the power cylinder. A third rotary valve directs the charge to supply alternately each end of the double-acting cylinder.

Ignition is by a continuous flame burning at a touch hole through the wall of each antechamber. Combustion begins as the charge enters the chamber. The expanding gases are free to pass into the main cylinder and push against the piston. There is a sliding valve to prevent pressure from escaping through the touch hole.

As the piston begins its return stroke a flat faced valve opens and allows exhaust products to be pushed out of the cylinder. The volume of residual exhaust gases remaining in the cylinder and adjacent passages is large.

Fig. 6-12   Wright double-acting engine. (From his English patent of 1833)

new to I-C engine practice. His patent drawings indicate a carefully worked out design on paper, but operational success would be doubtful. There is no record of such an engine ever being built.

An intriguing comment in the patent mentions the addition of pressurized air and a little steam pumped directly into the cylinder after each ignition. This would mix with expanding combustion gases entering past a one-way pressure operated valve inserted between the antechamber and the cylinder. Wright says, "by mixing with the condensed

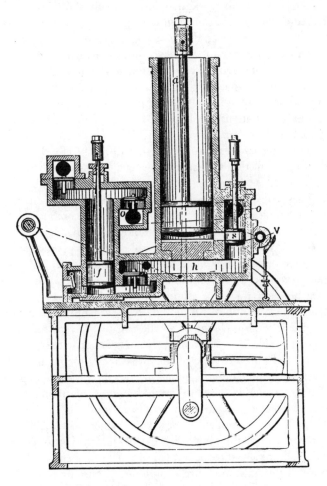

Fig. 6-13   Barnett "compression" engine of 1838, the first of three.
(The Smithsonian Institution)

[pressurized] air and steam the expansive force will be greatly increased."[36] Did he know something about the value of compression that he was not telling?

William Barnett: 1838

The ideas of William Barnett, an "iron founder" from Brighton, England, represent a growing awareness of the prerequisites for an efficient and practical I-C engine. His patent,[37] almost the sole source of what is known about his work, describes a structure which gives form to the theoretical compression engine suggested by Sadi Carnot. He gave no indication, however, that he recognized why his engine should be more efficient if he pressurized the combustible mixture before igniting it. Barnett's more practical contribution was a flame ignition system compatible with charge compression, and beginning with Otto, it was used in modified form on thousands of production engines.

Three design variations are disclosed in the Barnett patent, and like Wright's, all are based on the popular table pattern steam engine. Two plunger pumps separately measured and then dispatched fixed volumes of air and coal gas directly, or via an intermediate mixing chamber, into the cylinder. External supply pumps to compress the charge are shown for all three engines, but only in the third is further compression imparted by the power piston itself in the engine cylinder prior to combustion.

Barnett's first engine (Fig. 6-13) employed a single-acting power piston. The air pump, performing a double duty, supplied cylinder air from one side of its piston while the opposite side pulled exhaust gas from the previous cycle out of the combustion chamber. (He also said this extra function might be eliminated, and the exhaust could pass directly into the atmosphere.) A plunger-type valve opened the cylinder either to the incoming charge or to the exhaust. Except for the new flame ignition valve, all other valves were pressure operated.

Because of the above atmospheric pressure in the intake system, the conventional "touch hole" igniter flame method was no longer possible. Barnett's solution was to invent a means of timing a small, self-contained flame into the combustible mixture without the flame being blown out when suddenly exposed to a higher pressure. His igniter was a rotating, conical plug valve (Fig. 6-14) which had a gas jet extending into a hollow valve interior through the stationary end of the body. Valve ports first indexed to receive a continuously burning flame from an external gas jet. This ignited the gas already in the valve cavity supplied by the other jet. Further rotation shut off the outside flame port and uncovered another port leading into a receiver chamber by the cylinder. The novelty was that the flame continued to burn long enough within the valve cavity to ignite the charge when the internal ports indexed. Ignition was timed to begin in the receiver when the engine piston reached dead center and the plunger valve opened to connect the receiver with the cylinder. Even though the internal igniter port was under a higher pressure than the outside air, the valve flame was not snuffed out because there was no way for the pressure to escape and create a back draft. By the time the valve had rotated back to begin the cycle once again, fresh gas had entered from the internal jet to prepare for the new ignition flame. There was no lingering fire in the valve cavity because it had been extinguished by the charge explosion after the previous ignition plus the subsequent lack of oxygen. The igniting system seems roundabout, but as later improved by Otto, proved to be quite reliable.

A second engine in the patent (Fig. 6-15) was double-acting, both for the power piston and supply pumps. A third, auxiliary suction pump

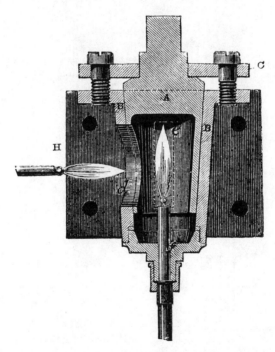

Fig. 6-14   Barnett rotating igniter cock – 1838. (The Smithsonian
            Institution)

was suggested for removal of exhaust gas from the cylinder. All of the pistons were timed to act in unison. Igniting valves for each combustion chamber were ported directly into the cylinder opposite the common intake and exhaust opening. When the piston was at the end of a stroke, a sliding plunger valve moved to let a pressurized charge enter the cylinder from an intermediate reservoir. With the charge in the cylinder, and the piston starting outward, the igniting "cock" admitted its flame to initiate combustion. One combustion chamber was open to an intake passage while the opposite chamber was exhausting. Most of the engine's other features were similar to those found in the first

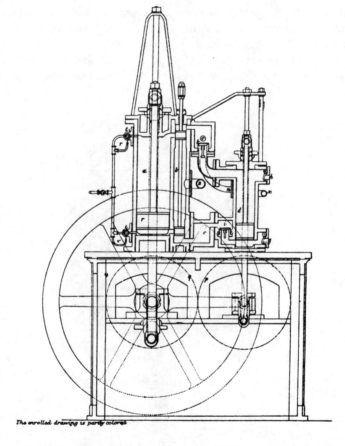

The scrolled drawing is partly colored.

Fig. 6-15   Barnett double-acting engine of 1838. Second of three.
(From his 1838 English patent)

engine, an important one being that expansion occurred throughout the entire power stroke.

Barnett's third engine has the greatest historical significance because of its compression in the power cylinder prior to ignition. No theory or advantage was given for this key idea, nor was its use mentioned in the patent claims. However, he did refer to it in the engine's description:

> ...[The] explosive mixture is ignited by coming in contact (whilst under pressure) with spongy platina. ..., and... the contact of the platina with the explosive mixture, aided by compression of the latter, produced by the ascent of the

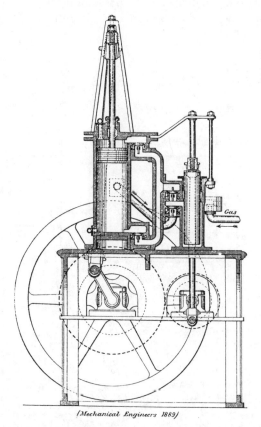

[Mechanical Engineers 1889]

Fig. 6-17 Barnett "compression" engine, cross-section view.
Third of three engines in his 1838 English patent.
(Proc. Institution of Mechanical Engineers, 1889)

piston, causes the mixture to ignite and explode, and the sudden and powerful expansion of the gases thus produced impels the piston to the bottom of its stroke.[38]

Spongy platina, a platinum-like wire compressed into a mass, caused ignition of the coal gas by catalytic action. This alternate method was proposed, but Barnett preferred his "flame igniting cock." (There is an analogy with the platinum used in catalytic mufflers for automotive exhaust emission control.)

According to Barnett's theory of operation, all of the new charge had been pumped into the upper chamber (Figs. 6-16, Plate and 6-17) by the time the piston ascended to the position shown. The piston continued upward under true compression conditions to top center where igni-

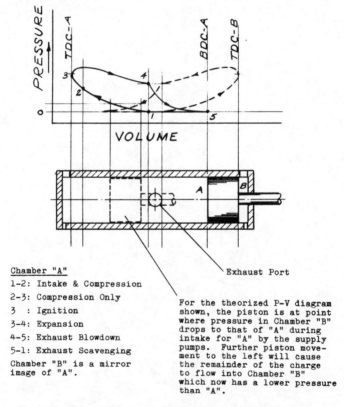

Chamber "A"
1-2: Intake & Compression
2-3: Compression Only
3 : Ignition
3-4: Expansion
4-5: Exhaust Blowdown
5-1: Exhaust Scavenging
Chamber "B" is a mirror image of "A".

Exhaust Port

For the theorized P-V diagram shown, the piston is at point where pressure in Chamber "B" drops to that of "A" during intake for "A" by the supply pumps. Further piston movement to the left will cause the remainder of the charge to flow into Chamber "B" which now has a lower pressure than "A".

Fig. 6-18   Theoretical pressure-volume diagram, Barnett double-acting "compressing" engine of 1838. (Author sketch)

tion occurred and then began its expansion stroke. An analysis of cylinder pressure versus time for this third design is shown in Fig. 6-18.

The engine, with its double acting piston, had three auxiliary pumps to perform gas and air pumping and suction scavenging. These operated at twice crankshaft speed and carried out their functions during a part of each cycle. (Only one pump is shown in the drawing.) All had pressure operated intake and discharge valves as did the inlet valves to the working cylinder.

The gas and air pump plungers had diameters sized to provide about a nine to one ratio of air to "hydrogen, or other inflammable gas." Their strokes were timed to ensure that the chamber of the cylinder firing next had received its full charge by approximately thirty degrees before top center. It was after this point that the cylinder piston further compressed the charge. There would have been some interval when inlet valves and exhaust port were both open because of the valves being actuated only by a pressure differential.

The scavenging pump plunger was timed so that suction began shortly after the crown of the piston uncovered a scavenge port midway along the cylinder. Following an initial pressure drop, most of the remaining exhaust gases were then sucked out and discharged into the atmosphere, possibly along with some of the next incoming charge.

It is not known for certain if these engines were ever made and tested, and if so, what problems resulted. One apparent design deficiency was that no provision was shown for cooling the cylinder, although it may be fair to assume Barnett must have been aware of the need. Nevertheless, his basic objectives were valid and proved to be a harbinger of the compression engines to come over thirty years later.

Contemporary, self-anointed experts in matters pertaining to power producers have never failed to advance their views on the futility of such things as *internal*-combustion engines. Thomas P. Jones, the Superintendent of the U.S. Patent Office who was aware of at least Brown's and Morey's engines, offered his opinion on the subject in 1833:[39]

> We are not prepared to say that there is not in nature any better power than that of steam, because we believe that our knowledge of the laws of nature, and the resources of art in applying them, will always be progressive; but we are fully convinced that this better power will not be the result of the firing of gunpowder, or of any other *explosive* mixture by which sudden and intermitting effects are produced.

Stuart Perry: 1844-1846

A liquid fueled engine was built by Stuart Perry (1814-1890), a resident of Newport in upstate New York. There are records of two Perry designs,[40] the second (1846) being an attempt to correct acknowledged deficiencies in the first (1844). Both Perry and Samuel Morey are good examples of men adapting their engines to burn fuels available in remotely located applications. Small and practical coal gas producers were not yet perfected to serve these areas. (Perry did suggest his engine could be modified to burn coal gas if the change was economically justified.)

Perry's approach, like Morey's, was to mix air with vaporized turpentine in a heated enclosure. By using an auxiliary air pump, part of whose output passed through a heated "retort," Perry claimed vaporization was enhanced. The result was an over rich mixture leaving the carburetor, but this was diluted by combining with the remainder of the air discharged from the pump. A throttle valve located between the air pump and the retort gave final control over the mixture ratio. A heating lamp could be extinguished after the engine reached operating temperatures; either the exhaust (1844 design) or cooling water (1846) provided sufficient heat for fuel vaporization.

A single, horizontal cylinder containing a double-acting piston was located directly over the air pump (Fig. 6-19, Plate). The slightly pressurized charge entered the cylinder through positively controlled inlet valves as the piston began its outward movement from dead center. Intake stopped about one-eighth of the way down the stroke where heat was applied to ignite the charge. The expansion characteristics would have been similar to Wright's double-acting engine, in that the complete charge was in the cylinder before the piston had traveled very far. Unlike production non-compression engines coming later, expansion occurred throughout most of the stroke.

Perry must have experienced severe overheating problems with his air cooled, first design because in his second patent he described means to cool not only the cylinder, but the piston and the stuffing box for the connecting rod. The piston was cooled by injecting water into a circumferential groove between the piston rings as the piston passed a supply port in the side wall at each end of the cylinder. Water sprayed directly into the cylinder when the piston had moved to completely uncover the ports. Perry claimed this served to cool and lubricate the cylinder.

In the earlier design, ignition was from a continuous flame admitted past a valve tripped open when the piston hit a pin projecting from the valve. Vapor bled directly from the retort was piped to supply a small flame at each ignition valve. This system was superseded in the second design. (Perry needed Barnett's flame cock because the greater than atmospheric cylinder pressure could blow out the flame when the valve was tripped open. The manner in which Perry described the earlier ignition process causes one to suspect he was aware of a potential weakness.) In his later method the continuously burning flames heated small "platina" cups filled with a fine platinum wire mass. The cups were maintained at an incandescent state and were insulated from the surrounding engine structure by a clay lining. Only when a cam-operated valve opened was the cup exposed to the combustible mixture. Perry thus differed from Barnett by keeping the wire mass at a uniform state of readiness as well as timing the point of ignition.

Intake and exhaust were first shown controlled by a large, rotating cylindrical valve driven by bevel gears off the output shaft. (Fig. 6-19, Plate) Slots cut crosswise on the valve indexed with ports in the closely fitting valve housing. The exhaust slots, when connected to their ports, allowed combustion products to flow around and heat tubular passages in the vaporizing box. The valving method adopted for the 1846 engine used modern engine practice: cams on a separate shaft operated poppet-type intake and exhaust valves through a pushrod and rocker lever arrangement. (Fig. 6-20)

A final feature of the improved engine was the addition of a compressed air tank for starting. Charged by a separate pump, it served to prime the cylinder. Each combustion chamber was filled with a burnable mixture by declutching the camshaft so that it could be turned by hand to open the valves. Air was not used to force piston movement.

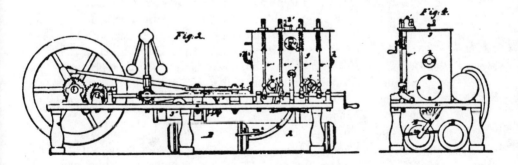

Fig. 6-20   Perry 1846 engine. (From the drawings of his U.S. patent)

Perry demonstrated his engine at his brother Samuel's store in New York City during 1846. It was described in *Scientific American*[41] "capable of working ten horsepowers," and by substituting rosin for turpentine, the "expense of feeding it" was reduced to about fifty cents per day. The engine derived "an astonishing power in proportion to the minute quantity of material from which the power is produced." The brief article closed by saying, "The ingenious inventor has had some difficulties to encounter in the construction of the first engine, but has a fair prospect of being well remunerated for his labor." Alas, a prediction never fulfilled.

Perry's work with engines occupied only a short span of a productive and prosperous life. Shortly after graduation from Union College in 1837 he went into a butter and cheese distribution business with his brother, a relationship lasting almost twenty years. After that, with his real interest in things mechanical, he became an independent inventor. He was granted a total of almost forty patents, some of which proved to be valuable and remunerative. There were significant ones for combination type locks (Linus Yale [1821-1868], the inventor of the Yale lock, was a Herkimer County native and friend of Perry) and hay tedders for turning and spreading hay in the field to hasten drying.[42] The failure of his engine to reach the market was only a minor setback in an otherwise successful career.

Alfred Drake: 1843-1855

Publicized demonstrations of Dr. Alfred Drake's non-compression gas engine served notice again of potential alternatives to steam. Drake displayed a working engine in his native city of Philadelphia in 1843 and then at a New York City machinery exhibit in 1855.[43] The operating characteristics appear to be the same for both, with the novel feature being a "hot-tube "igniter" (Figs. 6-21, Plate). This same ignition method was used on the first gasoline engines of Gottlieb Daimler and Wilhelm Maybach in 1883 (Chapter 12) and was found on engines built as late as 1900. For reasons unknown, Drake did not apply for patents until 1855. His U.S. patent of that year was followed shortly thereafter by one from Britain which issued to his "correspondent" in London, Alfred Vincent Newton.[44]

The Drake engine was double-acting with a single, horizontal cylinder (Fig. 6-22, Plate). A tank in the base containing the combustible mixture was slightly pressurized by air from an engine operated pump and from the coal gas supply; a valve in the gas line served to maintain the mixture at a desired nine or ten to one air:fuel ratio. Poppet intake and exhaust valves were actuated by a "rock shaft" driven off an eccentric on the crankshaft in contemporary steam practice. Cooling water circulated around a cylinder jacket and passed into a tube with one end axially attached to a cylinder head and the other extending into the cylinder over most of its length. The piston was hollow and its tubular rod telescoped over the fixed tube. By a series of ports in the piston and tube the piston was supplied with cooling water. (There appears to be no circulation path within the piston to prevent steam from forming.) Water exited the engine from a port in the exposed end of the piston rod. The model shows no crosshead bearing and guide at the outboard end of the piston rod. This would have forced all of the side thrust from the connecting rod onto the stuffing box seal at the one cylinder head, a construction no doubt changed in the full size engine.

Intake occurred during the very first portion of the outward piston stroke, and ignition occurred before twenty-five to thirty percent was completed. Cylinder pressure at the time of ignition must have been just at or below atmospheric.

The hot-tube igniter, so popular at the end of the nineteenth century, was a thimble-like cast iron piece projecting into a recess in the cylinder wall. The tube end was kept at a red heat by an internal flame whose air and fuel supply was from the same tank which fed the cylinder. An igniter assembly was positioned at each end of the cylinder so that after intake was complete the piston crown uncovered the recess, and the hot tube could ignite the charge.

The 1855 engine shown at New York's Crystal Palace reportedly had a sixteen inch diameter cylinder and with an eighteen inch stroke. No power rating was given.[45] Drake had difficulty at the exhibit with either the gas composition or maintaining a correct mixture ratio. As a consequence, the engine ran for a very little time.[46] Although Drake tried to launch a commercial venture with his engine, he apparently did not advance beyond the demonstration stage.

Barsanti and Matteucci: 1854-1864

Only an act of fate prevented two sons of Italy from being remembered as the founders of the I-C engine industry. Instead they closed an era of necessary, but financially unrewarding, searching and experimenting. What is generally known about Eugenio Barsanti (1821-1864) and his partner, Felice Matteucci (1808-1887), is based only on early developments and not later achievements. (Fig. 6-23, Plate)

95

Unlike their co-workers in the same endeavor, Barsanti and Matteucci were educated scientists and engineers. When they first met in 1851 Barsanti, a Piarist priest,[47] was a lecturer of mathematics and applied science at the Instituto Ximeniano in Florence; Matteucci was a practicing hydraulics engineer who had a distinguished academic background. Brought together professionally by a reclamation project on a nearby lake, the two remained close friends until Barsanti's untimely death.[48]

It is unclear how much Barsanti knew of the patents of earlier I-C engine inventors like LeBon and Brown, but he was aware of Volta's work and how it might lead to an improved engine. At the time he met Matteucci he was investigating the ignition of combustible gases within a closed cylinder. By 1854 the team had designed a free-piston atmospheric engine; this same design was the structure disclosed in their first British patent.[49] They gave no consideration to a non-compression engine because of the severe penalty paid in thermal efficiency from the lack of expansion. Cost estimates for a two-cylinder engine were given by Benini (Works and Foundry, Florence) in late 1853, and an order to build followed.[50] Manufacturing difficulties delayed completion until 1856 (Fig. 6-24, Plate). After acceptance it was installed in the Maria Antonia Railway Works near Florence, where it was used to power several machine tools.[51]

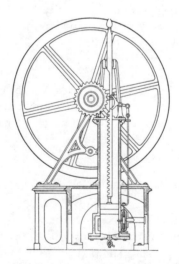

Fig. 6-25.   Cross-section view of the 1857 Barsanti and Matteucci engine. (Orsi, *Padre Eugenio Barsanti,* 1954)

A second British patent in 1857 incorporates improvements no doubt found necessary from operating experience with their first engine.[52] This patent also describes a simplified design which they implied had even greater promise. The engines of the 1854 and 1857 patents (Fig. 6-25) had a new feature later adopted by Otto and Langen in 1866: a rack and pinion gear to convert reciprocating into rotary movement. A drive train weakness (based on reports written forty to sixty years later) was the pawl and ratchet arrangement allowing the piston to move freely upward and engage only when it was traveling inward on the power stroke. Rivaz's chain and pulley were eliminated, but the pawl and ratchet were retained. The free-piston concept, first used by Rivaz, had the advantage of allowing outward movement against no significant forces other than piston inertia and friction. (The "free-piston" I-C engines built in the 1930s to 50s as high pressure, multi-stage air compressors and as gasifiers to drive turbines raised the paradoxical question of "how free is a free piston?" In the context of the atmospheric engines under discussion, "free" means declutched while moving in one direction). Stroke length depended on the size of the fuel charge: a weaker explosion produced, in turn, less piston travel and a lower cylinder vacuum, with the result being less force available from the atmosphere to produce power.

A major difference between the two 1857 engines was that the first, based on the 1854 design, had two pistons versus one in the latter and at that time, preferred version (Fig. 6-26). An auxiliary or charging and scavenging piston was not "free." It was operated by a crosshead linkage driven off eccentrics from the continuously rotating output shaft, the speed of which was stabilized by a flywheel.

Porting in a slide valve and its body allowed air to be sucked into the combustion chamber between the two pistons as the lower piston was pulled downward. After receiving the air charge, an arm extending from the still descending lower piston rod hit a trip stop on another rod fastened to the slide valve. The valve was then repositioned to briefly admit a charge of coal gas. With the lower piston and valve continuing further as a unit, the gas port was in turn cut off, and an electric spark from an igniter initiated combustion. The free piston was rapidly thrown upward to create a vacuum in the cylinder through the usual means of rapid expansion followed by upward piston inertia. Atmospheric pressure and its own weight returned the piston. The lower piston also began its mechanically timed upward movement, but not until the power piston had returned to its starting position. The slide

Fig. 7-3   Lenoir gas engine made by Reading Iron Works; Reading, England. (The Science Museum, London)

Fig. 7-9 Bisschop non-compression engine, 1870. (The Science Museum, London)

Fig. 7-8 Hugon vertical, non-compression gas engine in the Musée des Arts et Métiers, Paris (Author photo)

Fig. 7-12　Hugon 1/2 hp, horizontal gas engine, 1867. (The Science Museum, London)

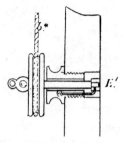

Fig. 6-27   Barsanti and Matteucci electric igniter. (From their
British patent of 1855)

were closed, and a spark was generated each time a gap formed between
the spring wire and the turning electrode. Sparking continued until the
lower piston was lifted off the cylinder base.

A unique offshoot of the original concept was a design by Giovanni
Battista Babacci, an engineer who joined with Barsanti and Matteucci.[54]
This new approach was a single cylinder atmospheric engine having
opposed pistons (Fig. 6-28, Plate). The pistons, one with a slightly
shorter stroke than the other, were free to move outward, but as before,
powered through a ratchet and pawl to a drive shaft on their inward
strokes. The two shafts were tied together by bevel gearing and a shaft
running parallel to the cylinder. The innermost position of the pistons
was determined by a cam hitting a tappet projection on the rack gear as
in the second design of the 1857 British patent. Even though each
piston was free to move outward and start inward in a generally random
fashion, they become re-synchronized with each other by timing when
the cams gave their added little push to locate the pistons at their
respective innermost points. A slide valve, fastened to a rod strung
between eccentrics on each output shaft, performed the intake and
exhaust functions. Ignition was still electric, and now a Rühmkorff
induction coil created the high voltage spark. (Although not the original inventor of the induction coil, Heinrich Daniel Rühmkorff (1803-
1877) improved it to the point that for many years his name was used
synonymously with "induction" to identify the type of coil.)[55] Benini
built an eight horsepower engine to this design in 1858.

The success of the opposed piston engine encouraged Barsanti and
Matteucci to start a company, "Società Promotrice del Nuovo Motore
Barsanti e Matteucci," in October of 1860.[56] A twenty horsepower ver-
sion generated considerable public interest when it was shown at the

Italian Exposition held at Florence in 1861. (A remarkable accomplishment, considering the limited power that was practical to extract from the largest Otto and Langen atmospheric engines yet to come.) This engine, built by another firm, was placed in service by the "Società Navigazione Lariana" of Como. The last opposed piston engine, a twelve horsepower, two cylinder model, was constructed by Escher, Wyss & Co. of Zurich.

Barsanti and Matteucci had two vital questions to answer: What model should be selected for the production engine, and who was going to build it? At least three manufacturers had already been tried and for one reason or another eliminated from consideration. The first decision was to return to the smaller, single cylinder engine having the auxiliary piston as shown in the 1857 British patent. A four horsepower model of this configuration was thought to hold the best market potential. The Bauer Helvetica Co. of Milan was given an order to build several of these engines in 1863. Tests were run on the first unit completed, and the performance was not to be equaled for some years to come, if the results may be believed. It consumed 800 liters of coal gas per horsepower hour to yield a fourteen percent overall efficiency and indicated efficiency of twenty-one percent!

Barsanti faced an uphill battle alone by now, and time was starting to run out. His friend and partner, Matteucci, was forced to resign because of ill health in 1862; there was also the emergence of the Lenoir engine as a potentially strong competitor. He needed a builder with an established reputation and a proven capability in the steam engine field; Soc. John Cockerill of Seraing, Belgium, met the criteria. Barsanti wrote a letter to Cockerill in December of 1863 specifically outlining the advantages of his engine over the Lenoir. (Data was given which showed his had one-fifth the fuel consumption.) An engine, shipped to Seraing for evaluation[57] was to be set up on Barsanti's arrival in March of 1864. The initial demonstrations were highly encouraging,[58] but before Barsanti could complete the tests and begin negotiations he became ill with typhus. He died on April 19th at the age of forty-two, in Liège. His remains were brought to Florence for burial.[59]

Cockerill immediately abandoned the project on written instructions from Italy. A few months later work began again in Florence under the new leadership of Fathers Antonelli and Cecchi, directors and stockholders of the company. They prevented Matteucci from assuming his rule as technical director, but he still came back to assist Babacci. The company's new efforts were concentrated on a hot-air engine which was doomed to failure; the new managers lacked the practical and business experience to carry on with what Barsanti and Matteucci had begun. Matteucci returned to his engineering practice.

The Barsanti and Matteucci story, as most often chronicled, ends in 1857 where it really began. While speculation with its advantage of hindsight is dangerous, one cannot help but consider the outcome if Cockerill and Barsanti had had a few good years together. The most criticized design feature of the engine was the ratchet and pawl drive. This was strictly a mechanical problem which was adequately resolved three years later by Eugene Langen. However, the fact remains the Barsanti and Matteucci engine did not go into series production, and it must be considered in that light regardless of the reasons for failing to do so.

Internal-combustion engines were now a reality. Inventors isolated from each other saw a need, and given a fuel, provided alternative directions away from steam. Atmospheric, compression and non-compression engines each had their advocates and were to have a chance to compete in the market place.

NOTES

1. William Cecil, "On the Application of Hydrogen Gas to produce a moving Power in Machinery; with a Description of an Engine which is moved by the Pressure of the Atmosphere upon a Vacuum caused by Explosions of Hydrogen Gas and Atmospheric Air," *Trans. Cambridge Phil. Soc.,* v. 1, Part 2, 1822, pp. 217-39.
2. John Venn, *Alumni Cantabrigianses:* Part II, (1752-1900), p. 547.
3. Cecil, *op. cit.,* p. 229.
4. Cecil, *op. cit.,* p. 230. Carbureted hydrogen is a mixture of hydrogen enriched with coal gas, i.e., adding a carbon compound to the gas.
5. Cecil, *op. cit.,* p. 237.
6. A. K. Bruce, "Samuel Brown and the Gas Engine," *The Engineer,* September 6, 1946, p. 214.
7. English patent No. 4,874 of December 4, 1823. The inventions covered in this patent were also protected by a U.S. patent issued March 2, 1824.
8. "Brown's Pneumatic Engine," *Mechanics' Magazine,* August 28, 1824, pp. 385-89. The drawing in the article is almost identical to that of the patent.

9. *Mechanics' Magazine*, April 16, 1825, p. 19.

10. Another Samuel Brown, a Royal Navy officer, received English patent No. 5,126 of 1825 for a chain driven means to pull a ship.

11. English patent No. 5,350 of April 25, 1826.

12. "Gas Engine Carriage," *Mechanic's Magazine*, June 13, 1826, pp. 79-80.

13. J.A. Whitfield, "Description of Cylinders, etc., to be applied on Mr. Brown's Patent Gas Principle to the working of a Carriage," *Mechanic's Magazine*, December 24, 1825, pp. 145-47. Whitfield was from the Bedlington Ironworks.

14. Seaton, *op. cit.*, p. 15.

15. "Mr. Brown's Gas Vacuum Engine," *Mechanic's Magazine*, February 3, 1827, pp. 82-84.

16. Seaton, *op. cit.*, p. 15.

17. "Brown's Gas Vacuum Engine," *Jour., Franklin Institute*, v. 15, 1833, pp. 274-75, and "The Croydon Canal Gas Vacuum Engine," *Mechanics' Magazine*, July 28, 1832, pp. 273-77.

18. Dugald Clerk, *The Gas, Petrol & Oil Engine*, v. 1, (New York, 1909), p. 5.

19. "Brown's Pneumatic Engine," *Mechanic's Magazine*, August 28, 1824, pp. 386, 389.

20. "Mr. Brown's Gas Vacuum Engine," *Mechanic's Magazine*, 1827, p. 83.

21. "Mr. Brown's Letter," *Jour. Franklin Inst.*, v. 5, 1828, pp. 206-207. Reprint of Brown's letter to the London *Times*.

22. "Gas and Vapour Engines," *Jour. Franklin Inst.*, v. 5, 1828, pp. 18-19.

23. *A Digest of Patents Issued by the United States from 1790 to January 1, 1839*, (Washington, D.C., 1840), p. 109.

24. Gabriel Farrell, Jr., *Cap't. Samuel Morey Who Built a Steamboat Fourteen Years Before Fulton*, (Manchester, 1915), p. 11.

25. The Morey patent copy is in the Baker Library, Dartmouth College, Hanover, New Hampshire.

26. English patent No. 5,402 of August 12, 1826, to Erskine Hazard, a citizen of the United States of America." (An article in *The Franklin Journal*, v. 1, 1826, p. 252, on the Morey engine, states that "a gentleman has gone to England for the purpose of obtaining a patent in that country." English practice allowed patents to issue in the name of the resident rather than the true inventor. See Chapter 3.)

27. Thomas Ewbank, *A Descriptive and Historical Account of Hydraulic and Other Machines for Raising Water...*, 4 ed., (New York, 1850), p. 473. An account of the demonstration is reported.

28. "An account of a new explosive engine generating a power that may be substituted for that of a steam engine. By Samuel Morey Oxford [*sic*], New Hampshire," *Am. Jour. of Science and Art*, v. XI, October 1826, p. 108. The idea was an adaptation of Sir Humphry Davy's mine safety lamp of 1816.

29. U.S. patent No. 125,166 of April 2, 1872, issued to George Bailey Brayton, p. 3.

30. *Ibid.*, p. 4.

31. Katherine R. Goodwin & Charles E. Duryea, "Samuel Morey, Precursor of Motor Power Development," *The Vermonter*, v. 36, May 1931, p. 142. Alice Doan Hodgson, in a letter to the author, adds new information and logical arguments on the friends' relationship to Morey. Rush and Muhlenberg were sons-in-law of Oliver Evans, and it was their foundry and machine shop in Philadelphia, the Bush Hill Works, that probably made many of Morey's engine parts, both steam and gas. Morey and Evans had become acquainted years earlier.

32. Wm. A. Duer, *Reply to Mr. Colden's Vindication of the Steam-Boat Monopoly*, 1819, p. 55. The source is referred to and quoted in a letter from Alice D. Hodgson to the author.

33. Alice Doan Hodgson, *Samuel Morey, Inventor Extraordinary*, (Orford, NH, 1961), pp. 18-19.

34. C. St. C. Davison, "The Internal-Combustion Engine, Some Early Stages in Its Development," *Engineering*, August 31, 1956, p. 258, suggests that Wright's first name was Samuel. A typographical error could have been made when the original hand written documents were transcribed into printed editions.

35. English patent No. 6,525 of December 16, 1833. (Wright).

36. *Ibid.*, p. 5.

37. English patent No. 7,615 of April 18, 1838. Brighton, the home given by Barnett in his patent, was the town nearest to a number of small iron foundries in Sussex County. The area was a principal source of charcoal iron. This information was kindly supplied by Mr. J.G.G. Hempson at Ricardo's, the great engine laboratory, located outside Brighton.

38. Barnett patent, pp. 5 and 6.

39. Thomas P. Jones, *Jour. Franklin Inst.*, 1833. Of interest is that Perry was granted an English patent, No. 9,972 of 1843, before covering the engine design shown in Fig. 6-19, Plate.

40. U.S. patent Nos. 3,597 of May 25, 1844, and 4,800 of October 7, 1846. A model for the earlier patent (Fig. 6-19) is on exhibit at the Museum of History and Technology, Washington, D.C. The second patent says Perry was a resident of New York City, but this was only for a short time. Documents in the Herkimer County, NY, Court House show most of Perry's life was spent in Newport.

41. "A New Gas Engine," *Scientific American*, v. 1, July 23, 1846.

42. *History of Herkimer County, New York,* 1879, and *Dictionary of American Biography,* (New York, 1934), v. 14, pp. 492-93.

43. *The Public Ledger,* Philadelphia, July 13, 1843 (an advertising reprint), and "The Ignition or Gas Engine," *The Railroad Advocate,* v. 2, December 22, 1855.

44. U.S. patent No. 12,715 of April 17, 1855, and British No. 562 of September 13, 1855, under the name of A.V. Newton. A patent model is on exhibit at MHT, Washington, D.C. (a model was once a required part of the patent application, if at all relevant. After 1870 one had to be furnished only when requested to do so by the Commissioner of Patents. This is a rare occurrence now.)

45. T.D. Stetson, "On the Ignition Gas Engine," *The Civil Engineer and Architect's Journal,* v. 19, (London, 1856), p. 340. See also, Frank A. Taylor, *Catalog of the Mechanical Collections of the Division of Engineering, United States National Museum,* Bulletin 173, (Washington, D.C., 1939), p. 146.

46. "The Ignition or Gas Engine," *The Railroad Advocate,* v. 2, New York, December 22, 1855.

47. "Piarist" refers to the "Order of the Pious Schools," a Catholic teaching order founded in 1617.

48. Vincenzo Vannacci, *L'invenzione del motore a scoppio realizzata dai toscani Barsanti e Matteucci', 1854-1954,* (Florence, 1955), pp. 8-10. See also: Giuseppe Orsi, *Padre Eugenio Barsanti ... 1853-1953,* (Pietrasanta, 1954), written for the engine's centennial.

49. British patent No. 1,072 of May 13, 1854 (Provisional only).

50. Vannacci, *op. cit.,* p. 15.

51. Vannacci, *ibid.,* p. 18.

52. British patent No. 1,655 of June 12, 1857. (A French patent of February 20, 1858, and an Italian patent, also of 1858 are similar to the British.)

53. A commonly used battery of the time developed by Robert Wilhelm Bunsen (1811-1899) of "burner" fame. The battery had zinc and carbon electrodes. The zinc rod was in a porous cup containing a dilute sulfuric acid solution. Outside the cup the carbon rod was in a concentrated nitric acid solution. The battery had a voltage of 1.9 volts per cell. Its chief disadvantage was the brown fumes from the nitric acid. See: Herbert W. Meyer, *A History of Electricity and Magnetism,* (Cambridge, 1971), p. 79. The de la Rive multiplier was named after August-Arthur de la Rive (1801-1873), a Swiss professor of physics at Geneva.

54. Patented in Italy in 1858. Babacci's name was not on the patent, although a later version patented in 1861 did list all three men.

55. Meyer, *op. cit.,* pp. 178-81.

56. Vannacci, *op. cit.,* p. 23.

57. This led to Hugo Güldner's erroneous conclusion that Cockerill built a Barsanti and Matteucci engine. See: Hugo Güldner, *Verbrennungskraftmaschinen,* 3rd ed., (Berlin, 1914), p. 627.

58. Details of problems in getting his engine through customs and the cooperation and helpfulness of the Cockerill people are given in an enthusiastic letter dated March 25, 1864, that Barsanti wrote to his company in Florence. See: Vannacci, *op. cit.,* pp. 31-32.

59. Orsi, *op. cit.,* p. 28.

Chapter 7

The Genesis of an Industry

Within a few years of its commercial introduction, the internal-combustion engine became a dependable enough source of power for a wide range of applications. Factories, print shops, hotels with luggage elevators and any business activity requiring small machine drives were all potential customers; there only had to be a nearby supply of illuminating gas. Initial reaction to the engine and its availability was enthusiastic, but users soon discovered that promised economy and reliability were often not as advertised. Nevertheless, these new entries in the power parade hastened the fulfillment of a need and desire for more efficient energy converters. The period of 1860 to 1867 saw the Lenoir begin, and the Otto and Langen atmospheric bring an end to the non-compression engine as a major thrust of development. The concept of compression before ignition also was openly discussed, although not seriously considered as a practical alternative.

The Lenoir Engine: 1860

Jean Joseph Étienne Lenoir (1822-1900) designed the world's first production I-C engine. (Fig. 7-1, Plate) Born in Mussy-la-Ville, Luxembourg (later ceded to Belgium), he moved to Paris at age sixteen where he became a metal enameler. In addition to developing new enamel materials he also invented an electroplating process. An interest in electricity led him to devise a railway telegraphy system and later to adopt electric ignition on all of his engines. Lenoir's engines were built under license,[1] but since large sales failed to materialize he never prospered from the ventures.

Probably less than 500 Lenoir engines were ever built, with most being made in Paris by M. Hippolyte Marinoni and by Lefebvre. (Fig. 7-2, Plate) The Reading Iron Works Ltd. of Reading, England, made about 100. (Sales agent for the English engines was the Lenoir Gas Engine Co. in London.) Koch and Co. of Leipzig and Kuhn of Stuttgart each tested an engine. An unknown small number were made by the

Lenoir Gas Engine Co. in New York, who advertised engines for one-half horsepower at $500 to four horsepower at $1,500.[2] The half horsepower model was probably the only size actually built in the United States.[3]

Lenoir's non-compression engine closely resembled a high pressure, double-acting steam engine in appearance, and the statement was made in his patent that it had operating characteristics like one. He specifically tried to disassociate his engine from the explosive-type atmospheric gas engines:

> ... my engine cannot be classed among gas engines. Indeed, the functions of the gas I employ do not consist in detonating or exploding it, thereby impelling the piston, as this has heretofore been done or suggested, but in the use of gas as a fuel that can be instantaneously and regularly ignited, and without producing any shock, for the purpose of heating the air that is mixed with it. The air thus dilated or expanded will act on the piston in the same manner as steam would in ordinary steam engines.[4]

The emphasis of his claim to invention was the method of admitting a combustible charge into the cylinder to achieve his "soft" combustion. This was actually accomplished at light loads more by cylinder conditions at the time of ignition (low pressure, etc.) than by what he thought caused it. There was knocking under full load because of the high rate of pressure rise after ignition. Little else was new and novel to the engine as an 1864 advertisement by the builder Lefebvre proclaims:

> The Lenoir engine uses Street's patented piston with direct and double action as developed by Lebon, the ignition is as with the Rivaz engine, the cylinder is cooled by water as in Samuel Brown's engine, it can be made to run on vaporized hydrocarbons as suggested by Herskine [sic] Hazard; on it can be found the same clever idea of Talbot's circular distributor. But in spite of all this the Lenoir engine sucks in gas and air through the action of the piston without necessitating any previous mixing, and for this reason it has a proper claim to be patented.[5]

The Lenoir engine (Fig. 7-3, Plate) was double-acting with power produced on each piston stroke. Flat slide-valves, parallel to and on opposite sides of the horizontal cylinder, separately performed the intake and exhaust functions. The valves, long enough to serve ports at each end of the cylinder, were moved by an eccentric on the crankshaft. The intake valve contained air and gas orifices sized to maintain a mixture at full power of about seven to one. A flexible rubber bladder damped gas line pressure fluctuations, and a flyball governor controlled speed by opening and closing a gas valve as required.

The "exceedingly delicate and troublesome"[6] electric ignition system consisted of two Bunsen-cell batteries, a Rühmkorff induction coil (like Barsanti and Matteucci), a distributor and lastly a spark plug in each cylinder head. An adjustable vibrating contact in the primary circuit of the coil induced high tension sparks (100 to 150 per second) across the plug gap in the secondary. The spark plug gaps varied from a suggested "one-sixteenth of an inch" for the American to "0.15 inches" for the English.[7]

Several designs of ignition distributors were tried. The first, as shown in the 1860 patent, made use of an insulated disc fastened to the end of the crankshaft. Located on the disc periphery were three conducting rings. The middle and continuous ring was connected to the outer, and oppositely placed to each other, segmented rings. Flat springs acted as sliding contacts on each of the rings. The length of the outer ring segments determined the time a spark plug was in the circuit, with the plug sparking at a rate set by the coil vibrator. The next design was a flat strip divided into two pieces and contacted by a slider operated off the connecting rod crosshead (Fig. 7-4). A final method returned to a rotary distributor, only now the insulated disc remained stationary and a rotor was driven off the end of the crankshaft. Sliding contacts on the rotor connected an inner ring on the disc face to an outer and concentric, but interrupted ring (Fig. 7-5). This improved rotary type was used on the French, English and American engines.

As the piston started outward from either dead center the intake slide-valve first moved to open only air ports. Gas was next admitted through small metering orifices (Fig. 7-6). Lenoir claimed by this manner a cushion of air at the piston reduced the explosion shock on engine moving parts. It is difficult to picture, however, a nonhomogeneous mixture existing in the combustion chamber at such low engine speeds. Before midstroke the valve closed; time was allowed for final mixing, and the plug (hopefully) began to spark. Cylinder pressure at the time of ignition was below atmospheric (approximately eleven psi absolute), and the peak combustion pressure reached an average of sixty psi.[8] A typical pressure-volume diagram for a Lenoir engine is shown in Fig. 7-7.

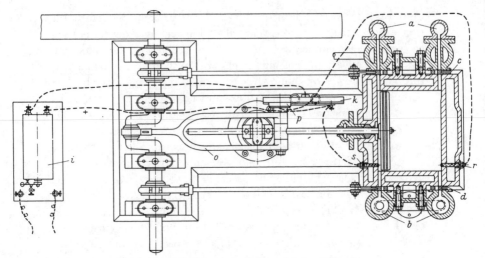

a – Gas supply; b – Exhaust outlets; c – Intake slide-valve;
d – Exhaust slide-valve; i – Induction coil; k – Sliding-type
ignition distributor; o – Connecting rod; p – Distributor slider in
crosshead; r, s – Spark plugs.

Section through cylinder

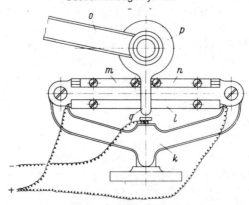

k – Frame with ground terminal; l – Full length, lower contact
strip; m & n – Contact strips for timing the sparking at plugs; p
– Slider mount on crosshead; q – Slider contact tongue.

Slider-type electric distributor.

Fig. 7-4   Lenoir engine, (Sass, *Gaschichte des deutschen
Verbrennungsmotorenbaues,* 1962)

Fig. 7-5.   Lenoir rotary distirbutor on end of crankshaft.

Expansion was very incomplete with a relatively high pressure in the cylinder when the exhaust ports opened. The manifestations of the incomplete expansion were an inherently low efficiency (four to five per cent) and a high heat rejection rate to the coolant. This latter necessitated large water jackets in the cylinder and heads plus an abundant supply of water. The suggested tank size for a one-half horsepower engine was 100 gallons. A three horsepower engine needed a 350 gallon reservoir. Cold water from the bottom of an overhead tank fed by gravity to the engine and returned through a pipe exiting just above the top of the tank water level.[9] Another cooling related problem was that an excessively hot exhaust caused slider distortion and sticking. The American engine reportedly solved this (as others also may have) by spraying a little water into the cylinder exhaust ports.

Mechanically, the engine was moderately successful, and the nuisance of continually cleaning spark plugs, recharging batteries, etc. normally would have been tolerated. One report stated, "The cylinders and pistons required frequent cleaning (with Philadelphia city gas daily and even oftener), and the electric igniting device demanded almost constant

111

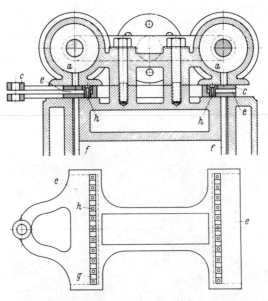

a – Gas supply; c – Slide-valve; e – Slots for air supply;
f – Inlet ports to cylinder; g – Openings for air;
h – Gas supply orifices.

Fig. 7-6   Lenoir intake slide-valve and gas-air induction system.
(Sass, *Geschichte* . . .)

attention to keep it in operation."[10] Unfortunately, a high consumption of costly illuminating gas, coupled with the maintenance irritants, were more than the customer would accept and proved to be the engine's downfall. Gas consumption figures varied, but the average usage was about 100 cubic feet per horsepower hour. This was neatly three times the fuel claims made for the engine when it was first introduced.[11]

Most of the European built Lenoir engines were three horsepower or less, although a few in the four to six horsepower range were also mentioned. The Lenoir on exhibit at the Science Museum in London, and representative of the English and French designs, operated there for two and a half years after its installation about 1865. With a nominal one-half brake horsepower, it developed an indicated one horsepower at 110 rpm from a cylinder of 5.5 in. diameter and a piston stroke of 8.5 in.[12]

Lenoir called attention to his engine with several publicity feats. In 1863 he reportedly placed a one horsepower model in a special vehicle and made a three hour round trip excursion out of Paris. Engine weight and cooling water volume were the main problems encountered.[13] Fuel was in the form of vapor "boiled off" gasoline in a vapor generator.[14] This stunt by Lenoir is not considered to predate the invention of a true automobile by Daimler and by Benz in 1886. A two horsepower engine in an auxiliary yacht owned by the Marquis d'Nare d'Aubais ran on the Seine River from Paris to Charenton several times a week for two years. The gas was generated on shore and then stored in pressurized tanks aboard the boat.[15]

By the late 1860s production of the Lenoir non-compression engine had ceased. This did not end an association of the Lenoir name with I-C engines, for in 1883 he designed a new family of gas "compression" engines of the Otto type (i.e., four-stroke cycle). Manufactured by Mignon and Rouart of Paris, these advanced design engines continued with electric ignition and had all poppet-type valves. Fuel consumption was only one-fourth that of his 1860 models.[16]

Lenoir did not die a prosperous man, and the only honors bestowed upon him during his lifetime were for contributions to telegraphy.

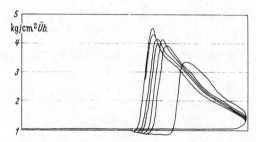

Fig. 7-7   Lenoir pressure-volume diagram. 4.2 kg/cm² = 60 psi
(Sass, *Geschichte . . .*)

The Hugon Engine: 1865

Direct competition to the Lenoir Engine began around 1865 with the introduction of a non-compression, double-acting gas engine by Pierre-Constant Hugon (1814-?). He was a director of a small company (Gaz Portatif) which sold "bottled" gas from horse drawn carts. Hugon began investigating the expansive force of burning gas not later than 1858.[17] He was granted several patents[18] on an engine whereby a gas explosion displaced (remote from the cylinder) a column of water, and in turn, the water moved a power piston. It was, in effect, a double-acting "water motor" with a hydraulic force acting on the piston, the purpose being to provide a longer and more uniform expansive force. Hugon abandoned

113

this indirect approach sometime before 1865, probably as a result of the publicity and potential success accorded Lenoir's engine.

Hugon's major contribution to I-C engine technology was his incorporation of Barnett's trapped-flame ignition cock into the slide-valve construction of the Lenoir. There was good reason for the slide-valve's almost universal acceptance, beginning with steam engines, since flat surfaces could be produced economically by known machine shop techniques. Clearances between the slider and its housing were simply set by adjusting screws at assembly or even during operation. Because of the higher temperatures found in I-C engines, however, special consideration had to be given to the lubrication and cooling of the slider when it was used for an exhaust valve. The Hugon slide-valve design was rather complicated, but it functioned well enough to demonstrate conclusively that, for then current gas engine state of the art, flame ignition was

Fig. 7-10   Hugon vertical engine, cross-section. (*The Engineer,* March 1867)

superior to other considered systems. Over the next twenty to twenty-five years every successful gas engine builder was to agree with Hugon.

The flame ignition system,[19] first used on a vertical engine introduced in 1865 (Fig. 7-8, Plate), included an inner or main slider and an outer, auxiliary slider (Figs. 7-10 and 7-11); each was operated by eccentrics on an overhead crankshaft. The cylinder had only a single port at each end to serve for intake, ignition and exhaust. Contained in a small cavity at the ends of the main valve slider was a gas jet relit for each power stroke from a continuous flame burning at a second, stationary gas jet. As the piston began to move away from the end of the cylinder, the two sliders also moved to connect that end with an external mixing chamber; a combustible air-gas mixture was sucked into the cylinder during the first third of the piston stroke. The main slider continued to move, cutting off its intake port, and next indexed the cylinder port to the transported flame in the valve igniter cavity. The charge in the port ignited and in turn set off the combustible mixture in the cylinder; the resultant explosion snuffed out the flame in the igniter cavity. Meanwhile, the auxiliary slider was repositioned to close off the passage from the mixing chamber to the main slider so that, on the main slider's return stroke, the mixing chamber could not be opened to the cylinder prior to completion of the exhaust stroke on that end of the cylinder. A "D" slot in the main slider allowed one end of the cylinder to exhaust while the other was drawing in and igniting the charge. Later engines had just one eccentric rod connected directly to the main slider. Movement of the auxiliary slider occurred only when a pin on that slider made contact with the ends of a slot in the eccentric rod. This provided the required short displacement of the auxiliary slider in a quick motion.

Gas and air were forced into the mixing chamber by bellows pumps driven off the crankshaft. (Fig. 7-10). The rubber bellows, along with flexible hoses to carry gas to the valve igniter cavities, had a limited life and caused occasional problems. On later engines the pumps were changed to metal and a mixing valve was added. A slightly higher pressure was necessary in the gas supplied to the igniter cavity than to the continuously burning jet so that scavenging and reliable lighting was assured in the cavity.

Gas consumption of the Hugon engine averaged twenty percent less than the Lenoir, with the normal range being eighty-five to ninety cubic feet per horsepower hour. This was due primarily to more positive ignition of a leaner air-fuel ratio. It simply was easier to kindle a fire in the cylinder from an already burning flame than to depend on the vagaries

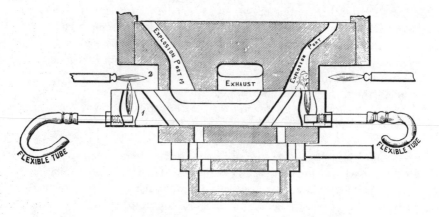

Fig. 7-11 Slide-valve flame igniter, Hugon engine. (Clerk, *The Gas and Oil Engine,* 1896)

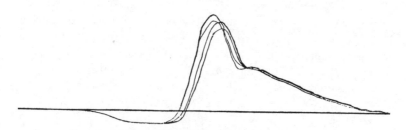

Fig. 7-13 Pressure-volume diagram from Hugon engine. 1/2 Hp at 75 rpm. (Clerk, *The Gas and Oil Engine,* 1896)

of a spark subject to plug deposits, breakage or external electrical problems. Ignition commenced earlier than the Lenoir to give a greater chance for expansion. Compare the pressure-volume diagram of the Hugon (Fig. 7-13) with that of the Lenoir (Fig. 7-7). Regardless of the unswept volume in the cylinder and its adjacent passages (approximately thirty percent), the Hugon engine was assured a burnable mixture in the cylinder port at the igniter flame. That part of the charge was the last into the port from the mixing chamber and was not diluted by residual exhaust gas as in the Lenoir. Hugon had, to a limited extent, a form of stratified charge engine where the mixture was locally rich for ignition and lean throughout most of the combustion chamber.

The low thermal efficiency of a non-compression engine meant that there had to be a high heat rejection rate. Hugon was aware of tests on the Lenoir showing eighty to ninety percent of the available heat of combustion was lost to the coolant and the exhaust. These tests by Prof. Tresca at Paris in 1861 gave fifty-three percent to the jacket water on a half horsepower engine. Results from a later trial on a one horsepower engine indicated sixty six percent of the heat went into the water (a figure to be suspect!).[20] It is not difficult to see why there were exhaust slider cooling problems.

Hugon alleviated the overheating condition by spraying water directly into the cylinder at the beginning of each charge ignition; the injection of water came from an auxiliary pump. Further tests by Tresca in 1866 on a two horsepower Hugon engine demonstrated a dramatic change in the distribution of heat rejection by the internal addition of coolant. There was now a twenty percent loss to the jacket water and twenty-four percent was carried off by the water injected into the cylinder and turned into steam.[21] Rather complete performance data from this test are worth noting:

Cylinder bore, in	13
Stroke, in	12.75
Speed, rpm (for 5 hours)	53
Cylinder pressure, max. psi	48
Air:fuel ratio	13:1
Horsepower, bhp	2
Brake specific fuel consumption, cu ft/bhp hr	91
Brake thermal efficiency, %	7.1*
Exhaust temperature, °C	186
Jacket water temperature (assumed max.), °C	42

The first Hugon and Lenoir engines had a "square" or "oversquare" bore-stroke ratio. Later engines reduced the bore diameter or increased the stroke which improved the proportion of cooling surface to cylinder volume.

Around 1867 a horizontal cylinder engine superseded the vertical, and this design enjoyed a moderate success for a few years until driven

*Based on a gas heating value of 727 Btu/cu ft, the brake specific fuel consumption, or bsfc, for an engine is the rate fuel is burned for one brake or usable horsepower for one hour. Relative consumption between different engines using the same fuel can thus be compared regardless of horsepower, size, etc.

off the market by the Otto and Langen atmospheric engine. The Hugon engine was built in England by Thomas Robinson and Sons of Rochdale.[22] (Fig. 7-12, Plate) Engine sizes were in the range of one-half to three horsepower as with the Lenoir. A one-half horsepower horizontal engine which replaced the Lenoir in the London Science Museum operated from 1868 until 1880.[23]

While a half horsepower engine hardly seems like a worthwhile effort today, the very slow engine speeds of that era meant their developed torque *was* a respectable figure. Thus, one-half horsepower at seventy five rpm translates into 220 lb ft. Horsepower was, unfortunately, a magic word in the nineteenth century as well as the twentieth, but the torque or turning effort of an engine is a primary performance factor; horsepower is a derived function of torque and engine speed. For example, a steam engine develops its maximum torque at stall, and the measured horsepower at this zero speed is, therefore, zero. An aircraft jet engine might develop 40,000 pounds of thrust before it begins to move the plane down the runway, yet its measurable horsepower, external to the engine, would still be zero.*

The Bisschop Engine: 1870

The most successful non-compression gas engine ever built was a "rough and ready" creation by the Parisian, Alexis de Bisschop. (Fig. 7-9, Plate). This small, single-acting motor cost little to buy and gave reliable service. The Bisschop engine arrived on the market three years after the Otto and Langen engine had all but driven off other non-compression makes. Nevertheless, it survived and proliferated because it supplied a need at the lower end of the power spectrum. The more popular models were of one-third horsepower or less, and while the specific fuel consumption was high at 150 cubic feet of gas per horsepower hour[24] (three times that of the Otto and Langen), the very small power ratings still allowed a low operating cost. A "one manpower" (one-twelfth horsepower) engine consumed only eleven to twelve cubic feet of gas per hour. With illuminating gas selling at an average rate of $2.50 per 1,000 cubic feet in the major cities, the fuel cost per hour ran less than four cents. An engine of this size sold in Paris for about $110 in 1878.[25]

---

*The relationship of thrust to horsepower is: Thrust hp = $\frac{\text{Thrust} \times \text{Intake Velocity}}{550}$, where thrust is in pounds and engine air intake velocity is in feet per second. One pound of thrust = one thrust hp at 375 mph.

Customers were attracted to the Bisschop engine for two other reasons: it was compact and required no cooling water. Floor space was reduced by making the cylinder vertical, and the height was kept low by offsetting the flywheel and placing it below the top of the crosshead guide. (Fig. 7-14) The linkage was arranged so that, at the time of maximum cylinder pressure, the piston rod and the rod tying the crank throw to the piston rod crosshead were almost parallel to each other. Piston side thrust thus was nil, and the crosshead guide structure consequently could be kept light. The engine was air cooled (a first) with large fins cast on the cylinder to carry away heat from the combustion chamber. The piston ran hotter than in other engines of that period and had to be fitted quite loosely in the cylinder. There were no piston rings, but the pressures (twenty-five psi and under) were low enough that blowby was tolerable.[26] Because of the hotter piston, lubricating oil was deliberately kept out of the cylinder to prevent carbon deposits from building up in the combustion chamber.[27] (Coal gas of the nineteenth century had an inherent lubricating characteristic and left a tar-like residue. In all probability many early designs were saved from failure for this reason.) Lubricating oil was needed only for the bearings. One of the Bisschop engines reportedly ran forty-seven days without stopping. [28]

Intake and exhaust were controlled from a single, spool-type valve actuated by bell crank linkage off an eccentric on the crankshaft. (Fig. 7-15) When the valve was "down" air and gas were drawn into the cylinder through metering ports and past flat, rubber check valves. Combustion pressure closed the flap valves, yet no fire reached back to the rubber valves because they were upstream of where a burnable mixture was formed. The spool valve moved slowly upward after ignition and opened the cylinder to the exhaust pipe at the end of the power stroke. Flywheel inertia carried the piston downward, and the exhaust gases were pushed out through the common cylinder intake and exhaust port. No governor was required to control engine speed.

Ignition was commenced by a gas flame directed through a port about one-third of the way up the cylinder. As the piston uncovered this igniter port, the below atmospheric pressure in the cylinder (intake was still occurring) opened an inwardly acting metal flap valve to allow a jet of flame to enter and ignite the charge. (Fig. 7-16) The resultant quick pressure rise closed the igniter flap valve to retain cylinder pressure. Since the combustion explosion usually snuffed out the ignition flame, a second, continuously burning flame was located below the igniter jet to relight it for the next cycle. A cold engine required about eight to ten minutes of

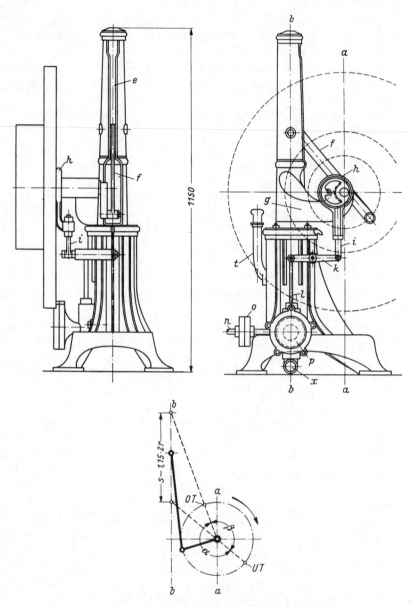

Fig. 7-14   Connecting rod and valve linkage of Bisschop engine
as built by Buss, Sombart & Co., Magdeburg, 1871.
Engine developed 1/3 hp at 110 rpm. (Sass,
Geschichte . . .)

120

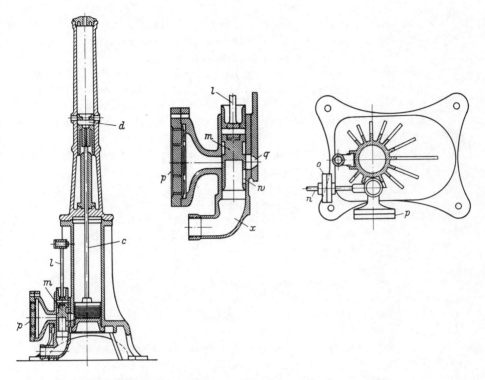

Fig. 7-15   Bisschop engine; air-gas supply and exhaust control by
a spool valve. (Sass, *Geschichte . . .*)

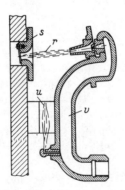

Fig. 7-16   Bisschop gas flame ignition system. (Sass, *Geschichte . . .*)

flame heating at the base of the cylinder before it could be started. Most engines had a gas jet located under the cylinder head for this purpose.

The Bisschop engine's success is evidenced by its continuous production for over twenty-five years by J.E.H. Andrew, Ltd. in Stockport, England. Andrews was reported to have built 2,000 of them by 1884.[29] Buss, Sombart and Co. of Magdeburg, Germany, produced the engine from 1878 to 1886.[30] Their one-third horsepower model had a bore and stroke of 100 mm by 290 mm and ran at 110 rpm; overall height was 115 cm. Mignon and Rouart of Paris was the principal French manufacturer. All of the engines were built under patent licenses from Bisschop.[31] The license was particularly important to Buss, Sombart because they needed an engine to build that would not infringe the Otto four-stroke cycle engine patent while it was in force. (Chapter 9) Almost every major technical museum contains one of these simple and practical little engines.

Non-Compression Gasoline Engines: Errani and Anders; Hock.

Independence from city gas mains and coal gas producers hastened the quest for liquid fuel engines. While cumbersome gasoline or light petroleum vapor generators were occasionally used if a gas supply was unavailable, the engine itself remained basically unchanged. During the the early 1870s there were, however, two attempts to build non-compression engines in which a highly volatile, gasoline-like fuel was sprayed directly into the cylinder. Neither fulfilled their inventors, dreams, but the concepts employed were a beginning.

Louis Charles Errani[32] and Richard Anders of Liège, Belgium, were explicit in their U.S. patent of 1873 about the fuel their single-acting engine was to use:

> We desire it to be well understood that in this apparatus we propose to use liquids only and not gaseous fluids, this not being a gas engine in which an explosion will take place, but an expansion engine in which the fine particles of the liquid, after having been commingled with the air, brought into condition fit for producing the best results from the expansion consequent to ignition.[33]

The significance of Errani and Anders is this clear distinction.

The fuel in the Errani and Anders engine did not come in contact with the air for combustion until it entered the cylinder. An engine

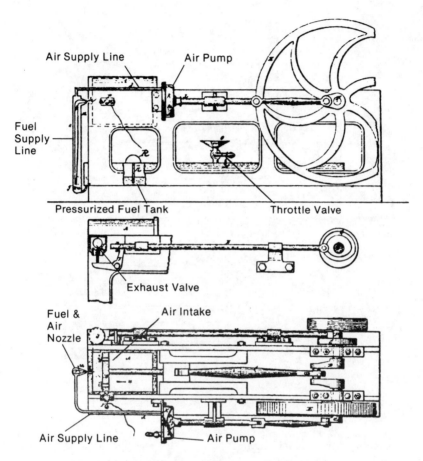

Fig 7-17   Errani and Anders non-compression gasoline engine,
1873. (From their U.S. patent drawings)

driven air pump with a rubber diaphragm pressurized a fuel tank
(Fig. 7-17); it also supplied a mixing nozzle to shred the fuel droplets as
they were sprayed into the combustion chamber by the tank pressure.
Timing of the crank operated air pump, in conjunction with a valve
arrangement in the pressure lines, limited the fuel-air spray to the first
part of the piston's outward travel. Most of the air, however, was pulled
into the cylinder through flap valves in the piston crown. Ignition was
by an electric spark, and the ensuing expansion was similar to that of
the Lenoir or Hugon. A hand valve at the air pump bled off tank air

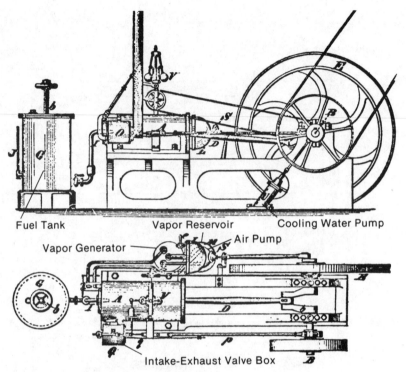

Fig. 7-18   Hock non-compression gasoline engine with flame
ignition. (From the U.S. patent drawings)

pressure to throttle the engine; opening it fully stopped the engine, and closing it gave maximum fuel delivery. There was no fuel specification offered other than its being "any suitable hydrocarbon liquid. "The engine apparently never went beyond the experimental phase, and the only accurate description of it is through the patent.

Fire insurance would have been a necessity for the owner of a Hock "Petroleum Dynamic Engine."[34] (Fig. 7-18) Julius Hock of Vienna constructed a rather dangerous machine using a flame ignition system to light off the volatile gasoline or naphtha sprayed into the cylinder. (Fig. 7-19) Hock specified in his patent a "petroleum of light, say about 69° specific gravity."[35] He used, in combination, a liquid fuel spray for cylinder combustion and vapor from a gas generator for ignition purposes. An air pump forced air through the vapor generator (Fig. 7-20) to

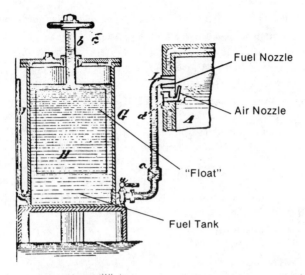

Fig. 7-19   Hock engine gasoline supply system. (From U.S. patent drawings)

supply directly a timed vapor jet blast (synchronized with the pump plunger), and indirectly, a second jet via a reservoir for a continuously burning pilot flame. The combustion fuel supply (Fig. 7-19) was from a tank containing a large, hand movable float to keep the liquid height about level with the spray nozzle at the cylinder. Immediately under the fuel nozzle in the cylinder was a small, vertically pointing air nozzle controlled by an inwardly opening check valve placed in the cylinder head.

As the piston began the intake portion of its stroke, the sucking action drew fuel and air through their respective nozzles. The air nozzle, directed into the incoming fuel, promoted mixing. The main air charge entered past a hinged intake valve leading into a combination intake-exhaust box. (Fig. 7-21). A flyball governor, acting through a tension spring, could override the normal opening of the valve. If speed increased, the hinged valve was opened further permitting more air to enter the cylinder via this valve. Cylinder pressure during intake was thus slightly raised, and the fuel quantity sucked through its nozzle reduced. A valve between the vapor generator and the reservoir kept the reservoir at a relatively constant pressure to assure the pilot flame a steady vapor supply. A shield protected the flame from any back blast escaping from the cylinder igniter flap valve. At ignition time the discharge from the air pump, less that needed to maintain pressure in the vapor reservoir, passed through fuel in the generator (a crude form of carburetor) and caused the air bubbles to draw off vapor. This flammable mixture went to the intermittent jet and caught fire as it passed the burning jet. The newly lighted igniter flame entered the cylinder past a flap valve (held slightly open by below atmospheric pressure during intake) and finally ignited the cylinder charge (if all went well). The strength of the igniter jet was regulated by a hand bleed valve at the air pump. Areas for possible operational problems are left to the reader's imagination.

The Hock engine was built for a limited time, but the general unreliability and danger,[36] plus the introduction of the Otto four-stroke cycle engine quickly ended its tenuous existence. The Julius Hock factory also made hot-air engines, one example of which is on exhibit at the Vienna Technical Museum.

With the exception of the "Economic Gas Engine" (Figs. 7-22 and 7-23), available in the United States during the 1880s,[37] no other non-compression engines were placed into production.

Francisque Million: 1861 Compression Engine

Lenoir and Hugon were only in the early phases of their own programs when a third Parisian, Francisque Million, proposed a compression engine and clearly outlined its advantages.[38] He revealed an excellent understanding of the reasons for those advantages. It is not known if even an experimental engine incorporating his advanced ideas was ever built.

Added to a basic Lenoir-type engine were separate, double-acting air and gas pumps (Fig. 7-24); both were operated from extensions on the piston rod crosshead. Million compared his engine to that of Wright and possibly Barnett (although neither was mentioned by name). He explained that most of the work put into the external pumps by the engine was wasted effort because they did not raise the cylinder pressure prior to ignition. Therefore, he says:

> ... these engines are very large in proportion to their power. On the contrary, by employing gases under the conditions above explained [i.e., auxiliary compressor pumps] these engines exert great power in proportion to their dimensions, the sudden ignition of the gases in the motive cylinder causing this latter to work at an operative pressure much greater than that of the pumps ... .[39]

126

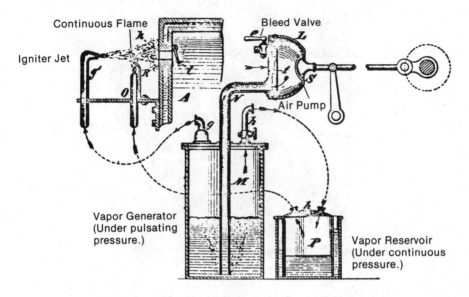

Fig. 7-20   Hock flame ignition system. (from U.S. patent drawings)

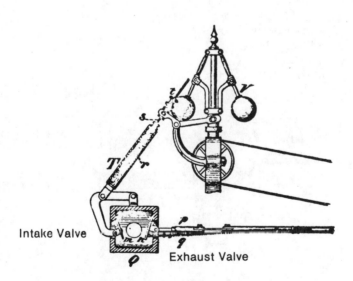

Fig. 7-21   Hock governor and valve design. (From U.S. patent drawings)

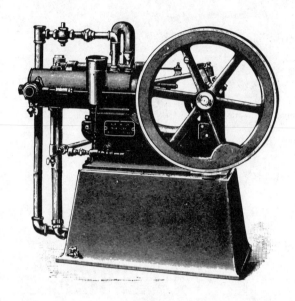

Fig. 7-22   *Economic* non-compression gas engine, ca. 1884. (Hiscox, *Gas, Gasoline and Oil Engines,* 1900)

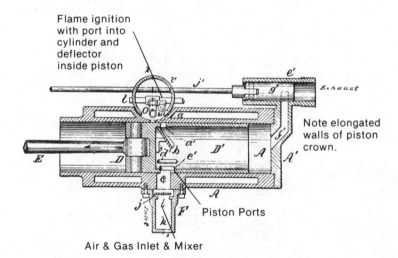

Flame ignition with port into cylinder and deflector inside piston

Note elongated walls of piston crown.

Piston Ports

Air & Gas Inlet & Mixer

Fig. 7-23   Cylinder section view, *Economic* engine. (Hiscox, *Gas. Gasoline and Oil Engines,* 1900)

Million went on to claim that compression prior to ignition was his invention alone:

> In the engine above described the mixtures are introduced
> under pressure into the motive cylinder: this is one of the
> characteristic features of this Invention and I claim the
> exclusive right to the principle upon which this engine is
> constructed and operated whatever may be the explosive
> mixtures employed and whatever may be their pressure.[40]

He apparently was not aware of Barnett's patent or else he did not correctly interpret Barnett. For that matter, neither did the British patent office, who were not at this time examining applications for prior art. Million would have been free to use Barnett's ideas, however, since the earlier patent had expired.

Excessive heating in the external pumps was recognized as a potential problem by Million. He suggested that if pressures of six or more atmospheres were desired, the compression should be in two stages with intercooling between the stages by "water circulating around the pipe through which the air passes."[41] This was in addition to cooling the pumps themselves by an engine driven water pump.

Another forward looking idea of Million was that he preferred a homogeneous mixture in the cylinder at the time of ignition. This was contrary to what almost everyone else advocated for many years. Vanes and wire gauze in the mixture supply pipe intermixed the pressurized gas and air prior to their entering the cylinder. Electric spark ignition was timed by a sliding rod which closed contact points in the secondary circuit of an induction (Rühmkorff) coil.

Million was not the only one proposing a compression engine in the early 1860s. Alphonse Beau de Rochas (whose name would not surface until the Otto four-stroke patent was challenged twenty years later) and Gustav Schmidt did the same. Schmidt, in a paper presented in 1861 at Vienna to the Society of Austrian Engineers stated:

> The results would be far more favorable if compression
> pumps, worked from the engine, compressed the cold air
> and cold gas to three atmospheres before entrance into the
> cylinder; by this 'a greater expansion and transformation of
> heat is possible.[42]

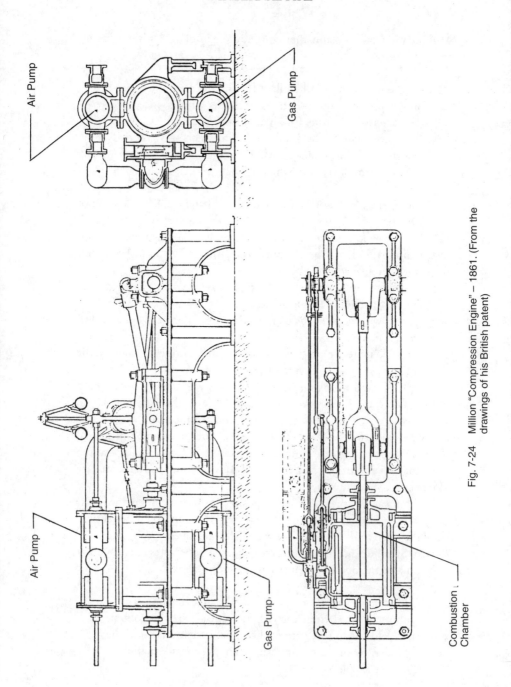

Air Pump

Gas Pump

Air Pump

Gas Pump.

Combustion Chamber

Fig. 7-24 Million "Compression Engine" – 1861. (From the drawings of his British patent)

Fig. 8-1   Nicolaus August Otto (1832-1891). (Werkphoto Deutz)

Fig. 8-2   Anna Gossi Otto (1839-1914). (Werkphoto Deutz)

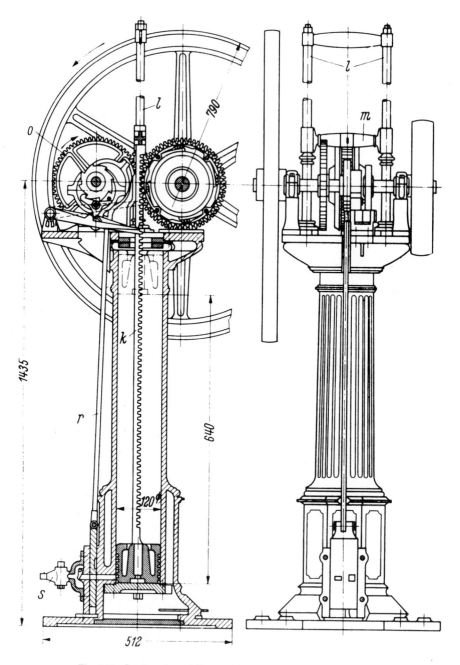

Fig. 8-5   Section view of Otto and Langen atmospheric engine,
1867. (Sass, *Geschichte* . . .)

Fig. 8-11   Otto and Langen atmospheric engine as exhibited in Paris, 1867. (Werkphoto Deutz)

Fig. 8-6   Eugen Langen (1833-1895). (Werkphoto Deutz)

Fig. 8-16   Otto and Langen engine in operating condition at the Deutsches Museum, Munich. (Deutsches Museum photo)

Möhlirhalle der Gasmotoren-Fabrik Deutz.

Fig. 8-12   Assembly area at Gasmotoren-Fabrik Deutz, ca 1872. (Werkphoto Deutz)

Million designed the engine Schmidt advocated, but a successful application was years away. This logical step of compressing the mixture to improve engine efficiency was seemingly avoided by engine builders for almost another fifteen years.

NOTES

1. Lenoir received patents in nine countries for his non-compression engine, beginning with France on January 24, 1860. British patent No. 335 of February 8, 1860, (under the name of J.H. Johnson) and U.S. No. 31,772 of March 19, 1861, followed. An "improvement" patent issued in Britain as No. 107 of 1861.
2. Lenoir Gas Engine Co. (New York City) catalog of April 2, 1866.
3. Fred J. Slade, "The Lenoir Gas Engine," *Jour. Franklin Institute,* v. 81, 3rd series, 1866, p. 178. The half horsepower engine produced its rated power at 185 rpm. The bore and stroke were 4-5/8 in. by 8-3/4 in.
4. U.S. patent No. 31,722, p. 1.
5. Friedrich Sass, *Geschichte des deutschen Verbrennungsmotorenbaues, von 1860 bis 1918,* (Berlin, 1962), p. 15. Quote given in French.
6. Dugald Clerk, *The Gas and Oil Engine,* 6th ed., (New York, 1896), p. 19. Clerk was a firm advocate of non-electrical ignition systems until after 1900. However, he was correct about the troubles found on the Lenoir engine.
7. Lenoir Gas Engine Co. cat., *op. cit.,* p. 14. Also: H.W. Dickinson, *Catalogue of the Collections in the Science Museum — Stationary Engines,* (London, 1925), p. 170.
8. Slade, *op. cit.,* p. 176. From tests on an 8.66 in. bore by 16.25 in. stroke engine.
9. Lenoir Gas Engine Co. cat., *op. cit.,* p. 9.
10. "On Atkinson's Gas Engine," *Jour. Franklin Institute,* v. 127, June 1889, p. 415.
11. Clerk, *op. cit.,* p. 15.
12. Dickinson, *op. cit.,* p. 170.
13. Henry H. Suplee, "Historical Review of the Development of the Internal-Combustion Engine," *Cassier's Magazine,* v. 33, November 1907, pp. 9-10.
14. Vapor generators of this probable type were advertised for the American engine as "optional equipment" at a cost of $100 to supply the half horsepower size. See: Lenoir cat., *op. cit.,* p. 19.

15. "Suction Producer Gas Motor Yacht 'Emil Capitaine'," *The Practical Engineer,* Sept. 15, 1905, p. 431.
16. Wm. Robinson, *Gas and Petroleum Engines,* 2nd ed., (New York, 1902), v. 1, pp. 324-26.
17. From information kindly supplied by M. Jacques Payen of the Musée du Conservatoire National des Arts et Métiers, Paris, during an interview.
18. British patent No. 653 of March 9, 1863, and U.S. No. 41,299 of January 19, 1864. French patents granted in 1858, 1860 and 1863 also show a progression of similar engine designs.
19. British patent No. 986 of April 6, 1865, French No. 66,807 of March 29, 1865, and U.S. No. 49,346 of August 8, 1865.
20. Robinson, *op. cit.,* p. 59.
21. Robinson, *op. cit.* p. 64.
22. "Hugon's Gas Engine," *Jour. Franklin Inst.,* v. 83, 1867, p. 264, as reprinted from the *London Engineering,* No. 62.
23. Dickinson, *op. cit.,* p. 170. This engine, made by F.B. Vallance, had a bore and stroke of 8.2 in. by 10 in. Indicated horsepower was 0.78 at 75 rpm. Mean effective pressure was 3.9 psi with a gas consumption of 85 cu ft/bhp hr.
24. Hugo Güldner, *Das Entwerfen und Berechnen der Verbrennungskraftmaschinen,* 3rd ed., (Berlin, 1914), p. 636. Güldner lists test data of Clerk, Richard, Schöttler and Witz for the Bisschop engine. There was a wide range of reported fuel consumption, partly due to the tests being on engines of different manufacturer and power, but the figures were all high.
25. "A New Gas Engine," *Scientific American,* December 21, 1878, p. 390. A "four manpower" (one-third horsepower) engine cost about $190.
26. Clerk, *op. cit.,* p. 133. Clerk shows a pressure-volume diagram similar to that of the Lenoir and Hugon.
27. Robinson, *op. cit.,* p. 76.
28. "A New Gas Engine," *op. cit.*
29. *Engineering,* September 19, 1884, p. 280.
30. Sass, *op. cit.,* p. 135. Sass reports that Buss, Sombart experimented with a one hp, water cooled model. See p. 137.
31. Under British patent No. 1,594 of 1872, for example. Improvement patents by Bisschop (British No. 579 of 1882 and U.S. No. 178,121 and licensees (Sombart, German No. 13,310 and U.S. 226,972 of 1880) followed.

32. Arthur F. Evans, *The History of the Oil Engine,* (London, 1930) pp. 14 and 115, refers to Errani as "Madam" and "this historic lady" and that "she" introduced a surface carburetor (a form of vapor generator) in 1869.
33. U.S. patent No. 140,021 of June 17, 1873, p. 1.
34. The title of Hock's U.S. patent No. 151,129 of May 19, 1874. The patent makes reference to the basic prior art of Errani and Anders.
35. Clerk, *op. cit.,* p. 393, said a fuel of this type would be classed as a "petroleum spirit" with a trade name of "naphtha" or "benzine" produced from an American crude. It could also be referred to as a gasoline. He said, "Liquid so inflammable and so capable of producing large volumes of explosive mixture are much too dangerous for successful use by the general public in engines."
36. Charles Singer, et al., *A History of Technology,* v. 5 (New York, 1958), p. 160.
37. Gardner D. Hiscox, *Gas, Gasoline and Oil Vapor Engines,* 3rd ed., (New York, 1900), pp. 130-32, describes this little engine. *Scientific American,* January 14, 1888, p. 30, carries an advertisement for a half hp, a one manpower and a dental engine for sale by the Economic Motor Co. of New York City. George M. and L.N. Hopkins were granted nine patents for the engine beginning with U.S. No. 284,555 of September 4, 1883. The engine was also patented in England under the name of Clark. (No. 4,260 of 1883, et seq.). All of their patents were assigned to the Economic Motor Co.
38. British patent No. 1,840 of July 22, 1861, issued in the name of William Edward Newton.
39. *Ibid.,* p. 8.
40. *Ibid.*
41. *Ibid.,* p. 13.
42. Gustav Schmidt, "Theorie der Lenoir'schen Gasmaschine," *Zeitschrift des Vereins deutscher Ingenieure,* 1861. Translation from Clerk, *op. cit.,* p. 16.

INTERNAL FIRE

Chapter 8

Otto and Langen

By mysterious ways which some call fate, luck or divine destiny, people are brought together in a manner affecting not only their own lives, but those they will never know. It happened to Nicolaus August Otto* (1832-1891) and Eugen Langen (1833-1895). Closely associated for half of their lives, each contributed a strength to complement the other's weakness. Otto, the inventor, and Langen the engineer and businessman, formed the first company exclusively to produce internal-combustion engines. The training ground they provided for dynamic management and the product they offered were to change the way we live.

Otto and His First Engines: 1861-1863
Otto was born in Holzhausen, a hamlet in the picturesque German Taunus between Frankfurt and the Rhine River. (Fig. 8-1, Plate) An innkeeper's son, his schooling and early working years were not determined by choice. Otto's mother (he was a small boy when his father died) had hoped to provide her son with a technical education, but it was denied him by worsening economic conditions in the country at that time. Her urgings that he become a merchant were dutifully followed after he felt it necessary to leave high school. For a while he clerked in a Frankfurt grocery store, and then his older brother Wilhelm, who had a textile business in Cologne, secured a job for him with a company in that city. Now a salesman of tea, sugar and kitchenware to grocery stores, his assigned territory was along the German side of the Belgian and French borders. Most of his days were spent in a mail coach running between Cologne and the towns he served.

The young traveler was twenty-seven when he met Anna Gossi (1839-1914) at a Cologne carnival. She was from Lorraine. (Fig. 8-2, Plate) They were not to marry until nine years had passed and Otto's

*Otto spelled his name "Nicolaus" and not "Nikolaus" as most write it today.

success was at hand. The long courtship, imposed upon them by his transient job and increasing obsession with engines, produced many letters to Anna. Luckily she preserved them for, in addition to his thoughts and travels, we find in them a partial record of his early engine experiments. Unfortunately for the history of technology (and at one point for Otto, too) no data or sketches accompanied these *Liebesbriefe*.[1]

Otto was intrigued with the potential of the Lenoir engine as soon as he read of it. Correctly perceiving that the future success of an I-C engine would largely be dependent upon its fuel source, he first devised an alcohol-air carburetor for use with mobile applications. He and his brother filed for a patent on the idea to the Kingdom of Prussia in January 1861, but the patent was not granted because of cited prior art. Nevertheless, Otto had plotted his future course.

Frustrating years followed. Although handicapped by lack of money and technical education, he explored almost every known variation of I-C engines. His share of a small inheritance, borrowed funds from his brother and friends plus his own savings went toward his attempts to surpass the Lenoir engine. Every spare moment from his full time job was devoted to what had become a second love.

Michael Zons (?-1911), a Cologne instrument maker who also ran a machine shop,[2] constructed for Otto in 1861 a small model of a Lenoir engine; Otto wanted to find out if the roughness exhibited by these engines when under load could be reduced. This was the genesis of Otto's great concern over piston shock loading at the beginning of combustion, a worry that continued until long after the four-stroke engine was introduced. Although he was unable to improve on the roughness without creating other problems, one facet of these first experiments was significant. He later wrote of initiating combustion with the piston at dead center. At first he drew in the mixture over only half of the stroke and immediately compressed it back to dead center. Ignition then occurred by manually closing the electric sparking circuit. He proceeded in this manner to increase the length of the intake stroke until it was over the entire piston travel. The resultant combustion with the full intake stroke compressed was so violent that the engine turned through several revolutions. The experience undoubtedly planted the seeds for his future compression engine; however, his immediate objective was to lessen the imagined piston shock. Otto may have read Gustav Schmidt's paper about the advantage of compression, but he did not pursue that line of thinking for another fifteen years.[3]

One final effort to improve on the Lenoir, revealed later by Otto (in court), raised more questions than it answered. Sometime in 1862 Zons built a flat, four cylinder, opposed piston engine for Otto. Each cylinder contained a free, "cushion" piston in addition to the power piston. (Fig. 8-3). A small plunger at the other end of a rod attached to the free piston acted as a dashpot or shock absorber as it moved in its closed ended tube. The only existing drawings of the engine were made by Otto from memory in 1885 for the German four-stroke patent litigation. Otto argued during the trial that the engine was of the compression type and a natural extension of his charge compression experiments on the single cylinder model. The engine was a reported failure, having quickly beat itself to death by higher than expected combustion loading. Although the German courts did not hold with Otto's statements regarding the disputed engine, there is little doubt that a four cylinder opposed engine with cushioning pistons was actually tested by Otto.[4]

Otto's problems with non-compression and possibly compression engines prompted him to consider the atmospheric type as a more feasible alternative. His first venture in the new direction was a one-half horsepower engine built in 1863, again by Zons. It proved unfit for sale, and, in retrospect, was a step backward from the operating Barsanti and Matteucci atmospheric engines. Several features of the Otto engine are worth noting, however. He utilized the cushion piston from his ill-fated four cylinder engine and added an adjacent air tank. The latter was to reduce the noise of air escaping from the vertical working cylinder and "to increase efficiency." (Fig. 8-4). Electric ignition, eccentric operated slide-valves and a crosshead-type power train to an overhead crankshaft were conventional. The engine was patented only in Britain since the German patent examiners failed to find, in their minds, any new concepts.[5]

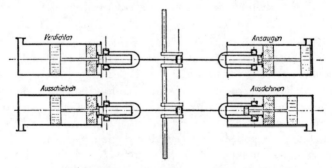

Fig. 8-3   Sketch of Otto's four cylinder, opposed-piston engine of 1862. (Goldbeck, *Kraft für die Welt*, 1965)

It is reasonable to assume that Otto was at least aware of Barsanti and Matteucci; to what extent is impossible to conjecture. Otto and Langen's English patent agent, Charles D. Abel, did inform them in 1865 of the Italians' work.[6]

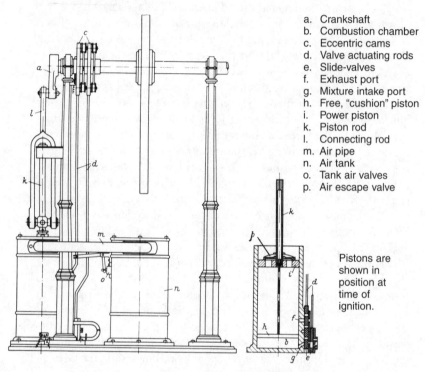

a. Crankshaft
b. Combustion chamber
c. Eccentric cams
d. Valve actuating rods
e. Slide-valves
f. Exhaust port
g. Mixture intake port
h. Free, "cushion" piston
i. Power piston
k. Piston rod
l. Connecting rod
m. Air pipe
n. Air tank
o. Tank air valves
p. Air escape valve

Pistons are shown in position at time of ignition.

Fig. 8-4 First Otto atmospheric engine, 1863. (Sass, *Geschichte des deutschen Verbrennungsmotorenbaues,* 1962)

Figure 8-4. Description and Operation of the 1863 Engine
A distinguishing feature of the engine was an airtight cylinder cover and a tank to receive the air forced from between the power piston and the cover. The piston rod passed through a stuffing box seal in the cover.

A cycle began with the free piston and the power piston at their innermost positions. As a flywheel rotated an overhead crankshaft, the power piston was pulled up and, in turn the free piston was lifted for the latter to draw in the combustible mixture through slide-valve ports. During the upward travel a tank air valve opened and exhausted the air that came from above the power piston; the valve closed as the piston

138

neared top center. Ignition of the charge under the free piston quickly forced it up to the much more slowly moving power piston.

Air trapped between the two pistons was forced through holes in the upper piston, past a one-way escape valve (a disc sliding on the rod), and into the air tank. This air did not exhaust and raised the pressure over the piston and in the tank. By the time the two pistons met at top center, their contact softened by the sliding dashpot in the power piston rod, a vacuum had formed in the combustion chamber as a result of expansion and upward inertia of the free piston. Rather than the conventional pressure differential of atmosphere-to-cylinder vacuum to create power for the working stroke, there now was a pressurized tank-to-cylinder vacuum differential.

An exhaust port, opened by the slide-valve when the combustion chamber lowered again to atmospheric pressure, served another function. After the free piston passed the port, it drew in air to keep a vacuum from forming between the two pistons and prevent it from reaching the desired end of its downward travel. Air deliberately trapped under the free piston kept it from hitting the cylinder head and gave it an upward bounce at the beginning of intake. Snubbing of the lower piston was also aided by the dashpot plunger pulling against its closed ended bore in the piston rod.

Eugen Langen

About all that Otto and Eugen Langen (Fig. 8-6, Plate) had in common before they first met was that the one sold sugar and the other refined it; their backgrounds were entirely different. Langen was raised with his five brothers and two sisters in a comfortable town house on one of Cologne's main avenues. His father was a school teacher turned accountant who went to work for a sugar refining company in that city; in time he became a partner and then the principal owner of the firm. A diversified interest included ownership of a nearby steel forging plant.

Eugen attended the *Karlsruhe Polytechnikum* (Institute of Technology) but did not graduate because of failing to take required exams in Latin. Ferdinand Redtenbacher (1809-1863), one of the most revered professors in the German engineering schools, was a teacher of Langen's. The professor was interested in this student who was afraid of Latin and gave him needed encouragement to at least complete the rest of his work. Langen's association and friendship with his mentor did not end when he left Karlsruhe. Another school friend and fellow student was Franz Reuleaux (1829-1905), whose influence and advice would contribute much to the ultimate success of Otto's and Langen's engines. Unlike Otto, there was no protracted courtship with a future wife; Langen married a girl from Basel, then living in Cologne, shortly after finishing school.

An apprenticeship in his father's forge shop at Troisdorff (against his own wishes) preceded Langen's joining the family sugar enterprise. The business and financial expertise gained there proved invaluable. Not considering himself fully occupied, the energetic young man invested in a new company to make a special coal grate for gas producers. Enough of the grates were sold in a few years, both in and out of Germany, to earn him a tidy profit and, in addition, to acquire an understanding of patents. By 1863 Langen had become the guiding partner in the sugar business, expanding it to refine beet as well as cane sugar. Productivity was also increased through processing equipment of Langen's own design.

With the family business running smoothly, Langen was restless to involve himself with something new. A note in his day calendar about this time refers to his reading of the Lenoir engine; so it was natural that his curiosity was strong when he heard of a struggling inventor working nearby on a new gas engine. Whether Langen was approached directly by Otto for funds or if it was through mutual acquaintances is not known. In any event, it was on February 9, 1864, "in a small shop on the Gereonswall that he heard the erratic thrashing" of Otto's first atmospheric engine.[7] Langen could see that there were technical problems to be solved, but he was intensely intrigued and quickly made up his mind to invest in the engine's future. Within a few weeks, with the help of his father and several business friends, Langen raised the capital to form a company that only briefly bore Otto's name but was for so long dependent on his guidance. Many times the story of invention does not take such a fortunate turn. In debt and discouraged "Ottos" never find their "Langens," and worthwhile ideas fall or lay dormant till a later day.

N.A. Otto & Company: 1864-1867

On March 31, 1864, Otto and Langen signed an agreement forming N.A. Otto & Cie., the world's first, and today as Deutz AG, the oldest company manufacturing I-C engines. Otto contributed his patents and workshop, and Langen financed the venture with 10,000 talers.* After outstanding debts were paid off, the new company was left with a cash

---

*A German monetary unit used until 1891 pegged to equal three gold marks. The word "dollar" derives from "Taler or Thaler."

balance of 2,000 talers.[8] Optimism ran high since it was assumed only a few details of the engine needed improvement. However, as anyone involved in development work well knows, the usual course of events seldom follows the initial script.

Three years passed before the combined efforts of Otto and Langen evolved a successful design. The new engine bore little resemblance to the machine Langen first saw; the free-piston drive, ignition and general mode of operation were all radically different. (Fig. 8-5, Plate) Langen's principal contribution, a one-way, wedging roller clutch, was probably the key feature that made the engine commercially feasible. Although the end result bore a striking similarity to the Barsanti and Matteucci engine, a detailed analysis of the Otto and Langen design and patent claims distinguish important differences. The power train and slide-valve mechanism of the 1867 engine were new, and it was on the basis of these elements that Otto and Langen were granted their patents.[9]

The new clutch, now called an "overrunning clutch," had minimum backlash and greatly increased torque transfer capacity. A cross section through the one-way drive (Fig. 8-7) shows four sets of rollers on curved, leather backed wedges at ninety degrees to each other. The rollers served to clutch and declutch the outer housing containing the pinion gear to the inner assembly keyed to the output shaft by alternately binding or running free as the piston descended on the power stroke or ascended on the explosion stroke. Service instructions written a few years later called for the leather pieces to be renewed every twelve to eighteen months in normal use. The internal parts of the "friction box" had to be oil free and were to be removed and wiped clean every six weeks.[10]

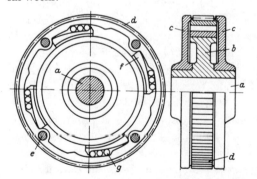

a. Power output shaft
b. Inner coupling half keyed to power shaft
c. Clutch housing
d. Ring gear
e. Housing bolts
f. Leather-backed curved wedges
g. Rollers
Direction of shaft rotation: Counterclockwise

Fig. 8-7   Section view of overrunning clutch, Otto and Langen engine; design of 1865. (Sass, *Geschichte* . . .)

The slide-valve was accurately timed to a "free" power piston by eccentrics, rachet and levers. (Fig. 8-8) Peculiar to such a free-piston engine was the independence of output shaft speed from piston stroke rate. The flywheel rotated at an almost constant speed, but the externally imposed load determined the stroke rate.

Numerous refinements to the slide-valve itself also contributed to the engine's success. (Fig. 8-9) The gas flame ignition system was improved over Hugon to provide good scavenging in the valve cavity without requiring a higher pressure in the gas supply to the igniter jet. Gas line pressure fluctuations were damped by a rubber bladder on the German engines and by a water-filled dashpot on those built in England. Spring loaded screws, adjusted by hand, set valve clearances. In addition to the obvious problems caused by the clearances being much too tight or loose, service instructions also informed that "if but a little too loose, the cover will be blown off almost imperceptibly; enough however to permit the explosion to escape. The light will then either be extinguished, or the succeeding explosions will be irregular."[11] It was suggested that the slide cover and slide be removed and cleaned "once or twice weekly" to open up the gas, air and exhaust passages. Tar deposits from coal gas may have helped to lubricate, but their presence was a nuisance in other ways.

While no governor appears on the introductory engine, Otto shortly thereafter designed one which was used for a few years. It worked well on a new engine but developed later problems. By overriding the seating force of an outwardly opening valve in the exhaust line, a flyball governor controlled back pressure to change the rate of piston descent during exhaust. (Fig. 8-10). The valve's normal function was to preserve the cylinder vacuum after the slide-valve moved into its exhaust position (the piston was still on the upper part of its stroke). The governor did not override the preset valve opening force under full load conditions. Here, exhaust was rapid, and the piston quickly descended to the bottom of the cylinder. If the load decreased and speed increased, however, the governor exerted more force on the valve to restrict exhaust flow; the time for exhaust was consequently lengthened since only piston and rod weight pushed on the combustion products. If the engine load was suddenly and completely removed, the valve was held completely closed, and the piston stopped entirely until shaft speed lowered. A problem with the governing method was that in time, when the piston and cylinder bore had worn, the exhaust could bypass the governor controlled valve and allow "running away" of the engine.[12]

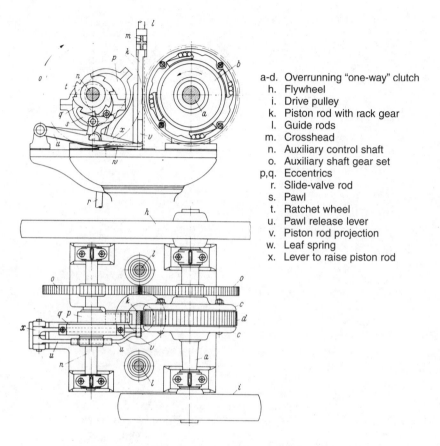

a-d. Overrunning "one-way" clutch
h. Flywheel
i. Drive pulley
k. Piston rod with rack gear
l. Guide rods
m. Crosshead
n. Auxiliary control shaft
o. Auxiliary shaft gear set
p,q. Eccentrics
r. Slide-valve rod
s. Pawl
t. Ratchet wheel
u. Pawl release lever
v. Piston rod projection
w. Leaf spring
x. Lever to raise piston rod

Fig. 8-8   Drive train and valve acutation mechanism, Otto and Langen engine. (Sass, *Geschichte . . .*)

Figure 8-8. Operation of Slide-Valve Actuating Mechanism

An auxiliary shaft (n) turns at the same speed as output shaft (a) through gear set (o). Two eccentrics (p, q), fastened together, are loose on the shaft (n). The eccentric (p) moves the slide-valve through rod (r). The other eccentric (q), pinned to the lever (x), lifts the piston rod (k) by the rod projection (v). Ratchet wheel (t) is keyed to shaft (n). Eccentric (q) carries a pawl (s) which strikes a cam nose on a second lever (u), also extending under the projection (v). Leaf spring (w) is compressed under the lever (u).

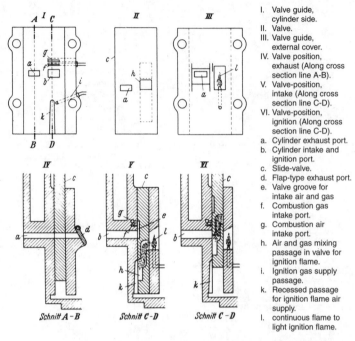

I. Valve guide, cylinder side.
II. Valve.
III. Valve guide, external cover.
IV. Valve position, exhaust (Along cross section line A-B).
V. Valve-position, intake (Along cross section line C-D).
VI. Valve-position, ignition (Along cross section line C-D).
a. Cylinder exhaust port.
b. Cylinder intake and ignition port.
c. Slide-valve.
d. Flap-type exhaust port.
e. Valve groove for intake air and gas
f. Combustion gas intake port.
g. Combustion air intake port.
h. Air and gas mixing passage in valve for ignition flame.
i. Ignition gas supply passage.
k. Recessed passage for ignition flame air supply.
l. continuous flame to light ignition flame.

Fig. 8-9   Slide-valve construction, Otto and Langen engine, 1867. The valve controlled intake of air and gas, flame ignition and exhaust. (Sass, *Geschichte . . .*)

The operating cycle can begin with the piston down and ready to draw in a fuel and air charge. The pawl hook is engaged with the ratchet, causing the two eccentrics to rotate. The slide-valve and the piston are both raised in a timed relationship. At ignition (where the slide-valve is highest) the rack projection quickly leaves the levers. As the eccentrics are rotated, the tail of the pawl moves away from the lever cam nose, even though the spring has raised the lever. When the tail next touches the lever it is to the "right" of the nose so that as the eccentric continues to turn, the tail is "caught" by the nose and the pawl hook is lifted from the ratchet. Slide-valve movement stops (this being the exhaust position), and remains stationary until contact is again made at the rod projection and the weight of the piston and rod pushes down the levers. The piston is pushing out the exhaust at this point. When the rod first contacts the lever (u) the cam nose falls away again and allows the pawl to re-engage the ratchet, The slide-valve returns then to its lowest, intake position and is ready for the next cycle to begin.

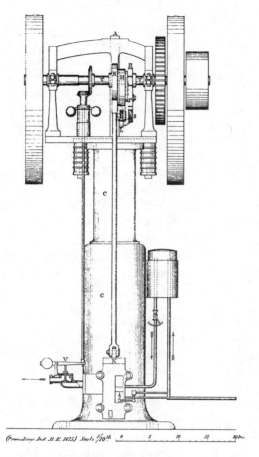

Fig. 8-10   Governor control for Crossley-built Otto and Langen engines. (*Proc., Inst. Mech. Engrs.,* 1875)

Gasmotoren-Fabrik Deutz AG

Otto and Langen chose the 1867 Paris Exposition as the stage to publicly demonstrate their engine (Fig. 8-11, Plate). What first appeared to be a public relations disaster for them was, at the last minute, changed into worldwide recognition and acclaim. All of the engine exhibits, including those of Lenoir and Hugon, were to be evaluated by a panel of experts. The clacking and pounding German entry with its Grecian column for a cylinder was looked upon as a curiosity by the French judges and was passed over for the more conventional "local" products. However, Franz Reuleaux, Langen's old school friend and now a professor in Berlin, represented the Prussians on the judging board. He suggested the prize be based on an engine's efficiency as well as performance. After tests lasting several days, the panel was astounded to find the Otto and Langen atmospheric engine consumed less than half the gas of the best non-compression engine. The strange looking machine was therefore awarded a grand prize with its accompanying gold medal. Felice Matteucci wrote to Paris contesting the award decision, claiming Otto and Langen had merely copied the Barsanti engine. The attempt to change the decision was futile.[13] As a result of the favorable publicity gained in Paris the small, young firm could not keep pace with the engine orders coming in.

A familiar problem faced the two partners: their company lacked sufficient capital to buy needed space and machinery to expand production. Langen, who had already more than tripled his original investment in the firm, sought additional help. Ludwig August Roosen-Runge, a Hamburg businessman whom Langen had met and befriended in England (while selling his coal grates) agreed to invest 22,500 talers and to become a limited partner. In March 1869 the company name was changed to "Langen, Otto and Roosen." Otto's contribution remained his efforts and ideas. (Langen still devoted less than full time to the engine works.) That same year the factory relocated to its present site across the Rhine in the Cologne suburb of Deutz.

The transfusion of a new partner and his money helped, but remained inadequate for the ever growing business. Langen, who could see the engine's great potential, asked his two brothers, and their partners in the sugar factory to join him in firmly putting the strapped engine company on a firm financial foundation. Langen and his brothers invested 200,000 talers and the partners 100,000. Otto, whose stock ownership became zero, accepted a long term employment contract under the new reorganization. On January 5, 1872, Gasmotoren-Fabrik Deutz AG* came into being with Langen in control and Otto handling the daily business operations under the title of technical director.

Creativity and business acumen were only part of what "Deutz" required during its years of rapid growth. Experienced factory management was also vitally necessary if the increased production was to be profitable. Langen recognized this fact and filled the gap with a recommended man whose own future was destined for fame. On August 1,

---

*AG (Aktiengesellschaft) indicates a joint-stock company, the German equivalent of "incorporated."

1872, Gottlieb Daimler (1834-1900) officially joined Gasmotoren-Fabrik Deutz as production manager. Daimler brought his protégé, a young engineer named Wilhelm Maybach (1846-1929), to head the design department. The bonus of a genius who became the world's most renowned engine designer was yet another stroke of fortune for Deutz.

Daimler carried excellent credentials. He was a trained engineer (a graduate of the Stuttgart *Polytechnikum*) with an impressive background in and understanding of manufacturing. From his teenage apprenticeship with a gunsmith, through his several years with a steam locomotive builder prior to joining Deutz, he never ceased to strive for quality in the products under his responsibility. Work periods in Paris and in several English industrial cities (made possible through a travel grant from an employer who thought highly of him) gave added experience for the task ahead of him at Deutz. Daimler, like Otto and Langen, was also impressed with the Lenoir engine and where its concept might lead. He recognized that a move to Deutz was an opportunity not to be ignored, but he was astute enough to drive a hard bargain with Langen on his employment terms: 1,500 talers per year plus five percent of the company's profits. He earned what he received, but in the process often made life difficult for Langen and Otto with his single-mindedness and sometimes obstinate demands. Daimler's decade at Deutz not only served his employer well, but also gave him the engine experience and financial means to ultimately be a founder of the automobile industry.

Although Maybach's star rose under Daimler's tutelage, its brilliance was never fairly assessed until shining in its own right many years later. Maybach was raised in an orphanage at Reutlingen after his father and mother died when he was ten. The *Bruderhaus* was an unusual institution. Established in 1837 by Gustav Werner, a Lutheran minister, it offered a compassionate home as well as learning and work opportunities. Associated with the orphanage was the "Bruderhaus Engineering Works" where Maybach received his basic technical and factory training. It was here that his talents were first observed by Daimler. (One of Daimler's jobs for a time was technical director of the Bruderhaus works.) Maybach went to work under Daimler at the Karlsruhe Maschinenfabrik in 1869, creating a team which remained together, except for a few short periods, until Daimler's death over thirty years later. The sensitive young designer, ever under the strong protection of his mentor, had a great capacity to learn through his own independent study. All of his work combined sound engineering with that rare quality of functional beauty.

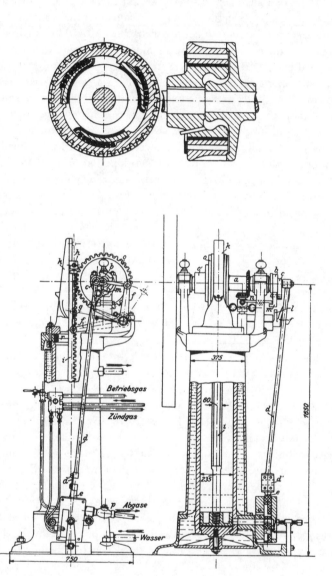

Fig. 8-13   Simplified, single shaft design and redesigned clutch,
Otto and Langen engine, ca. 1872. (Güldner,
Verbrennungskaftmaschinen, 1914)

One of Maybach's first assignments at Deutz was a redesign of the atmospheric engine to reduce manufacturing costs. Several troublesome operational areas were also improved upon. By the end of 1873 the task was completed, and Daimler incorporated the changes in his factory. (Fig. 8-12, Plate). The clutch, eccentrics and governor drive were now mounted on a common shaft. The governor force acted directly to control pawl engagement; piston stroke rate was no longer determined by restricting the exhaust. If speed increased, the pawl simply was kept out of engagement and stopped the piston lifting lever movement. Intake, ignition and exhaust all passed through slide-valve ports and a single port into the cylinder; there was no longer a check valve in the exhaust line. Modifications to the clutch included a reduction from four to three equally spaced sets of rollers and wedges (Fig. 8-13).

The design changes were patented,[14] but ownership of the patent was a disputed point. Although now generally recognized that the improvements were Maybach's ideas,[15] Daimler insisted the patent should issue in his name, and that he should own it. After a difficult time for all concerned, Langen compromised and permitted Daimler to be granted the patent, but Deutz was to retain all rights. Maybach's biographer called it a Pyrrhic victory for Deutz.[16] The issue was an opening engagement in the long and often bitter contest between the autocratic Daimler, the oversensitive Otto and, for the most part, the long-suffering Langen.

A limited power potential was the major disadvantage of the Otto and Langen engine. Restricted by height, the largest size never exceeded three brake horsepower. Composite published specifications by Deutz and a licensee[17] point out the height-power problem:

Nominal brake horsepower	1/4	1/2	1	2	3
Flywheel rpm	110	95	90	90	90
Piston stroke per minute	40	36	32	30	28
Engine gross weight, lbs.	900	1600	2750	4000	4450
Maximum engine height, ft. . . .	7	8.8	9.8	10.7	12.7
Cost, marks (1876)	960	1380	1890	2460	3000

Several tests, one by Tresca at the Paris Exposition in 1867 and the other by Dugald Clerk in 1884, give the representative data:[18]

	Tresca	Clerk
Brake horsepower	0.5	2.0
Flywheel rpm	81	90
Piston strokes per minute	—	30
Cylinder diameter, in	5.9	12.5
Maximum piston stroke, in	—	40.5
Maximum cylinder pressure, psi	—	54
Gas consumption, cubic feet/hour:		
Without ignition gas:	44	36
With ignition gas included:	48.7	42
Mechanical efficiency, %	—	68
Thermal efficiency, %	8	11.2

The indicator (pressure-volume) diagram from Clerk's test on a two horsepower engine (Fig. 8-14) illustrates a key difference between a steam atmospheric engine and one using internal combustion. At the time the distinction was either omitted or erroneously stated by builders and learned testers of the engine. Clerk took great pains to correct a mistaken idea.[19] Most writers previous to him assumed the cylinder vacuum was formed by a cooling and condensing of combustion gases when the piston completed its outward stroke. The process was considered identical to that of a Newcomen or early Watt engine. If such had been the case, the p-v diagram would not show a cylinder vacuum beginning at mid-stroke. Instead, the pressure would remain above atmospheric until near the end of the stroke when external cooling quickly condensed the gases to lower cylinder pressure.

The vacuum in an *I-C* free piston atmospheric engine was created by the inertia of the heavy piston assembly taking over after expansion by gas pressure ceased. At the time of ignition *(b)* (Fig. 8-14), the piston was stationary, having been lifted to that position by the eccentric lever L (Fig. 8-15). The piston did not move until combustion pressure built to a maximum at *(c)*, i.e., constant volume combustion. Consider the conditions at point *(d)*: Clerk calculated only eight percent of the available work was expended when the 116-pound piston and rod had moved to lower cylinder pressure to atmospheric. (Fig. 8-16, Plate) With a 1,560 feet per minute piston velocity at that point, the kinetic energy of the moving mass was sufficient to carry it to the end of the stroke against gravity and increasing cylinder vacuum. Externally imposed cooling, therefore, had little to do toward causing the vacuum.

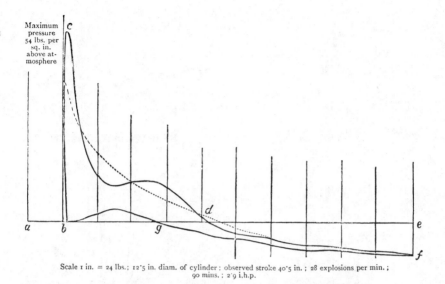

Maximum pressure 54 lbs. per sq. in. above atmosphere

Scale 1 in. = 24 lbs.; 12·5 in. diam. of cylinder; observed stroke 40·5 in. ; 28 explosions per min. ; 90 mins. ; 2·9 i.h.p.

Fig. 8-14   Pressure-volume diagram, Otto and Langen atmospheric engine. From a Clark test in 1884 on a 2 bhp
engine. (Clerk, *The Gas and Oil Engine,* 1896)

A high rate of acceleration by the projectile-like free piston was a source of another disadvantage. The recoil action of the vertically pointing cannon,particularly under full load operation, necessitated a strong foundation under the engine to counteract this force. Consequently, most installations were limited to the ground level.

The fifty to seventy-five percent reduction in fuel consumption achieved by Otto and Langen over Lenoir and Hugon was largely accomplished through greatly increased gas expansion. Using a similar air:gas ratio (around eight to one), they all began combustion without prior compression. The free piston design, however, allowed an expansion to ten times that of the original charge volume (*b* to *e* vs. *a* to *b* in Fig. 8-14) compared with a maximum of two and a half times in the Lenoir and Hugon non-compression engines (Fig. 7-6). The latter's much shorter piston stroke was limited by the throw of a crankshaft. The total expansion in the Otto and Langen engine was: a) that portion attributable to gas pressure pushing on the piston *(c-d)*, and b) that portion where the piston acted as in a vacuum pump to "pull" on the gases to complete the process *(d-f)*. Because of great expansion the

151

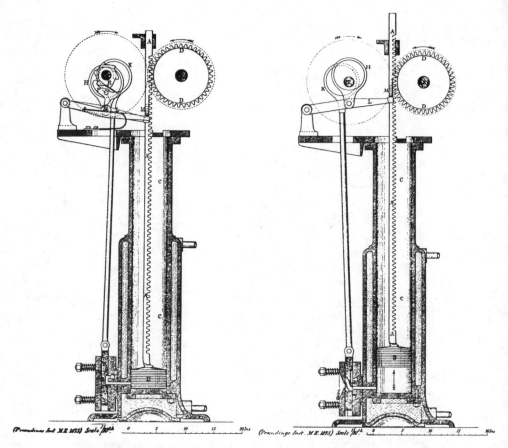

Fig. 8-15   Section view of Crossley's Otto and Langen engine.
(*Proc., Inst. Mech. Engrs.*, 1875)

temperature of the combustion gases at the end of the burning stroke
was much lower than in the earlier engines. As a result, the heat energy
lost to the exhaust was significantly reduced, and cooling of engine
components constituted no problem. Part of Carnot's teachings were
realized, but the lack of compression precluded an economy of size.

Atmospheric engine production figures for Gasmotoren-Fabrik
Deutz and its predecessor organizations between 1867 and 1876 illustrate the scope of the company operation and the effect of improvements instituted after Daimler's arrival in 1872:[20]

1867	7	1872/73**	245
1868	46	1873/74	348
1869	87	1874/75	589
1870	118	1875/76	634
1871	1197	1876/77***	222
1872*	141	1877/78	4

*January to July only.
**August to June hereafter (beginning year of G-F-D).
***Introduction of four-stroke cycle engine.

The total number of Otto and Langen engines built between 1864 and 1882 was 2,649 having an aggregate 2,828 nominal horsepower.

A World Industry

Otto and Langen established an international industry through their licensees and subsidiaries. Almost every major industrial nation built to the plans of Gasmotoren-Fabrik Deutz. The relationships began mostly with the atmospheric engine and continued after the introduction of the four-stroke cycle engine.

Francis William Crossley (1839-1897) and his brother, William John (1844-1911), of Manchester brought the Otto and Langen engine to England when they acquired the British patent rights in 1869. At the time the Crossleys were mainly building specialized machinery to fabricate india rubber and gutta-percha products. Although they had only been in business for two years, they had generated a respectable reputation for both quality and innovative design. Fortune, however, was not keeping pace with fame, and a new product was needed.

The two men brought good experience to their fledgling company. Frank Crossley had served an apprenticeship in the engineering works of Robert Stephenson at Newcastle, and W. J. Crossley went through his at the Elswick works of Sir W. G. Armstrong and Co. It was an uncle who made it possible shortly thereafter to buy the machine shop that started their industrial careers.[21]

At first, the atmospheric engines were marketed by Messrs. Simon of Nottingham, but soon the Manchester company took over that function also. No fewer than 1,400 of the Otto and Langen engines were built, with the Crossley brothers contributing several patented improvements of their own. From all accounts, quality was always of the highest.[22] (Their business philosophy was also influenced by a strong aversion to alcoholic beverages. While they did not refrain from taking orders from breweries, they refused to solicit them, and any profits accruing out of such sales were given to charitable organizations.)[23]

In 1881 Crossley Bros. became a private limited company, and on the death of Frank Crossley it was reorganized to a public limited one. The factory relocated in 1882 to the Openshaw site at Manchester where it has been ever since. This pioneering company which founded the British I-C engine industry remained its major manufacturer for many years.

About the time the Crossleys joined with Deutz, Felix Dehaynin also signed an agreement in Paris to have engines made in France under sub-contract. The venture was not satisfactory, and in 1872 a new, but similar, arrangement was formalized with Edouard Sarazin (?-1887). Approximately 200 atmospheric engines were built for Sarazin by Compagnie Parisienne d'Eclairage et de Chauffage par le Gaz. A stock company, with Sarazin and Deutz officials as principal owners, was formed in 1879 to build the four-stroke engine. Deutz maintained its interest in this company, Compagnie Française de Moteurs à Gaz, until 1896. Not very successful, the latter firm never produced the engines for which it was created. Most of the engines after 1878 were manufactured by Perin, Panhard & Co.[24] (Panhard & Levassor after 1886).

Langen & Wolf of Vienna was a subsidiary company established in 1872 to build atmospheric engines for central Europe. The firm was in existence for over fifty years and made in 1898 the first diesel engine in Austria.[25] Bauer & Co. of Milan (later Società Italiana Langen & Wolf) were the Italian licensees.[26]

Schleicher Brothers of Philadelphia, who exhibited an Otto and Langen engine at the Centennial International Exposition there in 1876, were the original United States representatives for Deutz. James (Jakob) and Adolph Schleicher were nephews of Eugen Langen from Antwerp, Belgium, who came to Philadelphia the same year as the exposition.[27] They were joined the next year by another man who would figure prominently in the future of the Otto four-stroke engine. Hermann Schumm (1841-1901) was hired in 1876 by Deutz because of his extensive engineering background to help with the introduction of the new engine. Schumm married a niece of Langen's and the Schleichers. Regardless of his family ties, he was an important factor in the success of the new firm of Schleicher, Schumm and Co. in Philadelphia. Schumm lived in the Maybach home when he first came with Deutz. Shortly thereafter, Maybach was given a three months leave to study industrial methods in the U.S. while the company was in transition from the atmospheric to the four-stroke engine. Schumm assumed Maybach's responsibilities during this time. Maybach visited his brother in New York, an executive with the piano firm of William Steinway, and stayed with the Schleichers while in Philadelphia.[28] It is highly probable that Maybach's report precipitated Schumm's sojourn in the United States.

Daimler Atmospheric Engine

It was not all smooth sailing for the management of Gasmotoren-Fabrik Deutz. By 1875 there was growing concern over reports and rumors of coming competition from: improved hot-air engines, a compression engine by George Brayton in the United States and an atmospheric engine designed by a former Deutz employee. The deficiencies of power limitation, weight, noise and recoil effects were not unrecognized by customers. Therefore, increasing activity was being devoted to this potentially serious situation. Daimler, the engineer, looked for an evolutionary answer in the form of a "second generation" atmospheric engine.

Daimler's design[29] attempted to extract the maximum from the atmosphere by means of a double-acting piston. (Fig. 8-17) On each side of the power piston was a free piston, all in a horizontal cylinder with open ends. The power or working piston was tied, through a crosshead on one end of the engine and connecting rods running the full length of the engine, to a crankshaft on the other end. Combustion alternately took place between one of the free pistons and the working piston when they were near the other free piston's outermost position. After ignition of the charge between the working and the "inner" free piston, combustion pressure and inertia quickly threw the inner piston to the opposite end of the cylinder where it was temporarily held fast. Atmospheric pressure, being greater than the cylinder pressure between the working piston and the newly latched free piston, pushed the other free piston (now unlatched) and the working piston as a unit toward the retained free piston at the other end of the cylinder. With all three pistons at the opposite end, the next combustion was initiated between the "new" inner piston and the working piston to repeat the same sequence of events in the other direction. The necessary piston motions for intake and exhaust were controlled by eccentrics as was a slide-valve on each end. Daimler asked Maybach to help him with a problem in the design, but Maybach "was not able to come up with the impossible solution" and consequently "there were no details about it in the patent description."[30]

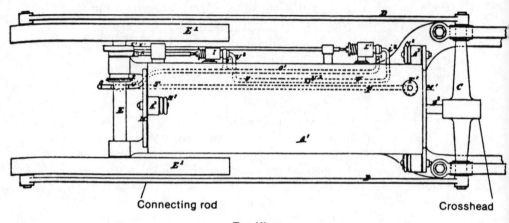

Connecting rod   Crosshead

Top View

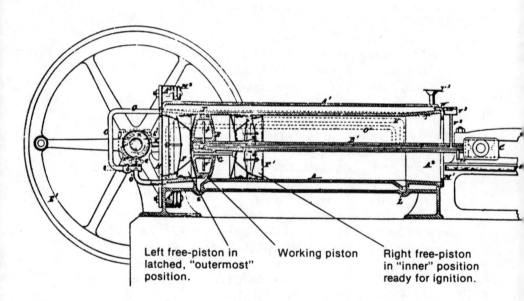

Left free-piston in   Working piston   Right free-piston
latched, "outermost"   in "inner" position
position.   ready for ignition.

Front Section View

Fig. 8-17   Three-piston, double-acting atmospheric engine by
            Daimler, 1875. (From his U.S. patent drawings)

156

Gilles Atmospheric Engine

Concurrently with Daimler's somewhat dubious effort, a new engine having related features was in limited production in Kalk, a Cologne suburb "up the street" from Deutz. Friedrich W. Gilles' design,[31] which competed with his previous employer, was built for a short time by Maschinenbau Humboldt AG, but the introduction of Otto's new engine ended any chance for its having an impact on Deutz.*

The Gilles single-acting, vertical engine had a free piston above, and working in opposition to, the power piston. (Fig. 8-18) The latter was tied to a floor level crankshaft by a conventional connecting rod. Ignition by gas flame occurred when both pistons were in the "down" position. The loose piston was quickly forced up and retained in the raised location by a latching mechanism. The vacuum generated between the two pistons caused atmospheric pressure to push up the lower, working piston and impart a torque on the crankshaft. Thus a long expansion stroke was achieved even though the working piston was directly connected to a crankshaft. Recoil vibration was less than in the Otto and Langen engine because the Gilles free piston was so much lighter, but the latching arrangement needed further improvement. There was no potential gain in power output.

The End of the Beginning

The ever helpful and concerned Franz Reuleaux alerted Langen in a letter dated July 1875 about companies who had competitive hot air engines. He prodded Otto and Daimler with an admonition to "get with it." ("Herr Otto must get off his hind legs and Herr Daimler off his front...")[32] Otto and Daimler were not seeing eye-to-eye by then and were pursuing their separate experimental activities within the company. Otto sensed the era of the atmospheric engines was over; Daimler refused to have faith in Otto's ideas for a simplified compression engine. It was left to Otto, the inventor, the creative tinkerer, to independently apply one of the most significant concepts found in the history of engines.

Close to 5,000 atmospheric engines were built to the basic Otto and Langen design. It became the catalyst, bringing together competent men, waiting factories and broad markets to set off an irreversible reaction that began the age of internal-combustion power.

*Humboldt merged into Motorenfabrik Deutz in 1930. Because Deutz production was by then mostly diesel and gasoline engines, the name "Gas" had been dropped in 1921.

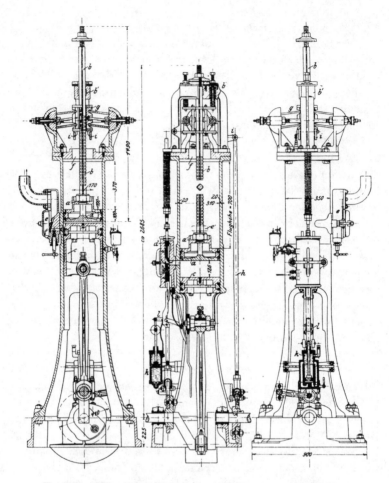

Fig. 8-18 Gilles atmospheric engine with the power piston tied to
a crankshaft and a second, free piston. 0.5 Hp at 46
rpm. (Güldner, *Verbrennungskraftmaschinen,* 1914)

❖ ❖ ❖ ❖

NOTES

1. See Eugen Diesel, et al., *From Engines to Autos*, (Chicago, 1960),
    pp. 36-46, for further details, in English, of Otto's early life. See
    also, Gustav Goldbeck, *Kraft für die Welt*, (Dusseldorf, 1964), pp.
    22-31, and Arnold Langen, *Nicolaus August Otto, der Schöpfer des
    Verbrennungsmotors,* (Stuttgart, 1949), pp. 11-47, for a more com-

prehensive story in German. Dr. Goldbeck's above book, *Power for the World*, was written to commemorate the centennial in 1964 of Klöckner-Humboldt-Deutz AG, as it was known then, was a leading builder of diesel engines and trucks in Germany.

2. Gustav Goldbeck, *Gebändigte Kraft*, (Munich, 1965), p. 36.
3. Schmidt's article on the Lenoir engine, along with his ideas and calculations for a compression engine, was also in [Dingler's] *Polytechnisches Journal*, CLX, 1861, pp. 321-37. (see also note 42, Chapter 7) Million's engine was not reported on in Dingler's Journal until 1866 (CLXXIX, pp. 329-40).
4. Lynwood Bryant, "The Origin of the Four-Stroke Cycle," *Technology and Culture*, v. 8, April 1867, pp. 195-97, suggests the engine was perhaps not constructed as Otto later showed and performed under a different mode.
5. British patent No. 2,098 of August 24, 1863. Claims were allowed only for the air reservoir addition and the construction of the pistons. The patent issued under the name of the agent, Richard A. Brooman.
6. Friedrich Sass, *Geschichte des deutschen Verbrennungsmotorenbaues von 1860 bis 1918*, (Berlin, 1962), p. 26.
7. Gustav Goldbeck, *Kraft für die Welt*, (Düsseldorf, 1964), p. 34.
8. *Ibid.*, p. 35.
9. A German (Prussian) patent of February 8, 1866; British No. 434 of 1866 (under the name of C.D. Abel); and U.S. No. 67,659 of August 13, 1867.
10. *Directions for Erecting and Working Otto and Langen's and Crossley's Patent Atmospheric Gas Engines*, Crossley Bros., Manchester, September 1878, p. 9.
11. *Ibid.*, p. 10.
12. Francis W. Crossley, "On Otto and Langen's Atmospheric Gas Engine and Some Other Gas Engines," *Proc., Institution of Mechanical Engineers*, London, 1875, p. 197.
13. Vincenzo Vannacci, *L'invenzione del motore a scoppio realizzata dai toscani Barsanti e Matteucci, 1854-1954*, (Florence, 1955), pp. 38-39.
14. British patent No. 414 and U.S. No. 153,245 both of 1874. The practice of a patent issuing in the name of an inventor's superior was not uncommon.
15. Sass, *op. cit.*, p. 38.
16. Kurt Rathke, *Wlilhelm Maybach*, (Friedrichshafen, 1953), p. 56.

17. *Directions for Erecting ... Otto and Langen's ... Engines ..., op. cit.,* p. 8. (specifications given for rpm and piston strokes); and *Prospect und Zeugnisse über atmosphärische Gaskraftmaschinen,* Gasmotoren-Fabrik Deutz, Cologne, 1876, pp. 8,9.

18. Data compiled from: Dugald Clerk, *The Gas and Oil Engine,* 6th ed., (New York, 1896), p. 141; Hugo Güldner, *Das Entwerfen und Berechnen der Verbrennungskraftmaschinen,* 3rd ed., (Berlin, 1914), p. 641; William Robinson, *Gas and Petroleum Engines,* 2nd ed., (London, 1902), p. 71.

19. Clerk, *op. cit.,* pp. 142-46.

20. Sass, *op. cit.,* p. 54.

21. *Crossley Brothers Limited, Pioneers, Progress, Leadership,* Crossley, (Manchester, ca. 1962), p. 3.

22. *Ibid.,* p. 4.

23. "Pioneers of Gas Power: 1. The Brothers Crossley," *Gas and Oil Power,* November 15, 1907, p. 32.

24. Archives, Klöckner-Humboldt-Deutz AG. (Now in the Cologne city museum)

25. Goldbeck, *Kraft ..., op. cit.,* p. 227. The technical museum in Vienna has a Langen & Wolf atmospheric engine, serial number 144, on exhibit.

26. Goldbeck, *Gebändigte, op. cit,* p. 159.

27. *Boyd's Business Directory,* (Philadelphia, 1876), p. 247, lists "Schleicher Bros." under "Gas Machines." *Gopsill's Business Directory,* (Philadelphia, 1876), p. 263, has "Schleicher Bros., Langen and Otto's Patent Gas Engine" listed under "Machinists." There are no entries for James and Adolph Schleicher under business or home in Philadelphia prior to 1876.

28. *Lebenslauf Maybach,* January 21, 1921, p. 101. A typed abstract in the K-H-D Archives from Maybach's handwritten memoirs.

29. British patent No. 71 and U.S. No. 168,623, both of 1875.

30. *Lebenslauf, op. cit.,* p. 101.

31. U.S. patent No. 179,782 of July 11, 1876. A patent model is in the Museum of History and Technology, Washington, D.C., and a production engine is on exhibit at the Deutsches Museum in Munich.

32. Sass, *op. cit.,* p. 40.

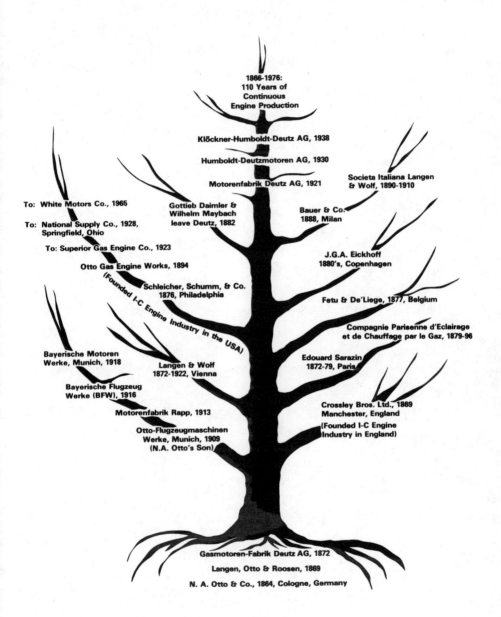

Fig. 8-19   Deutz Family Tree. (Compiled by author)

INTERNAL FIRE

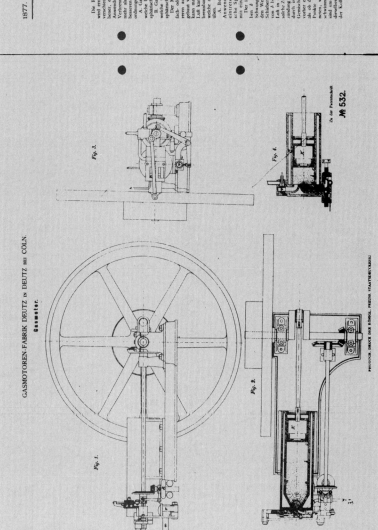

Fig. 9-1 Otto four-stroke German patent No. 532 of 1877 showing his ideas on charge stratification. (Werkphoto Deutz)

Fig. 9-2   Otto's experimental four-stroke engine of 1876 in the
Deutz Museum, Cologne. (Werkphoto Deutz)

Chapter 9

Otto's Four-Stroke Cycle

Neither the steam engine nor the horse were threatened by a pre-1876 internal-combustion engine, but the status quo was soon to change. In the spring of that year Nicolaus Otto's newest brainchild breathed its first life. A practical I-C engine had finally combined mixture compression and combustion expansion in the same cylinder. The performance of this direct ancestor to all modern reciprocating engines, from the outset, was far superior to all its competitors. The idea came at an opportune time, and customer demand soon exceeded productive capacity. Gasmotoren-Fabrik Deutz built 8,300 of the new engines between 1876 and 1889.[1] Their Philadelphia subsidiary, Schleicher, Schumm and Co., proclaimed sales of "over 25,000" by 1888.[2] Messrs. Crossley Bros., Ltd., the British licensee, had by the end of 1882 "erected at Openshaw (Manchester) no fewer than 5,000 Otto gas engines" in sizes from one-half to sixteen nominal brake horsepower.[3] The exciting era of the *neue Otto-Motor* began with a sudden vigor.

Otto's inventive mind was sparked by his awareness of an atmospheric engine's drawbacks and the repeated warnings by Reuleaux. For a while he considered an improved hot-air engine because it gave an opportunity to exceed the three horsepower limitation on the current Deutz product. Fortunately, the project was dropped (Reuleaux insisted any new engine should be of internal-combustion design[4]). Deutz even bought and tested Brayton's engine, with its separate compression and combustion cylinders (Chapter 10).* It was inevitable that Otto would refocus on his earliest experiments, his failures which diverted him to the atmospheric engine. Those crude, initial attempts involving compression, without an appreciation of what it could offer, were not abandoned because of an error in principle, but a lack of understanding. Supplied with fresh insight and the intervening years of experience, Otto decreed his new engine must compress and then burn the charge in the same cylinder.

*It did not arrive until after the four-stroke tests had begun.

163

This could be accomplished by stretching the total cycle of intake, compression, ignition, expansion and exhaust over four piston strokes or two crankshaft revolutions. Such a concept flew in direct opposition to the prevailing thought of making each piston stroke contribute its share of useful work as in the steam engine. Daimler was attempting to maximize the atmospheric engine's potential by also making it double-acting. To waste three strokes of the piston to create one power stroke was looked upon as sheer folly by Otto's contemporaries.

Of great concern to Otto was his old fear of piston shock loading. His first Lenoir test engine possibly had had a relatively small clearance volume over the piston, and if so, when he compressed a charge finally over a full return stroke he had fired the first high compression engine. Thus, it was no wonder that the resultant explosion was so violent! Remembering all of this, he ultimately concluded that the gas and air had to be selectively drawn into the cylinder in a carefully controlled manner.

A story Otto told about how his mixture stratification idea evolved is a classic of inventive inspiration. He was watching smoke rising from a nearby factory chimney one day while pondering the "shock" problem. He observed how the smoke first ascended in a solid, tight column until it was dispersed by the wind into a less and less dense, yet ever expanding cloud. The thought came to him that if first only air was brought into the engine cylinder, and then the gas and air mixture, the charge would be very lean near the piston and become progressively richer toward the source of ignition. The result would be gradual and shock free combustion. He also reasoned that the exhaust gases remaining in the cylinder, the volume of which equaled the space between the piston and cylinder head, should stay in a layer against the piston and further reduce shock loading. Thus by having the cylinder theoretically filled at the end of the intake stroke with three distinct strata, i.e. residual gas, air and lastly combustible mixture, his dispersed chimney smoke idea was realized. Otto built a hand-cranked model containing a piston in a transparent cylinder to observe the action of smoke entering during the suction stroke. Lighted cigarettes were held by the intake port, and a cam-actuated slide-valve controlled the air intake. The model, donated to the Henry Ford Museum by Deutz in 1934, was stated to have been built in 1872.[5] Thus the stratification idea must have intrigued him for several years before an engine incorporating it was built.

Because Otto strongly felt that a compression engine could not successfully operate without an accurate control over combustion, he emphasized stratification more than that of the four-stroke cycle. The first three of four descriptive claims granted in his basic German patent were devoted to stratification and combustion means.[6] Only the fourth claim protected the four-stroke idea. Otto's main claim in his U.S. patent reads:

> A gas motor engine wherein an intimate mixture of com-
> bustible gas or vapor and air is introduced into the cylinder,
> separate from a charge of air or other incombustible gas, in
> such manner and in such proportions that the particles of
> combustible mixture will be close together at the point of
> ignition, but will be more and more dispersed in the charge
> of air forward of that point, whereby the development of
> heat and the expansion or increase of pressure produced by
> the combustion are rendered gradual...[7]

His stratified-charge theory was later disputed, and in general discredited during titanic legal battles over his patent, but time may prove that the idea was a century too early. (Fig. 9-1, Plate)

The Prototype Engine

A prototype four-stroke cycle engine was operating in less than six months from the moment Otto decided he was ready to convert his ideas into hardware. (Fig. 9-2, Plate) Langen had assigned him an engineer, Franz Rings, and then left him alone. (Daimler was convinced this new and radical effort by Otto would be a waste of time.) From the very first the engine's performance lived up to Otto's expectations. The major difficulty experienced, irregular ignition at idle and light loads, was corrected by the time a production design was completed.

Functional and completely unadorned are the terms best describing the engine's overall appearance. It bore a similarity to the Lenoir engine with its single, horizontal cylinder and crosshead-guided piston. The vital differences were in the valving and the modifications to the gas flame ignition. The stratified charge was admitted through a redesigned slide-valve as was the ignition flame; exhaust was through a poppet valve activated by a rocker lever. Both valves were timed by an auxiliary camshaft turning at one-half crankshaft speed. The basic elements of all modern four-stroke engines are found on this first experimental model. Specifications and performance data have survived:[8]

Bore, mm	161
Stroke, mm	300
Max. compression pressure, atm	2.36 (34 psi)
Maximum power, bhp*	3
Rated speed, rpm	180
Gas consumption, cu m/bhp hr	0.95 (33.5 cu ft)

Fuel consumption was remarkably good and was close to that measured on production engines of comparable power.

A slide-valve, placed on the cylinder head, timed air intake and ignition. A second, cam-operated slide-valve, mounted directly over the camshaft, determined the timing of inducted gas. This valve could be overridden by governor linkage which slid the valve cam away from its follower if maximum speed was exceeded. Gas passed through a hand throttled valve before the engine timed valve. The intake and ignition slide-valve was reciprocated by a short crank throw on the end of the camshaft. (Fig. 9-3, Plate). As the piston began its outward stroke the valve opened an air passage into the cylinder. A row of small orifices in the valve cover led from the gas supply into the slider air passage, but no gas could flow until the gas valve opened (when the piston was about halfway out). Thus only air entered the cylinder during the first part of the intake stroke. A poppet-type gas valve, opened by a cam and bell crank, was used on the production engines. (Fig. 9-4, Plate).

When the engine was applied to electric power generation the speed could vary excessively with only an on-off control of the gas supply. A modulating valve reduced the problem, and all engines then used this design.

Otto, having more faith in flame ignition than electric, modified the system used on the atmospheric engine. With the cylinder now under pressure at the time of ignition, however, the valve design became more critical; the igniter flame could be blown out when it was exposed to the compressed charge (the same problem Barnett foresaw thirty years earlier). This trouble manifested itself on the Otto prototype as irregular ignition at idle and light loads. Part of the solution was the addition of a pressure equalizing circuit (Fig. 9-5), one of several refinements incorporated in a supplementary patent, German No. 2,735. Just before the flame cavity was opened directly to the cylinder, but after the gas

---

*The metric "horsepower" (Pferdestärke or Ps) equals 0.986 English and U.S. horsepower. Because of this small difference the two values are usually considered the same.

supply was severed, a branch passage off the cavity's gas supply line indexed with a second but much smaller port also leading into the cylinder. In addition to a more balanced pressure, the igniter flame in the cavity was enriched with a little extra puff of gas to strengthen it as the cavity met the pressurized cylinder charge.

Ignition on the "Silent Otto" was reliable within certain speed limitations. According to Clerk,[9] the engine performed well under full power at 80 to 100 ignitions per minute, but at 150 (300 rpm) the flame action was too slow. Time was too short for fresh air to purge the flame cavity of residual gases left from the last combustion cycle to make it ready for the next ignition flame. Neither did gas ignition come "free." Gas consumption also had to include that used by the continuously burning flame, about two percent of the total on a four brake horsepower engine.[10]

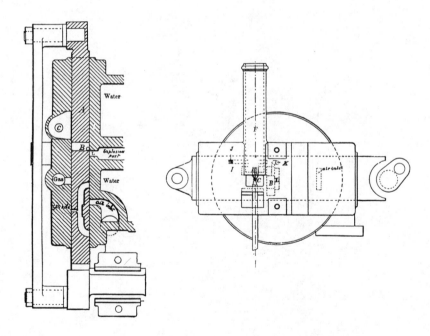

Fig. 9-5   Flame ignition system in the slide-valve. Deutz four-stroke engine, 1877. (Clerk, *The Gas and Oil Engine*, 1896)

Another significant modification to improve ignition and the ensuing combustion was also perfected on the prototype engine. An "explosion canal" in the cylinder head (Fig. 9-6) was designed to draw in a rich
mixture at the very end of the intake stroke. Thus when that portion of
the charge was exposed to the igniter flame in the slide-valve, a strong
jet of flame was generated to blast into the combustion chamber and
ensure quick, positive burning of the total charge. The optimum
passage diameter and exit orifice shape was determined experimentally
by cementing a number of different sizes and shapes into the cylinder
head. A sharp cornered orifice gave the best results, as Rings noted
in his log book on July 25, 1876.[11] Pressure-volume diagrams of
before and after situations of the *Schusskanal* illustrate the dramatic
difference.[12] (Fig. 9-7) The enclosed area formed by the curves as traced
on the compression and expansion strokes, minus the area of the
"pumping" loop (during exhaust and intake), is a measure of the "indicated" work produced by the engine. That is, before subtracting the
mechanical losses.

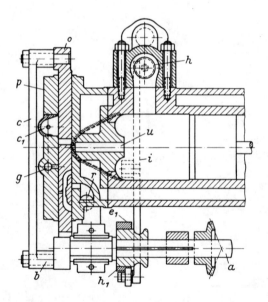

Fig. 9-6 "Explosion Canal" of Otto engine. The length and orifice
shape of the igniter passage was optimized to improve
part load performance. (Sass, *Geschichte des
deutschen Verbrennungsmotorenbaues,* 1962)

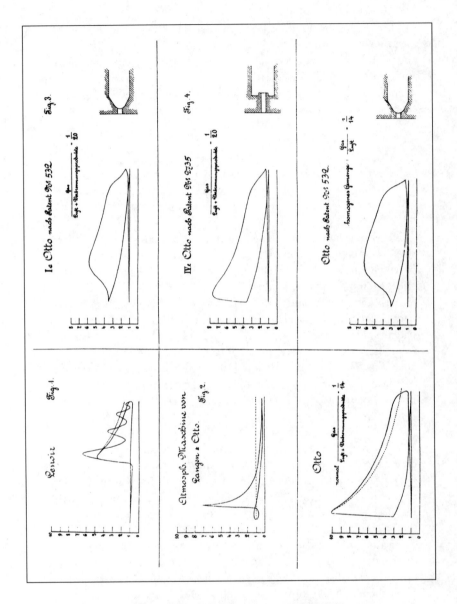

Fig. 9-7   Pressure-volume diagrams of Otto four-stroke engine
with various igniter passage configurations as compared
with the Lenoir and Otto & Langen atmospheric engines.
Fuel:air ratios are given for the Otto four-stroke.
(Werkphoto Deutz)

Otto's ideas concerning stratification changed somewhat between his first four-stroke patent (No. 532) and the follow on No. 2,735. The former stipulated discrete layers, with "slow," progressive burning from the ignition source and the latter intended a more rapid combustion from a small, locally rich charge into a lean but more homogeneous mixture. The patent claim covering this later thinking reads:

> The combination, in a gas motor engine, of a cylinder containing a weak or diluted combustible uniform mixture of gas and air with a separate passage or chamber containing a strong or undiluted mixture of gas and air, and provided with an igniting slide or valve, substantially as set forth.[13]

Deutz now had an encircling ring around almost every type of worthwhile I-C engine, including four-stroke as well as two-stroke if the latter engine appeared to contain layered or homogeneous mixtures and/or residual exhaust products!

Both patents 532 and 2,735 issued on the same date, Aug. 4, 1877, because of procedural changes caused by unification of the German patent system (Chapter 4), but there was a long interval between their filing dates. No. 2,735 was not applied for until June 1, 1877, one year after No. 532. Over one hundred production engines had been built by that time. The delay, plus the subtle change in Otto's stratification theory, became a factor in future litigation over the earlier patent.

The 1876 Production Engine

Wilhelm Maybach was placed in charge of redesigning Otto's prototype engine for production as soon as he returned from his trip to the United States. Many obvious refinements and improvements were required, but the general concept and layout were retained (Fig. 9-8, Plate). Two of these refinements merit a brief description because of their novelty.

Starting was aided by a compression release cam slidable along the camshaft. It was inserted under the exhaust cam follower to hold open the exhaust valve while the flywheel was turned over by hand. With the engine "spinning" the cam was manually moved away from the follower. Flywheel inertia carried the piston past a compression stroke so a charge could be ignited. Larger engines later used air starting by admitting compressed air into the cylinder during the power stroke.

Drip lubrication was supplied to the slide-valve and to the piston through a hole in the cylinder wall below the piston rings. The oil reservoir was in a bowl placed above the cylinder. A short wire, fastened to a belt-driven shaft turning in the bowl, dipped into the oil and then rubbed on a trough feeding to pipes connected to the lubrication points. As the shaft rotated, oil was picked up and removed from the wire, the quantity wiped into the trough being determined by engine speed.

Extensive testing on circa 1880 four-stroke Otto engines by independent engineers of the day provide good corroborative data. The following are results obtained by Professor Slaby[14] at Deutz in 1881 and Professor Thurston* at Stevens Institute, New Jersey in 1883.[15]

	Slaby	Thurston
Bore, in	6.75	8.5
Stroke, in	13.38	14
Compression ratio	2.65	2.63
Engine speed, rpm	157	158
Mean Effective Pressure, psi	52.9	—
Brake horsepower	4.4	8.1
Mechanical efficiency, %	87	84
Gas consumption, cu ft/bhp hr ..	32.4	29.1
Gas heating value, Btu/cu ft	547	617
Thermal efficiency, %	16	17

Although not given for these tests, the compression pressure would have been about 35-40 psi and the peak combustion pressure about 110-120 psi. Note the higher heating value of the gas used in the American test and the correspondingly lower volume consumed. No valid comparison of overall efficiency between gas engines can ever be made without knowing the Btu content of fuel. The approximate air:fuel ratio on these tests was between nine and ten to one.

The Achievement

One of the earliest pressure-volume diagrams taken from the Otto prototype engine is located in the Maybach archives. (Fig. 9-9) This historic curve, dated 9 May 1876, demonstrates why an "Otto" or

---

*Robert H. Thurston (1839-1903) is most remembered as an engineering educator (Stevens and Cornell) and as the first president of the American Society of Mechancal Engineers. His books on steam engines were considered classics.

constant-volume cycle was superior to a non-compression engine cycle. It traced an enclosed area far greater than any diagram yet made for such a small piston displacement.

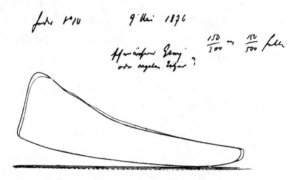

Fig. 9-9   Earliest recorded pressure-volume diagram of a four-stroke engine, made May 9, 1876. (Werkphoto Deutz)

What Schmidt and Million wrote about in 1861 was now a proven fact. A comparison between an Otto and Langen atmospheric engine and an Otto four-stroke engine dramatically illustrates what had been accomplished:[16]

	Otto & Langen	Otto (Crossley)
Test date	1884*	1882**
Brake horsepower	2	2
Approx. engine weight, lbs	4,000	1,250
Piston displacement, cu in	4,900	310
Power strokes per minute	28	80
Shaft speed, rpm	90	160
Mechanical efficiency, %	68	84
Brake thermal eff., %	11.2	14
Indicated thermal eff., %	16.5	16.7
Expansion ratio, approx.	10:1	2.5:1

*By Dugald Clerk at Oldham
**By Adams and Sprague at the Crystal Palace, London.

Otto verified that while a high expansion ratio, non-compression engine burned about the same amount of fuel as his new compression engine, it suffered badly relative to other vital parameters.

A reduction by a factor of three in weight and of over fifteen in piston displacement for an engine only slightly more efficient overall gave great cause for optimism at Deutz. The three horsepower ceiling on output suddenly disappeared. Objectionable noise and vibration became problems of the past. All of this was achieved with an engine having a compression ratio of only two and one-half to one! The significance of Otto's demonstrated concept may be expressed yet another way. Within ten years Benz and Daimler were driving automobiles, and only seventeen years after that Orville Wright was flying at Kitty Hawk.

The Otto Patent in the Courts

Gasmotoren-Fabrik Deutz and its licensees diligently protected their position as the world's sole supplier of Otto's new engine. Through litigation and threats of such action they pursued all builders who attempted to infringe the Otto patents. The issues involved not only the four-stroke cycle, but also any compression engine, which, in Deutz's judgment, did not in effect remove all residual gas from the cylinder at the end of the exhaust stroke! Competition was virtually eliminated. A "Letter to the Editor" of *Engineering* during the period of the Otto engine's total domination warned others of Charles Linford's fate after he lost an appeal in the English Courts in January 1882:[17]

> Sir — It may be of more than passing interest to some of your readers to know that Mr. Otto has been obliged again to take action against several firms for infringing his patent. It is well that the public should know, that after the action of Otto v. Linford (in which Linford was defeated and ordered to pay costs and cease to manufacture), purchasers and users of the Linford engine were obliged to pay royalty to Mr. Otto. The Otto patent has now been upheld in three countries.
>
> Yours truly,
Crossley Bros., Ltd
Robert Wilson, London Mgr.
>
> London, April 19, 1883

Even a two-stroke engine designed by Dugald Cleik and in volume production by Thompson, Sterne and Co. of Glasgow (his employer at the time), was a casualty of an infringement threat. "Otto v. Sterne" settled before coming to trial when the company agreed to withdraw the engine from the market.[18]

Otto's cherished patent, nevertheless, provided a legacy encompassing far more than an outpouring of legal decisions. It acted as a stimulus to basic research for proving or disproving the correctness of his ideas and for ingenious designs to circumvent his broadly interpreted patent claims. Dugald Clerk in England, Professor Aimé Witz in France and Professors Slaby and Schöttler in Germany, to name only a few, argued their theories in court about what went on in the cylinder of an Otto engine. Whether they were engaged as expert witnesses for the plaintiff or the defendant depended on their belief or disbelief in the stratification concept. Out of court they filled engineering journals with test data to reinforce their advocacy. As a direct result there grew a rapidly expanding base of understanding of the combustion process. It combined fuel chemistry, thermodynamics and novel instrumentation. The patent fulfilled its intended purpose: the holder was provided with an opportunity to freely exploit his property for a few years, and then the field was opened to a competition charged with pent-up energy and ready knowledge.

The first serious legal threat to the Deutz monopoly arose out of a patent opposition proceeding in 1882.[19] Deutz felt that a certain patent, granted to one Gerhard Adam of Munich, should not issue because it weakened the four-stroke claim of Otto's patent No. 532. Deutz lost the initial round of what turned out to be a three round fight. The Adam patent was allowed to issue under the title of "Improvements to the Gas Engine Patent No. 532,"[20] a result of a previous patent to Christian Reithmann (1819-1909), a Munich clockmaker. Reithmann was to testify later he had built and run his own engine on a four-stroke cycle before 1876. He had been experimenting with gas engines since the 1850s, but without notable success. Attention had been called to his work by a Munich Technical University professor in previous years. Reithmann was drug out of relative obscurity and became an unwitting tool of those Deutz competitors who sensed an opportunity to invalidate the Otto patent.

Round two began in December 1883 when Deutz sued Reithmann for his damaging testimony regarding the four-stroke priority. The engine in question (Fig. 9-10, Plate) was originally built in 1872 or 1873 and had various modifications added over the years. By the time of the trial several features did bear a resemblance to those found on a four-stroke engine, and with further changes and additions strangely permitted by the court, it was briefly demonstrated to run on that cycle. Despite inconsistencies and vagueness in Reithmann's testimony, the court decided in his favor on December 13, 1884.

Deutz appealed immediately, but as added insurance, they purchased from Reithmann just five days after the lower court decision all rights to his engine. The price was 25,000 marks and a small Otto engine, and the sale was binding regardless of the outcome of the appeal. Upon probing more deeply into the sequence of the modifications made to the Reithmann engine a higher court reversed the earlier decision and held that Otto was, in fact, the prior inventor. Deutz won round three and the fight. The Reitnmann story resurfaced in a 1903 classic text on engine history and theory by Hugo Güldner (1866-1929). For an unexplainable reason Güldner touted the engine and biased the story toward Reithmann by omitting mention of the appeals court decision.[21]

Enter Beau de Rochas

Not until 1884 did the emasculated engine builders of Europe find a way out of their dilemma, and then it was only by the chance discovery of an obscure writing. Early that year the journal of the Society of German Engineers (VDI) published a long letter written to the editor by C. Wigand in part telling of an old French pamphlet he had uncovered in which the essential concept of Otto's engine was spelled out.[22] Wigand was a patent attorney and friend of Ernst and Berthold Körting in Hannover, another of the frustrated engine manufacturers. (Gebr. Körting became one of the world's foremost builders of large gas engines.)

Wigand had found a tract based on an unpublished patent filed on January 16, 1862, to Alphonse Beau de Rochas (1815-1893), a French engineer who worked for the transportation department of the government in Paris. (Fig. 9-11, Plate) The patent, entitled "New investigations into the practical conditions for greater utilization of heat and in general of motive power with applications for railroads and navigation,"[23] had no drawings. In keeping with Beau de Rochas' sometimes unpredictable actions, he failed to pay the required fees so that the patent was never published. He did, however, have three hundred pamphlets lithographed from a handwritten copy of the fifty-three page patent application.[24] Buried within the rambling dissertation was a short section outlining possibilities for a new engine which would compress an air-gas mixture prior to combustion. It suggested that the cycle of operation take place in the same cylinder over four piston strokes. The stated process involved:[25]

1. Induction during an outward stroke of the piston;
2. Compression during the return stroke;
3. Ignition at the dead point, followed by expansion on the third stroke;
4. Discharge of the burned gases from the cylinder during the fourth and last stroke.

Beau de Rochas also suggested four engine conditions to design toward:

1. The largest possible cylinder volume with the minimum boundary surface.
2. The greatest possible working speed.
3. Greatest possible number of expansions.
4. Greatest possible pressure at the beginning of expansion. [See Appendix for the complete specifications of the patent relating to Compression engines.]

The Beau de Rochas tract could not have been more devastating to Otto's claim of invention for the four-stroke cycle engine. Handed the weapon that could break the hold of Deutz, Körting wasted no time in filing a suit against Otto to have his patent declared invalid. It little mattered that Beau de Rochas had proposed only a paper engine or that he had also let his patent lapse for non-payment of taxes a year after the grant. (An annual tax is required to maintain a patent in almost all countries, now including the United States.) During the German litigation Otto tried to establish prior invention by revealing his 1861 experiments with the single and four cylinder engines (Chapter 8). His testimony was not convincing enough to establish those critical dates to prove he had in fact "anticipated" Beau de Rochas. (Another example of the danger in not adequately documenting experimental work!) Otto's integrity was never questioned, and no one inferred he had ever seen the Beau de Rochas patent; nevertheless, the four-stroke claim was lost. He simply had the same idea at a later date as far as the court was concerned.

But is not invention more than the bare conception of an idea? Invention in its fullest meaning implies an effort by the inventor to transform his idea into a practical, useful creation. When this broader interpretation is applied to Otto's achievement then he, and not Beau de Rochas, has to be considered the true inventor of the four-stroke cycle engine. The U.S. Patent Office stresses this point. It requires an inventor to show "diligence" in "reducing his invention to practice." A second and later inventor may be granted a patent for the same idea if he perfected the idea before the first inventor, and the first inventor cannot prove diligence.

Beau de Rochas never defended his claim of invention in the years before the German trial even though, for example, an Otto engine won a gold medal at the 1878 Paris Exposition. One source suggests he had been out of the country for political reasons.[26] A friend of Lenoir, he worked in his later life for Mignon et Rouart, the Paris builder of Lenoir's new four-stroke engine. Two years before his death the French government recognized him as the inventor of the four-stroke cycle and awarded him three thousand francs. Textbooks sometimes refer to Otto's engine as operating on the "Beau de Rochas cycle."

The trial of "Körting v. Otto" originally centered on only the four-stroke claim. (Deutz also filed an infringement suit against the Körting Gas Engine Co., New York, in 1887, but it never came to trial.[27]) As the case unfolded, however, the stratification claims were also challenged. Expert witnesses for the plaintiff (Professor Schöttler for one) cast heavy doubt on the correctness of Otto's theories, particularly in view of his changed thinking in the later patent No. 2,735. Because Otto could not effectively refute the apparent demolition of his stratification ideas the court also held that all of these claims, too, were invalid. Thus on January 30, 1886, Deutz's competition won a complete victory. (Goldbeck suggests that governmental policy prevailing in Germany at the time was not in favor of patents which restrained broad industrial development of worthwhile products, and this may have been a factor in the decision.[28]) Deutz carried on an appeal for several years but with no success.

A case of equal import was being tried in London at the same time Otto suffered his legal demise in Leipzig. Fortunately for Deutz and Crossley, whose licensing arrangement was most profitable, the alleged infringer in "Otto v. Steel" lost.

The issue of the Beau de Rochas patent was strongly raised by the defense, but the judge disallowed its being entered in evidence. Although the British Museum library did receive a single printed copy of the handwritten tract in 1864, it was catalogued only under the name of the author and the French title and not by subject. The judge stated he must conclude that if he were to follow rules of the library the circumstances would have made the library's actual possession of no use to him. A single copy of an all but buried work did not, therefore, constitute publication of the work in that country.[29] All efforts were then concentrated by the defense on breaking the stratification claims since the infringement suit also involved the aspect of residual exhaust products. This time Otto's attorneys presented a more convincing argument even though the other side likewise had respectable data to substantiate its pleadings.[30] (Dugald Clerk, an expert witness for the defense, said he originally believed in the stratification concept of Otto, but after years of working on his own engine had changed his mind.) All of the claims in the British patent No. 2,081 (German No. 532) were upheld.*

Otto gave testimony at a deposition hearing in Cologne during the English trial that sheds light on another aspect of the stratification contradictions.[32] According to Otto, a ruling of the German Patent Office required him to accept a patent for his two-stroke cycle engine ideas containing contrary beliefs. The patent spoke of a completely homogeneous air and gas mixture in the cylinder at the time of ignition.[33] (The charge was drawn in and partially compressed in a separate cylinder prior to its entrance into the working cylinder.) This exactly opposite view to the teachings of the patent No. 532 was not helpful to Otto in the German trial. The circumstances were that Otto had experimented with a two-stroke engine and abandoned work on it because of poor fuel consumption and numerous other problems. The idea, however, was pirated and then patented under fraud in another German state. When all of the various state patents were unified under a single authority shortly thereafter, the German Patent Office finally awarded the "stolen" patent to Otto. Unfortunately, he had to take it "as is," yet he did not believe in the "intimate mixture" concept it described.

Although vindicated in England, the loss of the German patent was a blow to Otto's pride from which by all accounts he never recovered during the five years remaining to him. Deutz and most of the world attached his name to the four-stroke compression engine, but Otto felt there was more to its inherent success than its taking two revolutions of the crankshaft to complete a cycle.

Follow-on Developments at Deutz

Deutz did not rest on the laurels of its success with the "A" engine introduced in 1877. While the basic design remained virtually unchanged until 1895, output was continually increased; Crossley offered a one hundred horsepower, single cylinder model in the mid-1880s. Space saving, vertical engines of one to eight horsepower were also produced in quantity. (Fig. 9-12, Plate)

---

*Mr. Justice Pearson, the presiding judge, also commented during the trial "you have confirmed in me an idea which I have had for a great many years that all patents are bad."[31]

A problem arose when the engines were applied to electric generators for the newly introduced direct current arc lights. Speed fluctuations with the slow speed, one cylinder engine caused undesirable flickering. Otto solved this by a "twin engine." Two identical cylinders adapted from a standard engine lay side by side, and their pistons acted on a common crankshaft. With a power stroke on every revolution, speed variation was reduced to an acceptable limit. Each exhaust valve had its own camshaft, but the intake and ignition slide-valves were controlled from only one of those shafts. Twin engine generator installations began in 1880 with the lighting of the Berlin opera house and the cathedral at Cologne (to celebrate its completion). Of the 24,000 gas engines Deutz had built by the turn of the century 1,150 were "twins."[34]

Daimler's independent solution to the speed problem was by a double-expansion compound engine; only a few were made.[35] Horizontal high pressure cylinders straddled a single, low pressure cylinder. Ignition and combustion occurred in the outer cylinders and their exhaust passed through poppet valves into the center cylinder for further expansion. The crank throw for the low pressure piston was 180 degrees from the two throws for the outer pistons, thus providing a power stroke for every one-half shaft revolution. (One of these engines ran in Langen's sugar refinery for a brief time.)

More significant developments at Deutz during the first ten years of four-stroke engines involved ignition and carburetion. It was Otto who in 1884 pioneered a low tension magneto for an electric ignition system. (Fig. 9-13, Plate) The spark plug for the engine using this system had both a fixed and a movable electrode. When the latter was rocked away from contact with the stationary rod, by a small bellcrank whose shaft passed through the igniter assembly in the cylinder head, a spark was induced across the gap. (Fig. 9-14)

Deutz introduced a gasoline-fueled engine about the same time as the magneto. The fuel was vaporized in a surface carburetor by bubbling air up through a fuel reservoir on the engine's suction stroke. (Fig. 9-15) An air valve at the carburetor and an air-vapor throttle valve controlled mixture strength and flow rate. Engine cooling water discharge circulated through a large water jacket around the carburetor to enhance vaporization. A hand pump at the tank supplied the carburetor. By 1885 Deutz was building their "AB" engine incorporating both the surface carburetor and the low tension magneto for "make and break" ignition. (Fig. 9-16, Plate) The carburetor with this model was warmed by either exhaust gas or water from the engine.

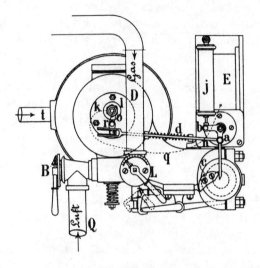

Fig. 9-14   Cylinder end view of electric ignition system used on
Deutz engine, 1884. The magneto was combined with
a "make and break" spark igniter in the cylinder.
(Werkphoto Deutz)

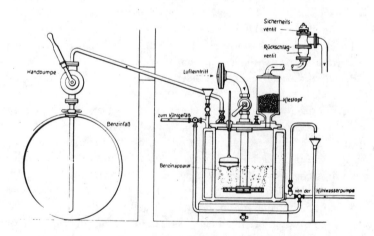

Fig. 9-15   Gasoline surface carburetor for Deutz engines, 1884.
(Werkphoto Deutz)

The slide-valve limited engine speed and cylinder pressure. If the slider clearance adjusting screws were tightened to reduce flame and pressure leakage, the wear rates became excessive. Continued exposure to high temperatures caused burning erosion around the flame ports, and the small intake passages restricted the charge flow into the cylinder. Crossley abandoned the slide-valve on all models by 1888, adopting a poppet intake valve and hot-tube ignition. (Fig. 9-17, Plate) A small, timed valve connected the combustion chamber to the inside of a closed ended red-hot tube. (Fig. 9-18). Deutz eliminated the slide-valve on the electric ignition, gasoline engines and was gradually phasing it out on other models. The small, vertical engines changed to a hot-tube igniter.

Both Deutz and their licensees profited by a free exchange of information on each other's new developments. Crossley was in the forefront with new innovations on ignition and speed regulation. The whole family of Otto engine manufacturers had golden years for sales as the expanding markets could not be supplied fast enough. In the United States, Schleicher, Schumm and Co. continued to be a major supplier of I-C engines. (Fig. 9-19, Plate) In 1894 the Schleichers sold their interest to the Deutz management, and the company name was

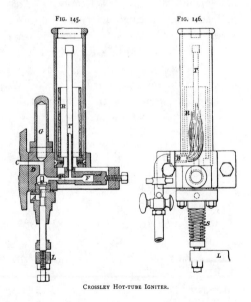

FIG. 145.   FIG. 146.

CROSSLEY HOT-TUBE IGNITER.

Fig. 9-18   Section view through Crossley hot-tube igniter system.
(Robinson, *Gas and Petroleum Engines,* 1890)

181

changed to "The Otto Gas Engine Works."[36] Hermann Schumm was by this time on the Board of Directors at Deutz and after Otto's death provided its technical leadership.

What began in 1876 as a confident hope soon became a standard of comparison. The tradition established at Gasmotoren-Fabrik Deutz in those early years gave the company an esprit which has enabled it to weather the storms of financial chaos, competition and wartime destruction, and to enter its second century as an engine builder. Langen the businessman, Daimler the production organizer and Maybach the engineering genius left their heritage, but what they accomplished was based on the imagination of August Otto.

A Postscript: The Genesis of BMW [37]

Gustav Otto (1883-1926), the only son of August and Anna to live to adulthood, never worked for Deutz but became an engineer and aircraft designer in Munich. Using part of the inheritance from his father, he founded in 1909 "Gustav-Otto-Flugzeugmaschinenwerke, München." It was an airframe company eventually to produce planes for World War 1. In 1916 a new company, Bayerische Flugzeugwerke AG absorbed the Otto works. Otto used the money he received to pay off the debts accrued while developing a practical airplane and was thereafter not involved with BFW. Some of the engines for the Otto biplanes were supplied by Motorenfabrik Rapp GmbH, a small engine firm founded in 1913, also in Munich. In 1918 the Rapp name changed to Bayerische Motorenwerke AG, and after BFW stopped production in 1919 the engine works moved into that facility. It is interesting to note that BMW uses 1916 as the date of their founding, the year the "Otto Werke" became BFW.

NOTES
1. Friedrich Sass, *Geschichte des deutschen Verbrennungsmotorenbaues von 1860 bis 1918,* (Berlin, 1962), p. 54.
2. Advertisement in *Scientific American,* January 1, 1888, p. 45.
3. *Engineering,* February 15, 1884, p. 136.
4. Arnold Langen, *Nicolaus Otto, der Schöpfer des Verbrennungsmotors,* (Stuttgart, 1949), pp. 65-66.
5. Correspondence dated February 27, 1934, to Henry Ford's secretary from Humboldt-Deutzmotoren AG via Ford Motor Company, Cologne. Henry Ford Museum Archives, Dearborn.

6. German patent No. 532 of August 4, 1877. A fifth claim only referred to general construction features as described in the specifications.

7. U.S. patent No. 194,047 of August 14, 1877. The equivalent British patent was No. 2,081 of May 17, 1876.

8. Sass, *op. cit.,* p. 44.

9. Dugald Clerk, *The Gas, Petrol and Oil Engine,* v. 2, (London, 1913), p. 264.

10. Dugald Clerk, *The Gas and Oil Engine,* 6th ed., (New York, 1896), p. 172. (Slaby tests of Otto engine at Deutz, August 1881.)

11. Sass, *op. cit.,* p. 52.

12. Eugen Langen, *Vortrag des Herrn Kommerzienrat Eugen Langen gehalten in der Sitzung des Kölner Bezirksvereins deutscher Ingenieure am 2. Marz 1886 über das Urteil des Reichgerichtes vom 30. Januar 1886 betreffend die Patente der Gasmotoren-fabrik Deutz,* (Cologne, 1886), Pl. 11.

13. U.S. patent 196,473 of October 23, 1877, Claim 1. It and British patent No. 2,177 of June 4, 1877, correspond to the German No. 2,735. The Crossley brothers, Francis and William, have their names added in addition to Otto's as inventors on these U.S. and British patents.

14. William Robinson, *Gas and Petroleum Engines,* 2nd ed., (London 1902, p. 112. The 1883 test was performed by Brook and Steward under Thurston's direction and is sometimes listed under their names.

15. Clerk, *The Gas and Oil Engine, op. cit.,* pp. 170-79.

16. Clerk, *op. cit.,* p. 141; Robinson, *op. cit.,* p. 112; and Hugo Güldner, *Das Entwerfen und Berechnen der Verbrennungskraft-maschinen,* 3rd ed., (Berlin, 1914), p. 112. The data given is calculated from the "raw" specifications and performance figures to make the comparison more meaningful.

17. *Engineering,* April 27, 1883, p. 391.

18. *Engineering,* January 15, 1886, p. 47, and Robinson, *op. cit.,* p. 200.

19. Before a patent finally issues in Germany (and Great Britain, among others) it is published as approved by the patent office and exposed to the public for challenge. If no one opposes the granting of the patent within a specified time the patent issues.

20. Sass, *op. cit.,* p. 60. German patent No. 43,549.

21. Güldner, *op. cit.,* pp. 647-49.

22. *Zeitschrift des Vereines deutscher Ingenieure,* XXVIII, January 12, 1884, pp. 45-47.

23. The patent No. 52,539 was issued "without examination and guarantee," the usual French practice. See: Gustav Goldbeck, "Otto and the Otto Engine," *The Engineer,* November 21, 1952, p. 679; Lynwood Bryant's two comprehensive articles, "The Silent Otto," *Technology and Culture,* VII, Spring 1966, pp. 184-200, and "The Origin of the Four-Stroke Cycle," *Technology and Culture,* VIII, April 1967, pp. 178-98; and Sass, *op. cit.,* pp. 56-58 and 162-66.

24. Eugen Diesel, et al, *From Engines to Autos,* (Chicago, 1960), p. 72. The section on Otto is written by Dr. Goldbeck.

25. Bryan Donkin, *Gas, Oil and Air Engines,* 2nd ed., (London, 1896). An "Abstract Translation" of the Beau de Rochas patent by Donkin is printed in its entirety in the Appendix.

26. Bryant, "Origins...", *op. cit.,* p. 185, fn. 10. See also: Jacques Payen, "Beau de Rochas, Étude Bibliographique," *Documents Pour L'Historie des Techniques,* Cahier No. 2, (Paris, 1962), pp. 3-24.

27. *Nicolaus August Otto vs. The Korting Gas Engine Company, Ltd.,* Complainant's Record, Circuit Court of the U.S., Southern District of New York, April 2, 1889.

28. Eugen Diesel, *op. cit.,* p. 74.

29. "High Court of Justice, Chancery Division. Before Mr. Justice Pearson, Otto v. Steel," *The Engineer,* January 29, 1886, p. 93.

30. *The Engineer,* December 18, 1885, p. 483.

31. *The Engineer,* January 15, 1886, p. 47.

32. *The Engineer,* December 4, 1885, p. 434.

33. German patent No. 14,254 of December 31, 1879. See also: Sass, *op. cit.,* pp. 73-74.

34. Sass, *op. cit.,* pp. 70-71.

35. They were built to German patent No. 10,116 of August 15, 1879. (British No. 3,245 of August 12, 1879 and U.S. No. 222,467 of December 9, 1879.)

36. During World War I the U.S. Government expropriated the company's Philadelphia assets, and in 1923 they were sold to the Superior Gas Engine Co., Springfield, Ohio. From 1923 to 1928 when the National Supply Co. bought Superior, the Philadelphia plant was known as the Otto Works of the Superior Gas Engine Co. In 1937 the Otto name was dropped and all production moved to Springfield. White Motor Co., Cleveland, acquired National Supply in 1955.

37. Gustav Goldbeck, "Gustav Otto, Ein Lebensbild aus dem deutschen Flugzeug-und Automobilbau 1905-1925," *Technik Geschichte,* VDI, 1972, No. 3, pp. 213-26.

Chapter 10

Brayton and His " Ready Motor"

The man who gives the world a new power and teaches his brethren how to wield it, has a royalty of his own, and deserves that Hero worship which enthusiasts offer at the shrine of greatness.

—Brayton Prospectus[1]

George Bailey Brayton (1839-1892) labored to be that man. Although an active participant in the power parade, he never became its leader. Brayton designed the first commercial gas engine of American origin in 1872 and followed with the world's first practical oil burning engine three years later. All compressed an air:fuel mixture prior to combustion, but the compressing (of air and fuel in the gas engine) was performed in an auxiliary pump. An unacceptably low thermal efficiency prevented the Brayton engine from successfully competing with the Otto. Nevertheless, the thermodynamic cycle fitting this engine lived on to be used for the modern, continuous-combustion gas turbine. The term "Brayton Cycle" conjures a specific picture in the mind of a mechanical engineer, but its genesis is little known.

Born in East Greenwich, Rhode Island, Brayton (Fig. 10-1, Plate) spent much of his life in New England and was a product of the emerging industry in the United States. His father was superintendent of a cotton textile mill who had enhanced his income through several inventions for loom attachments. George Brayton's formal education stopped before high school and consisted of learning the machinist trade in Providence. He showed an early aptitude for mechanical innovation, with a breech loading gun and a tank riveting machine being early ideas. While employed by the Exeter Machine Works at Exeter, New Hampshire, for several years, he developed a sectional steam generator used in home and building heating. The "Exeter" heating boiler became the principal product of the company.[2] It was there that his prototype

185

gas engines were made, and William Burlingame, the Exeter owner, later supported him financially.

Combustion engines had intrigued Brayton for many years; his earliest experiments using camphene (an explosive mixture of turpentine and alcohol) as a fuel began in the 1850s. By 1870 he devoted his total effort to the development of a new concept of an internal-combustion engine. Although his first engines used less fuel than either the Lenoir or the Hugon, they were not as efficient as the Otto and Langen. Nevertheless, they were fairly reliable and available in higher power ratings than the cumbersome Otto and Langen. The introduction of Otto's four-stroke engine in 1877 denied Brayton the chance for a success in the market place.

The uniqueness of the Brayton engine lay in its method of compressing, burning and then expanding the air and gas or oil charge. Brayton built "compression" engines at least four years before Otto, but mechanical and throttling losses associated with the compressing method greatly reduced the inherent potential exploited by Otto. Air and gas were compressed by a piston in a separate cylinder, as Schmidt had proposed, and then piped to a power cylinder via a storage tank. (Fig. 10-2, Plate) A flame jet burning in an antechamber at the inlet to the combustion chamber ignited the incoming pressurized charge when the piston moved past top dead center. Continuous combustion was maintained at a constant pressure as the piston traveled outward until the inlet valve closed. Air reservoir pressure remained always higher than combustion pressure. Expansion began after the inlet closure, continuing until the exhaust valve opened at the end of the stroke. Brayton engines were "two-stroke" with a power stroke on each crankshaft revolution. Most were single-acting, but beginning about 1876 some double-acting engines also appeared. A similarity of the combustion process to that of the gas turbine can be seen, exemplifying why the Brayton cycle lends itself to a thermodynamic analysis of the turbine.

For a few years, beginning in 1872, gas-fueled engines were built in limited numbers. A too frequent backfiring of the burning mixture into the gas-air charge stored in the reservoir became an insurmountable problem to overcome and forced Brayton to abandon the use of gas as a fuel. The explosions were not destructive, but necessitated purging the reservoir of burned gases and relighting the igniter flame.

The gas engine was patented in the United States and Great Britain in 1872.[3] followed by oil engine patents two years later.[4] Brayton's last protected improvements to an oil engine issued in 1890.[5] Both the gas and oil-fueled engine patents of the 1870s describe a single cylinder using one face of the piston for pumping and the other to be acted upon by the expanding gases. (Fig. 10-3) Almost all of the production engines utilized a separate pumping cylinder.

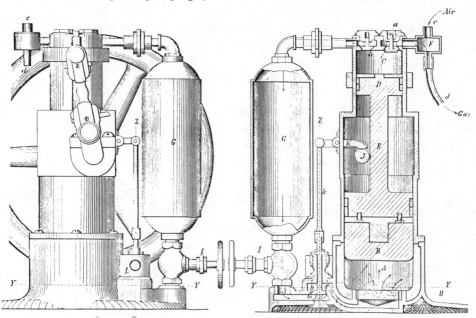

Fig. 10-3   Brayton gas engine of 1872. Power and pumping pistons are combined. (From his British patent drawings)

Brayton Gas Engine – 1872

Whether the air pump and combustion chamber were on opposite sides of the same piston or in separate structures, the operating principle was unchanged. The air and gas were drawn into the pumping chamber past cam-actuated valves at a ratio of twelve to one, according to Brayton. In practice the mixture was considerably richer. When air pump pressure reached about sixty pounds per square inch (up to eighty on later engines) a preset, pressure loaded valve opened to discharge the mixture into a receiver. In production engines this was a tank located in the base. A relief valve at the receiver prevented excessive pressure buildup by either the air pump or an explosion resulting from a flashback of burning gases in the combustion chamber.

The combustion cylinder was water jacketed, being served by mechanically operated intake and exhaust valves. Power was transmitted from the piston to the crankshaft through a pedestal-mounted rocking beam, a peculiar characteristic of most Brayton engines.

At the heart of all of Brayton's designs was the unique ignition and combustion system. Pressure in the combustion chamber, always lower than that in the receiver, was relatively uniform until the intake valve closed; this was a point never exceeding forty percent of the piston stroke. (Fig. 10-4) Expansion then commenced and continued until the exhaust valve opened with about ten psi in the cylinder at the end of the stroke. The exhaust valve remained open until the piston again reached inner dead center and was ready to begin the next cycle.

The element making possible such a means of ignition was based on a principle first incorporated in the mine safety lamps of Sir Humphry Davy and the great Northumbrian engineer, George Stephenson in 1815.[6] These men discovered that a flame will not travel back through a small passage into an inflammable mixture. Wire gauze or fine wire screen, as first used by Davy, was inserted between the igniter flame and

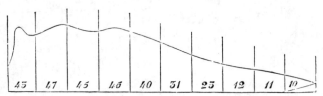

Mean pressure 30·2 lbs. per sq. in.   8 ins. dia. cylinder.   Stroke 12 ins.   200 revs. per min.
—Brayton Petroleum Engine.   Motor Cylinder.

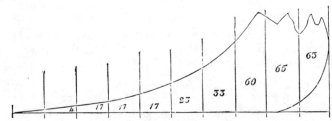

Mean pressure 27·6 lbs. per sq. in.   8 ins. dia. cylinder.   Stroke 6 ins.   200 revs. per min.
—Brayton Petroleum Engine.   Pump Cylinder.

Fig. 10-4   Pressure-volume diagrams of pump cylinder and "motor" cylinder, Brayton oil engine. From Clerk tests of 1878. (Clerk, *The Gas and Oil Engine*, 1896)

the intake valve. (Fig. 10-5) The action of the wire screen may be easily demonstrated by placing a fine mesh over a Bunsen burner and then igniting the gas on the upper side of the screen. A flame will not develop under the screen even when raised and lowered. Brayton fully described in his patent how he could prevent flame propagation from the burning charge back into the receiver by interposing a stack of wire screens. The fresh charge passed through the screen pack to be ignited the other side and then proceed out into the main combustion chamber. Screen life was limited, however, and when a rupture did occur the gas in the receiver exploded causing the discomfiture of the operator when the safety valve released; a screen replacement was also usually required. (See Morey, Chapter 6)

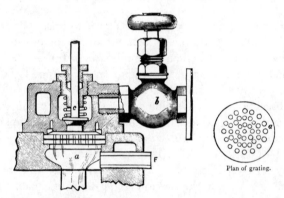

Fig. 10-5   Flame grating and mixture supply valve (c). Pilot air
and gas supply enters through line (F). (Clerk, *The Gas
and Oil Engine,* 1896)

A flame for ignition was sustained by the bypassing of a small, constant flow of combustible mixture from the receiver to the jet in the antechamber on the downstream side of the wire screen stack. A large pressure drop through the intake piping, valve and screen always assured that the igniter jet supply pressure remained higher than that in the antechamber to prevent a snuffing out of the flame. Excessive throttling of the incoming charge was a significant source of the engine's poor efficiency.

The earliest test of a Brayton gas engine for which data is still available was performed on January 18, 1872, by Horace McMurtrie, a Boston consulting engineer. This engine was probably the one built by the Exeter Machine Works during October and November of 1871.

William Burlingame supplied a testimonial letter saying that while at his factory the engine had run at speeds "from 60 to 500 revolutions a minute as desired..." and could operate on either gas or the "vapor of carbon oils"[7] The engine was in Boston for the McMurtrie test:[8]

Power piston: bore and stroke, in	8 x 12
Pumping piston: bore and stroke, in	8 x 6
Engine speed, rpm	180
Receiver pressure, psi	75.4
Maximum cylinder pressure, psi	68
Gross (indicated) horsepower	9
Brake horsepower	4.1

The great reduction from indicated power to brake power pointed out a basic fault: creditable performance from the combustion chamber negated by high mechanical and pumping losses. Tests made a year and a half later on a demonstration engine in New York City by Prof. Thurston give fuel consumption data. His figures, as published in a Brayton brochure,[9] are misleading, for Dugald Clerk points out he did not deduct the fuel used to drive the air pump.[10] This addition increased the consumption from 32 cubic feet of gas per brake horsepower hour as stated by Thurston to 69.3. Thermal efficiency in turn was reduced to slightly over seven percent with the change. Thus, while better than the Lenoir and Hugon, the Brayton fell far short of equaling the Otto and Langen.

Almost all published information on Brayton's gas-fueled engine was in the form of testimonial letters emanating from trials or observances of a small group of engines. While he generated an enviable amount of publicity, particularly about the gas engine's instant availability and smooth operation, the few units actually made signify it was not yet in a form ready for general acceptance. A Brayton gas engine was expected to be exhibited at the Vienna International Exhibition in 1873, but it failed to show up in time to be judged.[11]

Brayton Oil Engine

Introduced in 1875, the oil fueled engine version differed only in the fuel supply and ignition system. A plunger pump was driven by an eccentric on the shaft controlling the intake and exhaust valves. Because check valves of that era could not adequately seal the small fuel volume moved on each stroke, a reciprocating flat-faced valve was inserted in the pump suction and discharge lines. It was timed with the pumping plunger by an adjacent eccentric. (Fig. 10-6)

Most of Brayton's basic oil engine patent of 1874 is devoted to constructional details of the vaporizing chamber. Fuel under pressure from the plunger pump flowed into an annulus filled with felt that ringed the incoming air passage. (Fig. 10-7) Compressed air from the receiver passed the oil soaked felt when the intake valve opened. (Brayton now called the inlet valve an "injection valve" in his patent. This later gave rise to claims by some that his design "anticipated" Rudolf Diesel's high pressure, air injection fuel system.) By the use of a deflection plate he was able to create sufficient turbulence at the surface of the felt exposed to the air to vaporize, or carry in spray form, enough fuel to create a combustible mixture. From that point the charge passed through the "gauze flame intercepter" to finally contact the ignition flame fed by oil. The design used in production engines for the first few years was a sandwich construction of wire screen inserted between two honeycombed grating plates. Later there was only a grating. Air receiver explosions were eliminated, but a sooting up of the cylinder was an occasional nuisance.

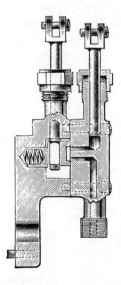

Fig. 10-6   Fuel pump with spring-loaded slide-valve, Brayton oil
engine, 1876. (Clerk, *The EGas and Oil Engine,* 1896)

Fuel requirements apparently were not too critical, although contemporary sources and the patents refer to "light hydrocarbons" and "light petroleum" indicating an oil close to kerosene or furnace oil.

Extensive testing of a Brayton oil engine by Dugald Clerk in February 1878 yielded a poorer fuel consumption than for the gas engine. Brake specific fuel consumption was about eight times that attainable from a modern diesel. The nominal five horsepower test engine, built by the New York and New Jersey Ready Motor Company, was tested at the Crown Ironworks in Glasgow. Clerk reported the following results: [12]

"Motor cylinder" bore and stroke, in . . . . 8 x 12
"Pump cylinder" bore and stroke, in . . . . 8 x 6
Mean engine speed, rpm 201
Mean dynamometer reading, bhp 4.26
Brake specific fuel consumption, lb/bhp hr 2.75
Air pump maximum pressure, psi* 65
Receiver pressure, psi 60
Motor cylinder maximum pressure, psi* 48
Motor cylinder mean pressure, psi 31
Motor cylinder indicated horsepower 9.49
Pump cylinder indicated required horsepower 4.10
Mechanical friction horsepower 1.13
Fuel specific gravity (kerosene type) 85
Brake thermal efficiency, % 4.75
*See Fig. 10-4.

Although Clerk was disappointed with the efficiency of the tested engine he predicted, "The cycle is a good one, and under other circumstances is capable of better things.. ." [13] He went on to add that it was "quite unsuitable for a cold cylinder engine." The gas turbine was the fulfillment of this prediction. Clerk's exposure to the Brayton engine undoubtedly influenced him to pursue work on a two-stroke engine. He commented that the engine had performed useful work and operator reports of starting ease and "almost absolute steadiness" were not uncommon. While the efficiency was low, fuel was inexpensive, and the operating cost per hour was on the order of only a few cents. [14]

Thompson, Sterne & Co., Glasgow, the firm then employing Dugald Clerk, was apparently a licensee of Brayton during the latter 1870s. Several contemporary articles have illustrations of the Brayton gas

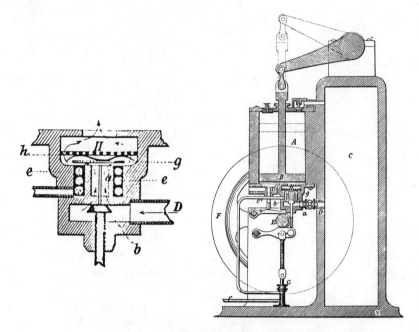

Fig. 10-7 Brayton oil engine. Pumping cylinder (A) above combination working and pumping piston (B), air reservoir (C); cam (E) to actuate fuel pump (G) to feed wick (e) under grating (h). (From his British patent of 1874)

engine (with the separate pumping cylinder) showing the Thompson, Sterne name on the base casting. One refers to a "Mr. Clarke, who has charge of the engine in ... [England]." Clerk himself adds a slight contradiction by saying that "Messrs. Simon of Nottingham introduced it into this country" in a modified form.[15]

George Brayton was an entrepreneur as well as an inventor, and the commercial enterprises he fostered spanned a period of twenty years. Those companies, with approximate starting dates, participating in the construction and/or sale of Brayton oil engines were:

The New York and New Jersey Ready Motor Co.,
    New York City, 1875
The Pennsylvania Ready Motor Co., Philadelphia, 1876
The Brayton Petroleum Engine Co., Boston, 1882
Otto Henniges, Berlin, was a licensee for a short time.

193

Engines bearing the nameplate of the N.Y. & N.J. Ready Motor Co. carried an address of an agent, the H.S. Manning Co. (later Manning Maxwell and Moore). It is not known where the engine was actually manufactured.

At the International Exhibition of 1876 in Philadelphia the Pennsylvania firm demonstrated a ten horsepower engine having a double-acting, vertical cylinder. Their sales brochure of that year listed the availability and specifications of several models:[16]

Horse-power	Bore & Stroke Power Cylinder	Floor Space	RPM	Weight	Price
1	5 x 7 in	2x 4^1/2ft	200	900 lb	$ 350
3	7 x 9	2^1/2 x 5	180	1400	450
5	8 x 12	2^1/2 x 6	160	2100	600
10	10 x 15	3 x 7*	140	4000	1000

*Height to the top of the beam was eight feet in this vertical cylinder engine.

The five horsepower model with an open frame and underslung rocking beam was a standard design and is that most often found in museums. (Fig. 10-8, Plate)

A new ten horsepower double-acting engine was announced in 1877 by the Pennsylvania Ready Motor Co.[17] Horizontal pumping and power cylinders gave it a resemblance to the more conventional gas engines. (Fig. 10-9, Plate) To survive the heat generated in the double-acting cylinder the piston was also water cooled. Two tubes parallel to the piston rod, one end fastened in the hollow piston crown and the other mounted on the rod's crosshead slider, were connected by flexible hoses to a cooling water supply and return. A later version had an enclosed base (Fig. 10-11, Plate) and was only single-acting. Power was accordingly reduced by one-half.

Sometime during the 1870s Brayton built several horizontal marine engines which were installed in river craft. (Fig. 10-10, Plate) A pre-1880 brochure of the Brayton Petroleum Engine Co. illustrates the engine in an open launch. Clerk said they ran on the Hudson River for a few years.[18] Another source, which probably should be given more credence, indicated that an engine was placed in a government boat on the Exeter River near Portsmouth, New Hampshire. It "was not a success, but it did run now and then with a great deal of coaxing."[19]

Fig. 10-1   George Bailey Brayton (1830-1892). (The Smithsonian Institution)

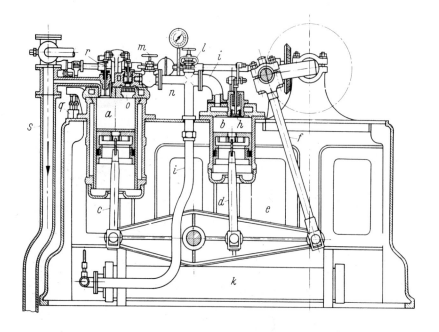

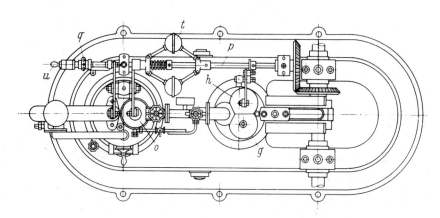

Fig. 10-2   Top and section views of Brayton oil engine, 1876, showing working cylinder (a), air pumping cylinder (b), air
reservoir (k) and fuel pump (q). (Sass, *Geschicht . . .*)

Fig. 10-8   The Brayton kerosene-burning engine as it appeared in
Scientific American, May 13, 1876.

BRAYTON'S HYDROCARBON ENGINE.

Fig. 10-9   Brayton double-acting engine of 10 hp. (*Scientific American,* Jan. 13, 1877)

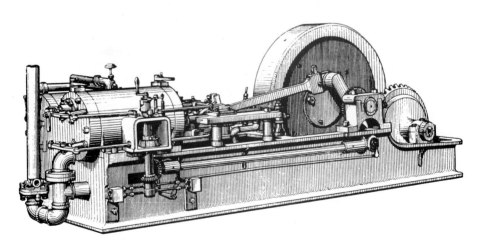

Fig. 10-10   Brayton horizontal marine engine. Clerk, *The Gas, Petroleum and Oil Engine,* 1909.

BRAYTON PETROLEUM OIL ENGINE.

Safety! Economy! Convenience! No Boiler, No Coal,
No Engineer, No Danger, No Steam, No Ashes,
No Explosion, No Fires, No Extra Insur-
ance, Almost no Attendance.

Speed and Fuel thoroughly regulated by Governors.
Started instantly with a Match. Always ready to
give out its full power at once. Expense
ceases when Engine is stopped.

ADVANTAGES CLAIMED FOR THE OIL ENGINE.

Always ready; power developed to its full capacity in a few
seconds. Simple in arrangement; easily understood and adjusted.
Compact; occupying less space than any other Engine. Does not
deteriorate by constant use. Less cost for foundations in general.
A perfection of workmanship not found in other engines. Complete interchangeability of parts, thus reducing cost of repairs.
The perfection of steady motion and close governing. Every engine
thoroughly tested and proved under load before leaving works.
Every engine shipped complete, requiring no setting up of any kind,
except to bolt to foundation, connect water supply for circulation,
and exhaust with chimney. Less cost for fuel, and less attendance
required, than for any other engine. Will not enhance cost of
insurance in any building.

PRICES.

Floor space occupied by	Height.	Weight.	Prices.
2 H. P. Engine, 3 ft. by 7½ ft	3 ft. 6 in.	1,300 lbs.	$350 00
3 " " 3 " " 8 "	4 " 0 "	1,600 "	450 00
5 " " 3 " " 9 "	5 " 6 "	3,000 "	600 00

Fig. 1301.

Fig.. 10-11 Brayton engine as offered in an H.S. Manning catalog,
ca. 1880. (The Smithsonian Institution)

Fig. 10-12   Vehicle built in 1904 for patent infringement suit to prove
workability of design in the Selden patent of 1877. Power was
from a three cylinder Brayton-type engine. (Collections of
Greenfield Village and the Henry Ford Museum, Dearborn)

Fig. 10-13   Brayton engine ca. 1878 with axial pumping and
working cylinders. This engine is on exhibit at the
Museum of History and Technology, Washington,
D.C. (The Smithsonian Institution)

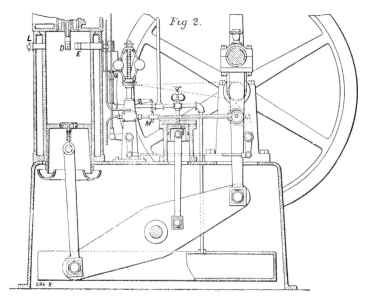

Fig. 10-14   Last design of Brayton's oil engine as it appeared in
Engineering, July 15, 1892.

Brayton and the Selden Automobile

Information concerning Brayton's engines surfaced during the famous trial over the Selden automobile patent. Volumes have been written about the legal battle George B. Selden (1846-1922) and the powerful Association of Licensed Automobile Manufacturers fought against the young Henry Ford and his struggling company. (Ford Motor Company was the financially stronger litigant by the end of the trial.) In the courts from 1903 to 1911, it was finally decided that the Selden patent was in fact valid, but limited to the use of a Brayton-type engine. Since Ford never built such an engine he did not infringe the patent.

Briefly, the story begins in the mid-1870s. Selden was an engineer oriented lawyer who became a patent attorney in Rochester, New York. Like many others, he dreamed of a horseless carriage, and from 1875 to 1878 he experimented with a number of power plants, the last being a multi-cylinder Brayton engine. The design included three pumping cylinders, an air tank and three power cylinders. In 1879 he filed a patent application for a "Road Engine" which supposedly described a complete vehicle. (The application was witnessed by George Eastman of Kodak fame.) Through numerous legal delays permitted by the Patent Office, he was able to prevent issuance of the patent (No. 549,160) until November 1895. By this time the automobile industry in the United States had expanded and the patent, sold on a royalty basis by Selden to the A.L.A.M. (Winton was one of the founders), suddenly became a potent weapon requiring every car manufacturer to pay a sizable royalty for each vehicle they built. Almost all complied, with Henry Ford being a major exception.

In 1904 a car now in the Ford Museum (Fig. 10-12, Plate) was built to the patent description to prove its viability, and its power plant was an engine made by Selden in 1877. The car ran but that was about all.

Trial testimony brought out various aspects of the Brayton engine and its prior use. Several people stated they had ridden in a Brayton powered street car operated by the Providence, Rhode Island, Union Railway Company during the winter of 1872-1873. According to the witnesses (Brayton's then-remarried widow and his brother-in-law) a four horse-power engine was "placed in the car at the center of one side in the space usually given a stove. A water coil was on the roof and under the seat was a 5-gallon naptha tank."[20] The car had a wheelbase of about six feet, an overall length of about thirteen feet and a weight close to three tons. Later, a twelve horsepower engine was reportedly installed. The car, not allowed to run on streets, used only trackage outside the city limits.

Anyone who could climb on got a ride since the experimental vehicle did not charge for passengers. Speeds up to fourteen to sixteen miles per hour were attained, and with the larger engine a five percent grade was negotiated. The street car tests lasted about six months, ending with a lack of funds caused by the economic slump of 1873.

Also figuring in the Selden trial was the Brayton engine now on exhibit in the Smithsonian Museum of History and Technology. In 1907 Brown University at Providence was requested to test this engine. (Fig. 10-13, Plate) From a working cylinder of six by nine inches, a maximum of two and a half brake horsepower was developed at 270 rpm. Fuel consumption, using a blend of 95 percent kerosene and 5 percent gasoline, was 2.8 pounds per bhp hour.[21] Construction date of the engine is thought to be around 1878.

Brayton Oil Engines of 1890

The last oil engine made by Brayton was based on his patent of 1890. *Engineering* reported the engine as available in England.[22] (Fig. 10-14, Plate). Ignition was started from coils of platinum wire placed in the end of a tube. The vaporized oil and air charge ignited as it passed the incandescent wire mass. Starting was accomplished by preheating the platinum with a torch through a glass-covered door. The underside of the air pump piston directly charged the tank in the base of the engine, and air entered the combustion chamber through a pressure-operated flat valve on the piston crown.

An optimistic description in 1892 of the vaporization method for Brayton's last engine offers a provocative comparison with that of an engine first patented by Rudolf Diesel in the same year:

> The oil is finely divided —atomised in fact — in a large quantity of air, and is flashed into flame instantly. The combustion resembles that of flour dust, suspended in the air, and which is so rapid that it constitutes an explosion. The combustible material is divided into infinitely small particles, and each particle is surrounded with an ample supply of oxygen, to which it exposes a surface which is very great in relation to its bulk. Under these conditions combustion is exceedingly rapid, and spreads from particle to particle with amazing celerity. The oil is burned suspended in air; its combustion is complete, and is not impaired or delayed by metallic surfaces on which deposits can accumulate.[23]

Diesel engineers still wish that, with all conviction, they could say this has been achieved.

Brayton died in Leeds, England, while working on a new oil engine. His efforts extended from the time of Lenoir to Diesel. Often unorthodox, his thinking acted as a stimulus to others. Clerk summed it up by saying, "His perseverance deserved a better reward."[24]

NOTES

1. *Brayton's Ready Motor,* (Boston, 1872), p. 3. Quoted from an anonymous source.
2. *Exeter and Its Leading Business Men,* (Exeter, 1891). An advertisement.
3. U.S. patent No. 125,166 of April 2, 1872, and British No. 432 of February 10, 1872 (issued to Brayton's London agent, Wm. R. Lake). A working model is on exhibit at the Museum of History & Technology, Washington, D.C.
4. U.S. patent No. 151,468 of June 2, 1874, and British No. 2,209 of June 25, 1874 (also issued to Lake).
5. U.S. patent No. 432,260 and British No. 11,062, both of July 15, 1890.
6. See: Samuel Smiles, *Lives of the Engineers: George and Robert Stephenson,* (London, 1879), pp. 89-108, for an account of the development of this most vital invention by Stephenson and Davy, and the ensuing controversy over who was first and which design was better. It was a good example of the "trained scientist" looking down on the "lowly mechanic."
7. *Brayton's Ready Motor,* (Boston, 1872), p. 14. A prospectus.
8. *Brayton's Hydro-Carbon Engine,* Pennsylvania Ready Motor Co., (Philadelphia, ca. 1876), p. 5. Mainly testimonial letters.
9. *Ibid.,* pp. 7-12.
10. Dugald Clerk, *The Gas and Oil Engine,* 6th ed., (London, 1896), pp. 157-58.
11. *Reports of the Commissioners of the United States to the International Exhibition Held at Vienna, 1873,* edit. by Robert H. Thurston, v. 111, (Washington, D.C., 1876), pp. 164-67. Prof. Thurston included a report on the engine with results from his own tests made at Stevens Institute.
12. Clerk, *op. cit.,* p. 159.
13. *Ibid.,* p. 162.

14. "Brayton's Hydro-Carbon Engine," *The Engineer,* July 19, 1878, p. 48.
15. Clerk, *op. cit.,* p. 152.
16. *Brayton Ready Motor or Hydro-Carbon Engine,* Pennsylvania Ready Motor Co., (Philadelphia, ca. 1876), p. 3. A catalog.
17. "Brayton's Hydrocarbon Engine," *Scientific American,* January 13, 1877, pp. 19-20
18. Dugald Clerk, *The Gas, Petrol and Oil Engine,* v. 1, (London, 1909), p. 29.
19. Correspondence from H. N. Welch, Exeter, N.H., to the Henry Ford Museum, June 1930. Ford Museum Archives.
20. Extracts of Selden trial testimony (from v. 9 of Defendant's Records, pp. 198-398) sent to the Museum of History & Technology by Charles E. Duryea, November 9, 1935. The quote is from p. 2 of Duryea's covering letter.
21. The tests were under the direction of Prof. Kenerson of Brown University.
22. "The Brayton Petroleum Engine," *Engineering,* July 15, 1892, pp. 88-89.
23. *Ibid.,* p 89.
24. Dugald Clerk, *The Gas, Petrol and Oil Engine,* v. 1, (London, 1909), p. 29.

Chapter 11

The Two-Stroke Cycle

Not everyone accepted the premise that the four-stroke cycle was the only solution for a compression engine. A dedicated few believed a power stroke *could* be generated with each crankshaft revolution. This conviction, abetted by a need to circumvent Otto's patent, stimulated the development of what soon came to be known as a two-stroke cycle engine. The difficulties associated with such a cycle were not easily overcome, and its successes in the pre-1900 era were limited. Upon the expiration of the Otto patent most early builders of two-stroke engines switched to the four-stroke. A demand for small, high output gasoline engines in marine and portable applications and for very large gas engines, however, ultimately generated a sizable two-stroke market. The introduction of the diesel engine added another opportunity for acceptance.

Between 1879 and 1881 two-stroke designs of James Robson, Dugald Clerk, Wilhelm Wittig and Wilhelm Hees made their market debut. Karl Benz started his first engine, a two-stroke, on the last day of 1879. The early 1890s were developmental years for the distinctive opposed piston engines of Wilhelm von Oechelhäuser and Hugo Junkers. Concurrently, Joseph Day was working on a valveless design which became a forerunner of modern outboard engines. Others built two-stroke engines before 1900, but the above were *the* pioneers.

The unique designs of James Atkinson, although long since abandoned, also generated much interest in the 1800s. Atkinson gas engines burned even less fuel than the Otto as a result of their greater expansion on the power stroke.

Inherent problems associated with a two-stroke cycle engine sometimes outweighed potential advantages. Economy of operation almost never equaled that available in a four-stroke. The time available to accomplish intake and exhaust were reduced by more than one-half; the ignition rate doubled for the same engine speed as a four-stroke. There were additional mechanical losses associated with a needed scavenging of exhaust products from the cylinder and losing part of the incoming charge out the exhaust. The cooling system burden also increased. Special lubrication problems usually associated with two-stroke engines (piston pins, for example) were not yet a factor because of the slow speeds.

Dugald Clerk

Sir Dugald Clerk (1854-1932), whose work has already been quoted numerous times, devoted at least ten years of his early career to the development of two-stroke gas engines. (Fig. 11-1, Plate) That he never achieved success with his own creations was a great personal disappointment, but this failure diverted him into areas which benefitted the entire internal-combustion engine industry.

The Glasgow-born Scotsman's education in chemistry and physics was subsequently called upon in his major contributions towards an understanding of the processes occurring inside an engine cylinder. Clerk became one of the first Englishmen to combine science and technology in the design of I-C engines. For example, he was the first to use the technique of an air standard cycle analysis to compare thermal efficiencies of I-C engines.[1] Sir Harry Ricardo (1885-1974) wrote in his memoirs of lectures he attended as a student that, besides Clerk being the accepted leading authority on I-C engines,

> His lectures were a pattern of lucidity, and he had a gift for explaining the theory of thermodynamics in simple terms that his largely schoolboy audience could readily understand. I made up my mind that if ever I came to lecture on such subjects I would do my best to follow his example.[2]

Those who have studied Ricardo's own classic works know that he more than fulfilled this youthful promise to himself.

In 1877 Clerk joined the firm of Thompson, Sterne and Co., Glasgow, having become interested in I-C engines the previous year.[3] One of his early assignments was an investigation into the merits of the Brayton engine. (Clerk may even have called the Brayton engine to his company's attention.) The results of the Brayton tests (Chapter 10) might have been influential in his design philosophies for the two-stroke cycle. A distinguishing characteristic of a Clerk-cycle engine, as it was called in England for many years, was a separate displacer or pumping cylinder to provide low pressure scavenging and charging of the power cylinder.

The first Clerk two-stroke engine built by Thompson, Sterne was based on his British patent of 1878[4] and was demonstrated at the Kilburn Royal Agricultural Show in June 1879.[5] (This date is usually considered to mark the initial exposure to the public of a two-stroke compression engine. Thompson, Sterne became L. Sterne and Co. about 1883, which helps to date the few Clerk engines in museum collections.) The Kilburn gas engine, rated at two brake horsepower, had two horizontal and equal cylinders of six inch diameter by eight inch stroke. One performed the functions of intake and compression, the other for producing power and then exhaust. The pump crankshaft throw lagged that for the power by ninety degrees and forced a gas and air mixture past a check valve into an intermediate reservoir maintained at seventy psi. (Like Brayton to this point.)

Compression was not generated in the power cylinder as its poppet exhaust valve remained open until near the end of the inward stroke. The exhaust gas left in the cylinder was supposed to act as a cushion for the piston. The clearance space at inner dead center was three-fourths of an inch. When the piston had moved outward about two inches, ports in a slide valve opened to admit the pressurized charge from the reservoir. Ignition was by means of an incandescent platinum cage contained in the slider. A speed of 300 rpm meant the ignition rate capability more than doubled over that feasible in the new Otto engine. Combustion, as in the Otto engine, was by constant volume rather than continuous combustion, a basic difference between the Clerk and the Brayton engine.

Difficulties with the "Kilburn" engine resulted in Clerk's abandonment of the high pressure charging concept. Occasional backfires causing explosions in the reservoir unexpectedly stopped the engine; an annoyance but not a catastrophe. More significantly Clerk said that "It knocked badly with rich mixture; even with weak mixtures of coal gas and air the knock could still be heard."[6] A larger engine (ten by eighteen inch cylinders) was built to this initial design. It knocked so severely that "the blow could be felt in the ground outside the building about 100 ft. away, and was also heard at long distances."[7] Clerk was not at all hesitant to tell of troubles with his engines, particularly in later papers and texts. (This makes his writings all the more valuable as historical documents.) He later deduced that the reason for the knocking (high rate of pressure rise) was because of extreme turbulence in the entering charge. It was particularly true of that last part being ignited and entering the cylinder.

Before the end of 1880 Clerk had a second generation engine running (Fig. 11-2, Plate). The new design,[8] placed in limited production the following year, was successful enough for the British to make his name synonymous with that type of two-stroke engine. National pride was also involved. The Germans had Otto and Diesel and the French, Carnot (and by some Beau de Rochas), so it was natural the British should use the two-stroke opportunity to join the "cycle club." In due course the United States was enrolled, thanks to Brayton's contributions. Clerk was not reticent in the promotion of "his" cycle since he himself adopted the term in his widely read writings.

The time and method of intake, compression and exhaust were radically altered from the original design. The pumping cylinder was retained, but its piston, now called a "displacer," only raised the gas:air mixture to five psi maximum rather than compression pressure. The inner movement of the displacer piston now led that of the power piston by ninety degrees. Exhaust ports in the combustion cylinder were uncovered by its piston crown near the end of the expansion stroke. (Fig. 11-3)

When combustion cylinder pressure dropped below displacer pressure after the exhaust ports opened, the fresh charge entered past a damped, free-floating inlet check valve (Fig. 11-4) at the "point" end of a conical cylinder head. Uniflow scavenging followed, i.e., the exhaust products were displaced by the incoming mixture in a one-direction flow. Timing was compromised to leave a little residual exhaust gas in the cylinder rather than lose part of the fresh charge out the exhaust ports. On the piston's inward stroke the ports were covered, and compression of the combustible mixture commenced as in the Otto engine.

Since Clerk by this time no longer believed in Otto's stratification theory his objective was to find an optimum timing to balance performance against economy. He reported that the reduced turbulence of the entering charge, through its introduction into the deep conical recess, permitted an increase in compression ratio over the earlier design and still "no knock was experienced under any circumstances."[9]

A clever modification in the slide valve made ignition by gas flame feasible for two-stroke engines. (Fig. 11-5) The slide valve now performed only one duty, that of introducing the flame into the compressed cylinder charge. Clerk's system apparently worked so well his 1881 engine ran at 400 rpm without misfire. This was over three times the rate at which the early Otto igniter could reliably function. The secret was to end a dependence on externally created natural drafts to

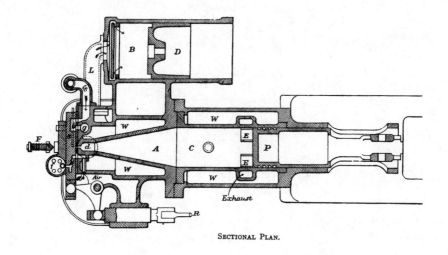

SECTIONAL PLAN.

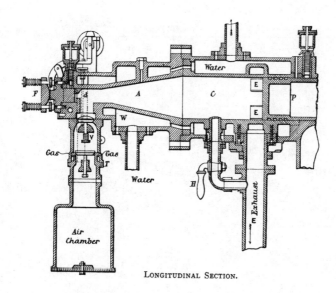

LONGITUDINAL SECTION.

Fig. 11-3   Section views of Clerk 1881 two-stroke engine.
(Robinson, *Gas and Petroleum Engines*, 1890)

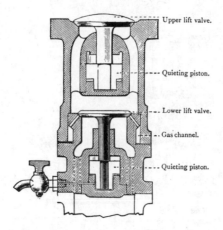

Fig. 11-4 Section view of intake valve and mixing chamber, Clerk two-stroke engine, 1881. (Clerk, *The Gas and Oil Engine,* 1896)

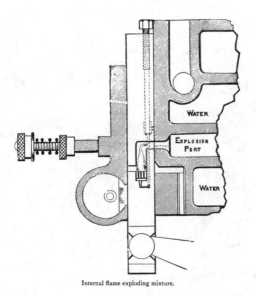

Fig. 11-5 Clerk flame ignition system. Slide-valve shown in position to ignite charge in combustion chamber. (Clerk, *The Gas and Oil Engine,* 1896)

scavenge the igniter cavity in the slide valve. (If the speed increased much beyond 125 ignitions per minute in the Otto engine the cavity ignition mixture had insufficient oxygen to burn.)

When the slider was in its flame relighting location (Fig. 11-6), a small passage connected the cylinder with the igniter flame cavity. An already combustible mixture, flowing into the cavity under increasing compression pressure, ignited from the pilot flame. To prevent a backfire into the supply passage a small metal grating was placed in the passage where it entered the cavity. A "chimney" for the vigorously burning jet in the cavity allowed circulation, and an adjustable metering valve in the supply passage regulated the bleedoff pressure from the cylinder. Clerk said if this pressure was excessive an annoying "popping" explosion could be heard when the cavity opened to the pilot flame. For cylinder ignition the slider moved quickly to cut off the pilot flame and chimney and to index the cavity with an "explosion port" in the cylinder.

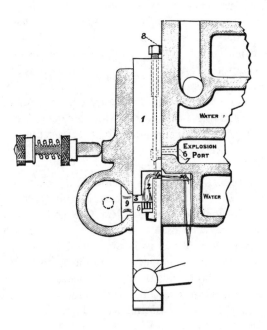

Fig. 11-6   Clerk flame ignition system. Slide-valve positioned for relighting of ignition flame from pilot flame. (Clerk, *The Gas and Oil Engine*, 1896)

The Clerk design was constructed in sizes rated 2, 4, 6, 8 and 12 brake horsepower models. Results from some standard L. Sterne and Co. factory tests in 1885 are worth noting:[10]

Brake horsepower, rated	2	6	12
Power cylinder: bore-stroke, in	5 x 8	7 x 12	9 x 20
Displacer cyl.: bore-stroke, in	6 x 9	7 1/2 x 12	10 x 20
Average test speed, rpm	212	146	132
Compression pressure, psi	38	48	57
Peak pressure, psi	155	195	238
Mean effective pressure, psi	43	53	65
Brake horsepower	2.7	7.2	23.2
Mechanical efficiency, %	75	80	85
Gas consumption, cu ft/bhp hr (includes gas for ignition)	39	30.3	24.1

Brake thermal efficiency on the six horsepower model was slightly under thirteen percent, or about four percent less than that of a comparable Otto engine of the same period.

The Clerk engine was introduced to the United States in 1882[11] where it was built for several years by the Clerk Gas Engine Co., Philadelphia. It would appear from the advertising copy (Fig. 11-7, Plate) that all had not gone well for earlier editions. An 1884 H.S. Manning (later Manning, Maxwell and Moore) catalog lists five Clerk models of the same sizes as that produced by L. Sterne, but no prices are quoted. It can be presumed that the engines were made by the Philadelphia firm.

Sometime in 1885 L. Sterne ceased building the Clerk engine, due probably to the lack of its being a potentially commercial success and the threat of an infringement suit by Otto. One contemporary writer spoke of low efficiency with the Clerk engine and that "probably none were working by 1898."[12] Additionally, in studying Clerk's personal test data the author could find no engine serial numbers higher than 300 as late as 1884. Clerk, who by this time had gained a reputation among the gas engine manufacturers, left Glasgow and found another home for his engine at Tangyes Ltd. in Birmingham. They built an unknown number during 1886-1887.[13]

It was at Tangyes where his friendship with another engineer named George Croydon (later Lord) Marks brought to pass in 1888 the life-long partnership firm of Marks and Clerk, Chartered Patent Agents.

(At the time neither specialized legal training nor examinations were required.) As a patent attorney and a much in demand expert witness, Clerk attained the financial success denied him as a somewhat disillusioned engine designer. For example, Clerk acted as an expert witness for the Selden interests in their long trial against Ford, and Henry Ford was so impressed by Clerk's performance that he personally asked Clerk to be his attorney on English patent matters (which Marks and Clerk did for many years).* Other prestigious men numbered among the firm's clients around the turn of the century were Charles Parsons of steam turbine fame and Thomas A. Edison. The well deserved honors and awards Sir Dugald Clerk, the "dour little Scotsman," received for his continuing contributions are too numerous to mention.

James Robson

If James Robson (1833-1913) had been a writer as well as an inventor a battle of words might have erupted over whether the two-stroke engine ran on the Clerk or Robson cycle. Both men concurrently perfected engines firing every revolution, and for a short time the same firm produced them.

Robson was born at North Shields, England, where the river Tyne flows into the North Sea, and spent over half of his life in the Newcastle area. The son of a building contractor, he had no engineering training but was apprenticed to an ironmongery and hardware business run by an uncle.[14] He was in his early thirties when his uncle died leaving him as proprietor of the business, but because of his father's increasing age, his full services were required in the construction activities. Up to that time Robson had built several working gas engines. This interest stemmed from youthful experiments using gas to heat an incubator. A resulting explosion could have ended his life at age nineteen, but Fortune looks after many young inventors. Having observed the expansive power of combustible gas mixtures, Robson turned to the task of harnessing that power.

A small non-compression engine of the strictly experimental variety was built in 1857. Its vertical cylinder of three and a half inch bore had a piston with a six inch stroke driving an overhead crankshaft (Fig. 11-8). The cylinder head was bolted in the base of a wooden box partly filled with cooling water. A board floating on the water's surface

*A very enlightening interview with Mr. Norman Waddleton, of Marks and Clerk, London, provided the author with much helpful personal information regarding Clerk.

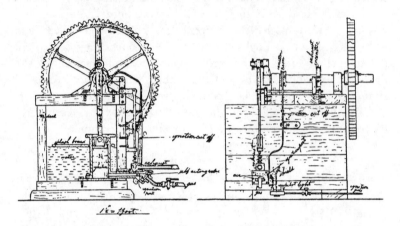

Fig. 11-8   Drawing by James Robson of his first atmospheric gas
engine made in 1857. (Robson, *A Brief Memoir of
James Robson,* 1915)

kept it from splashing into the open end of the cylinder. Upward piston movement drew in the combustible mixture past a "self-acting" valve, and ignition by a gas flame occurred after the piston had moved about half way out the stroke. It was known as the "Cogwheel Engine" by Robson's people because the flywheel was a spur gear from from an old quarry crane. The engine was destroyed in 1865 when an end wall of the building housing the hardware business in South Shields fell into a basement being excavated next door for a new theater. It was about this time when Robson returned to North Shields to work with his father, and with the press of business, all engine developments ceased for a few years.

A horizontal, double-acting engine, similar in appearance and operation to a Lenoir, followed in 1858-1859. The engine reportedly developed three horsepower and drove an eighteen inch circular saw at his father's North Shields contracting company for about nine years. Its end came when frost cracked the cylinder water jacket. Two similar engines were built by Robson and placed in North Shields business establishments.[15]

Of particular interest was the ignition means on these engines. A "make and break" system (Chapter 12), it consisted of a rotating interrupter cam at each end of the cylinder, a battery and a Rühmkorff coil. The cams were on a long shaft driven through bevel gearing operated off the crankshaft. (A grooved cylindrical cam also on the shaft operated sliding exhaust valves.) A cam finger, acting through a leaf spring for snap action, pivoted a small lever inside the cylinder away from its contact point. This assembly was set in a brass block, insulated from the cylinder head. The lever shaft pivoted in the block, but the stationary contact pin, also passing through the block, was insulated from it. This basic construction was used years later by many engine builders after reliable magnetos became available.

Shortly before his decade-long hiatus from engines began, Robson designed a small, manpower rated engine that he ultimately patented in 1880.[16] It was subsequently built for a short while by R. Waygood and Co., London, under the name of the "London Gas Engine." There were two vertical cylinders, the smaller one for combustion having a crank operated "pump" piston to draw in the charge as it was pulled upward. When it reached the top, combustion began and the expanding gases passed into the larger cylinder and forced upward a free piston. In doing so a stack of springs above the piston was compressed. A rack gear on the piston rod meshed with a ring gear on a one-way wedging roller clutch (viz. Otto and Langen) which was engaged when the stored energy in the springs pushed the piston back down. It was not an atmospheric engine since an exhaust valve was open when the piston moved inward.

Robson returned to his avocation about the time Clerk began his first experiments. In 1877 Robson was granted his first patent on a two-stroke engine utilizing compression,[17] another step in his evolving ideas. This design had a single, horizontal working cylinder with valves at each end leading into storage cylinders where combustion was initiated. These two cylinders were arranged one over and the other under and parallel to the working cylinder. Both ends of the working cylinder were closed off, the outer where expansion took place and the inner (crankshaft end) acting first to draw in a charge and then alternately to pump the charge into one of the auxiliary cylinders at a maximum pressure of about thirty-five psi. Valving was by eccentric-operated sliders. Thus there was a combustible, compressed charge ready to drive the piston toward the crankshaft on each revolution. It would appear that adequate scavenging of the auxiliary cylinder might have caused serious power and fuel consumption problems. Robson built only one of these engines where it ran in his North Shields shop until his next edition was completed.[18]

The design culminating in a production engine was patented in 1879.[19] It was much simplified, and in refined versions was produced by Tangyes until about 1891 when they came out with a four-stroke after expiration of the Otto patent. The engine featured a single, double duty cylinder as before (pumping and power), but the pumped charge now was raised to only the pressure required for scavenging the power cylinder. A tank in the engine base was maintained at this pressure. Exhaust ports backed up by a slide valve, were located near the outer third-point of the cylinder. A governor controlled the gas valve, and ignition was again from a flame.

As the piston moved outward on its power stroke, the gas and air mixture drawn in on the previous stroke at the opposite end of the cylinder raised the storage pressure to about six psi. The exhaust valve opened when the piston reached the exhaust ports. After the cylinder pressure dropped below that of the receiver an inlet valve opened to scavenge and charge the cylinder. On the piston's inward stroke the ports were covered, the exhaust valve closed, and the charge was compressed to about thirty-five psi. The underside of the piston could pull in a fresh charge all the way up the stroke, even though the exhaust ports became uncovered, because of the backup exhaust valve.

The first of these engines was made in early 1879[20] in North Shields and ran there until Robson left in 1880. Tangyes Ltd., manufacturers of high quality steam engines of all sizes, had been looking for a promising gas engine to build in their Cornwall Works at Birmingham, and after several false starts, heard of Robson's developments. He granted Tangyes the rights to his 1879 patent and moved to Birmingham to assist in getting the engine in production, sometime in 1881. He remained at Tangyes until retirement, working on engines and other products he invented.

Over the years about 300 Robson engines were shipped from the Cornwall Works[21] in 1/2, 1, 2-1/2 and 4 "nominal" horsepower sizes; obtainable brake horsepower was about one-third more. The large size engine consumed close to thirty-five cubic feet of gas per brake horsepower hour with the smaller ones using an increasing amount as the sizes decreased. Their consumption was comparable to that of the Clerk engine.

Whether it was Robson or Clerk who actually built the first two-stroke engine in England is not important. Their efforts were concurrent and their ideas sometimes overlapping, but each did evolve a distinctive design: Clerk with two operating cylinders; Robson with one, double-acting cylinder and a low pressure storage reservoir. Both saw their ideas modified and adapted by others to later engines, yet their own creations remained overshadowed by the success of the Otto-Crossley engine.

Wittig and Hees

Two-stroke activity began in Germany at almost the same time as in England, but the effort was kept in check. Infringement threats from Deutz over the Otto patent, followed by a premature release from that threat in 1886 when it was declared invalid, deterred two-stroke developments and afforded an earlier opportunity to produce the more forgiving four-stroke.

Wilhelm Wittig and Wilhelm Hees owned no crystal ball to forewarn them about this short term potential. The inventor-engineer duo had worked at Maschinenbauanstalt Humboldt AG in Cologne-Kalk and then moved to Hannover where they were employed by Hannover'sche Maschinenbau AG.[22] They designed and patented a two-stroke engine in 1879[23] and then sold it to their company that same year. The company welcomed this opportunity to grab on to the coattails of Otto's success because their principal business of building locomotives was greatly depressed at the time. (They had tried with little success to market a small opposed-piston atmospheric engine Ferdinand Kindermann patented in 1877.)

The engine bore some similarity to the first Clerk, i.e., two cylinders with mixture compression in one and combustion in the other, but there was no intermediate reservoir. (Fig. 11-9) Both cylinders were vertical with the crankshaft overhead. The crank throws lay in the same plane so that as the pistons moved downward the pumping cylinder was compressing as the power cylinder was exhausting. The end of the latter cylinder extended below the other to maintain a large clearance volume under the power piston while the pumping piston almost touched its cylinder head.

Just before inner dead center an exhaust valve closed and a transfer valve between the two cylinders opened to charge the power cylinder at compression pressure. The charge also passed through a slide valve controlling a flame ignition system. The transfer and exhaust valves were of the poppet type, and all, including the slider, were actuated by eccentrics on the crankshaft. Air intake to the pumping cylinder was past an "automatic" check valve, and gas entered through an eccentric-timed poppet valve, the lift of which could be overridden by linkage

a) Working cylinder; b) Pumping cylinder; c) Transfer pipe;
d) One-way valve; e) Gas entrance; f) Air entrance; g) Gas valve;
h) Air valve; i) Exhaust valve; k) Ignition slide-valve; l) Eccentric;
m) Governor; n) Control linkage for valve spindle g).

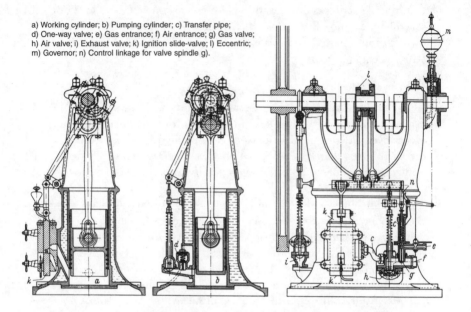

Fig. 11-9　Wittig and Hess two-stroke gas engine from their 1879
design. (Sass, *Geschichte des deutschen Verbrennungsmotorenbaues,* 1962)

from a flyball governor. Engines were built in outputs of 2, 4, and 8
horsepower. The largest had pumping and power cylinder bores of 200
mm and 250 mm respectively with equal strokes of 300 mm. Rated
power was developed at 100 rpm. Tests by Schöttler in 1881 on the four
horsepower model (3.75 bhp at 103 rpm) gave a gas consumption of
1.24 cubic meters (44 cu ft)/bhp hour. The bores and strokes for this
engine were 165 mm (pump) and 200 mm (power) by 180 mm.[24]

In 1880 Hannover'sche made gasoline fueled two-stroke engines to
the Wittig and Hees design. After passing a timed valve, liquid fuel was
sprayed from a nozzle (due to intake suction) into the air stream controlled by an orifice in the intake pipe. This engine was installed in a
"street locomotive" and is believed to be the first internal-combustion
engine in Germany to power a railed vehicle.

Production of the Wittig and Hees engines ended in 1881. In
December of 1880 Deutz had written a letter to Hannover'sche stating
the Otto patent was being infringed. Hannover'sche decided it was not
and continued sales. The matter came to a head when a Wittig and

Hees engine was displayed at a Cologne fair, a place too close for Deutz's comfort. The engine was impounded by a court order, and after a lengthy suit and countersuit Hannover'sche agreed in 1882 to pay a ten percent royalty on all two-stroke engines it built. In the meantime the locomotive business had greatly improved with orders increasing from only nine in 1880 to over 100 the following year. The profitability looked better there, so the two-stroke engine was dropped. Twenty five years later the company, now called Hanomag, began to build I-C engines once again.[25]

The Wittig and Hees design did not die with its demise at Hannover'sche. George Lieckfeld, the engineer in charge of the project there, moved in 1881 to Gebrüder Körting, a steam engine builder in Hannover. He no doubt had a premonition of what was going to happen. Lieckfeld started Körting in the I-C engine business with a close copy of the Wittig and Hees design.[26] Called the Körting-Lieckfeld, it was made in limited numbers until 1884 when it was further revised into a similar looking engine operating as a four-stroke. This was the engine that brought Deutz and Körting into patent battles and which ultimately caused the German Otto patent to be invalidated.

Karl Benz

Karl Benz (1844-1929) survived his days with two-stroke engines to become the co-founder of an industry building on internal-combustion power. Financial desperation directed him to construct his first engine, and sheer determination, soon to be combined with a dream, sustained him.

Born in Karlsruhe and raised there by his mother, Benz knew of struggle from an early age. (He was a baby when his father, a locomotive engineer, died from a job related incident.) His interests always lay in the physical sciences, and at sixteen he passed the entrance exams for the Karlsruhe *Polytechnikum,* one of Germany's first and best engineering schools. While there he came under the guiding influence of Ferdinand Redtenbacher, the same professor who encouraged Eugen Langen to continue his engineering studies. The great teacher used to urge his students, even before Lenoir, to search for a new form of power to supercede the inefficient steam engine. Benz had the honor to be one of the student pallbearers for Redtenbacher on his death in 1863.

A series of jobs at several companies after graduation in 1864 convinced Benz that the only way to success would be through his own business. He wrote of his trainee days at Karlsruhe Engineering Works in the locomotive department: "After twelve hours of boring and filing in semidarkness, I got to understand the hard way the old saying 'apprenticeship is mastership.'"[27] Benz left three years before Daimler was to arrive as the new chief engineer.

In August of 1871 Benz and a local machinist began to solicit business under the firm name of "Karl Benz and August Ritter, Machine Shop." Ritter and Benz soon had differing opinions regarding the future of the business and decided to part company. Benz bought out his associate with an advance payment on his fiancée's dowry. Shortly thereafter, on July 20, 1872, Bertha Ringer of nearby Pforzheim and Karl Benz formed a marriage partnership lasting fifty seven years. (Bertha Benz had just seen her ninety-fifth birthday when she died in 1944, some fifteen years after Karl.) The contract machine business was never very prosperous, having been sustained mainly by a boom period after the Franco-Prussian War. Bankruptcy was almost at hand by 1877, and for several years the financial wolf was at the Benz family door.

After the "Otto Silent" introduction, Benz became intrigued by the commercial possibilities of an I-C engine and decided that here was his salvation. Dugald Clerk had shown him how to circumvent the four-stroke patent by building an engine to fire every revolution. Taking what time he could spare from his failing business, he designed and built an experimental two-stroke engine. It ran for the first time on New Year's Eve of 1879, and Benz' own words best describe the occasion:[28]

> After supper my wife said, "Let's go over to the shop and try our luck once more. Something tells me to go and it will not let me be." So there we were, back again, standing in front of the engine as if it were a great mystery that was impossible to solve. My heart was pounding. I turned the crank. The engine started to go "put-put-put," and the music of the future sounded with regular rhythm. We both listened to it run for a full hour, fascinated, never tiring of the single tone of its song. The longer it played its note, the more sorrow and anxiety it conjured away from the heart. It was the truth that if sorrow had been our companion on the way over there, joy walked beside us on the way back.

Several more years passed before Benz could offer his engine for sale. Capital needed to begin the new venture luckily came from an unexpected source. Emil Bühler, a court photographer, financed him to start "Gasmotoren-Fabrik in Mannheim" on April 15, 1881. This was changed to a stock company eighteen months later. Criticism by a few of the nine stockholders concerning the engine program and its potential caused Benz to pull out and to try to start over again with almost less assets than before. The company continued on for several years building the Benz two-stroke engine under a free license.

Fortunately, some months later, on October 1, 1883, he was able to found a new company, "Benz & Cie., Rheinische Gasmotorenfabrik in Mannheim," with the help of Max Rose, a businessman, and Friedrich Esslinger, an engineer. This partnership lasted seven years and gave Benz an opportunity to carry out his ideas. Fear of the speculative nature of Benz' later zeal to build automobiles ended the business relationship between this trio, but those events are for another chapter.

The engine built by Benz & Cie. was probably the best designed two-stroke offered in the pre-1885 period. Donkin said:[29]

> In it the problem is again treated, how to obtain a motor impulse for every revolution, without the additional complication of a second pump cylinder... In the opinion of Professor Witz, the difficulty is more completely and satisfactorily solved in this than any other [two-stroke] engine.

Dugald Clerk made no reference to the Benz engine in his earlier editions and only an offhand comment in his expanded two volume work of post-1900 to the effect that Benz also built a two-stroke.

The Benz solution was to use the underside of the piston as a pump (Robson), but only to pump low pressure scavenge air. (Fig. 11-10) The gas was pumped by a separate, small piston. The scavenge air discharged into a receiver in the engine base past a slide operated valve. Poppet-type intake and exhaust valves were timed to loop scavenge the power cylinder since the air inlet was pointed toward the piston. With this basic design the continued problem of premature combustion in either the displacer cylinder (Clerk) or the receiver (Robson) was eliminated.

An electric ignition system first used in 1882 incorporated a quite modern looking spark plug. (Fig. 11-11) The system included a battery, an induction (Rühmkorff) coil and a make-and-break contact at the external side of the platinum electrode plug. Benz made many contributions in this area, and all of his production engines had spark systems.

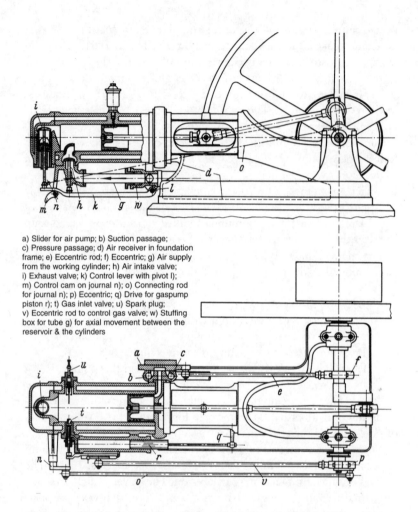

a) Slider for air pump; b) Suction passage;
c) Pressure passage; d) Air receiver in foundation
frame; e) Eccentric rod; f) Eccentric; g) Air supply
from the working cylinder; h) Air intake valve;
i) Exhaust valve; k) Control lever with pivot l);
m) Control cam on journal n); o) Connecting rod
for journal n); p) Eccentric; q) Drive for gaspump
piston r); t) Gas inlet valve; u) Spark plug;
v) Eccentric rod to control gas valve; w) Stuffing
box for tube g) for axial movement between the
reservoir & the cylinders

Fig. 11-10   Section view of Benz two-stroke gas engine, 1884.
(Sass, *Geschichte . . .*)

Another distinctive feature was a compact governor-controlled gas
valve.[30] A vertical spool valve, directly connected to the governor shaft
was raised and lowered by the action of the flyball weights. As speed
increased the spool moved so that the full diameter land gradually shut
off the gas supply port. A bypass passage with a needle valve gave a final
adjustment for the no-load speed.

216

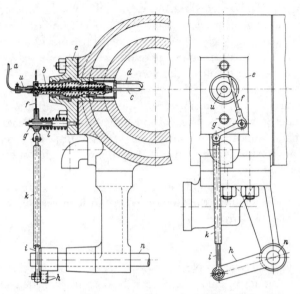

Fig. 11-11   Benz electric ignition system with porcelain-insulated spark plug and external contact breaker. 1882 design. (Sass, *Geschichte . . .*)

Performance data from 1886[31] showed a gas consumption of 25 cu ft/bhp hr (707 liters/bhp hr) versus 37.7 cu ft/bhp hr for a Clerk engine. Both had a 4 horsepower nominal rating but were producing 5.6 bhp at 153 rpm on the Benz and 190 rpm on the Clerk.

Benz & Cie. built two-stroke engines until Otto's patent was invalidated in 1886. (Fig. 11-12, Plate) The German Patent Office had refused to grant Benz a patent on his basic two-stroke ideas because of Otto, but he was able to get protection in Britain and the United States.[32] There is no record of Deutz claiming infringement because the loop scavenging precluded any attempt to claim charge stratification.

Fielding Uniflow Scavenge Engine – 1881
John Fielding of Gloucester, England, built on the groundwork laid by Robson. His "under-piston scavenge" two-stroke engine used piston pumping action to pressurize a closed crankcase.[33] Upward deflected intake ports, circumferentially arranged around the cylinder wall were uncovered by the piston as it neared bottom dead center. Before expos-

ing the ports, a cam-actuated exhaust valve in the cylinder head opened. This is the arrangement adopted on most modern uniflow scavenged engines whereby the cylinder port area is cooled from incoming air, and the hot exhaust passes through more readily cooled poppet valves in the cylinder head rather than cylinder ports.

The closed crankcase for scavenge air also allowed Fielding to use it as a lube oil reservoir, a possible first. Piston pin lubrication in the vertical cylinder was by a method possible only on slow speed engines. A bicycle chain, looped around one sprocket free to turn on the pin, and a second attached to the crank throw, dipped into the sump and carried oil up to the pin.

Fielding, who was to build four-stroke engines under the company name of Fielding and Platt in Gloucester, had little market success with this first small two-stroke.

Nash "Two Port" Engine – 1888

Lewis Hallock Nash of New York City patented one of the earliest two-stroke engines to eliminate all cam or eccentric actuated valves.[34] Scavenge air was provided by under-piston pumping directly into a sealed crankcase. Air and gas were drawn into the crankcase past a one-way valve. Exhaust ports in the cylinder wall were uncovered as the piston neared bottom center, followed next by the intake ports. A conduit housing a second one-way valve connected the crankcase with the inlet ports. To achieve loop scavenging a large deflector plate projected from the piston crown to divert the incoming charge up toward the cylinder head. Throttling was by a governor-controlled plug valve in the pipe leading to the inlet ports.

Between 1883 and 1897 Nash was granted forty patents on various engine designs and modifications. All of these were assigned to the National Meter Co. of New York City who built a popular line of "Nash" two and four-stroke, gas and gasoline engines well past 1900.

The "Nash" set a pattern for the American style of two-stroke engines adopting crankcase scavenging (outboards, etc.) with a "reed valve" interposed between the carburetor and crankcase. European practice, in general, is of the "three port" design as first built by Day.

Day "Three-Port" Engine – 1891

The barest of mechanism distinguished Joseph Day's (1855-1946) patented three-port engine of 1891.[35] (Fig. 11- 13, Plate) Day made use of Fielding's closed crankcase to store scavenge air, but like Nash, had the exhaust pass through cylinder ports. (Maybach designed four-stroke engines in the mid-1880s with a pressurized crankcase, although for another purpose.) A third cylinder port, added below the intake and exhaust, was uncovered by the lower end of the piston skirt as it moved upward. The charge was then sucked through the open port rather than past a one-way valve as in the Nash. Timing for all functions thus was piston controlled. A high vertical plate offset to one side of the piston crown deflected the incoming charge to induce loop scavenging. Untimed ignition was from an exposed hot tube.

Clerk reported that a Day engine rated at one nominal horsepower produced 3.3 indicated horsepower at 180 rpm from a cylinder with a bore and stroke of four and a half by seven and a half inches.[36] He said the gas consumption should have been less than forty cubic feet per brake horsepower hour, or better than a Robson-Tangye.

The gas engines were made by Day and Co. of Bath, England. Gasoline fueled ones of 2-1/2 hp to 30 hp, chiefly for marine use, appeared in 1906 and remained in production for almost twenty years. They mostly came from the Day Motor Co. Ltd., Putney.[37]

James Atkinson

James Atkinson (1846-1914) was an ingenious English engineer who attacked the problem of improving efficiency right at the source: maximizing expansion of combustion gases. His engines also produced a power stroke with every revolution, but in most unconventional fashions.

Born near Manchester into a family of engineers, his career spanned steam, gas and oil engines. He served his apprenticeship with a marine engineering company in Jarrow, a town next to South Shields where at about the same time Robson was building his first gas engines. Until Atkinson directed his full attention to the gas engine in 1882 his activities centered around steam engines and ships. The first evidence of his interest in non-steam power is a patent granted in 1879 for a hot-tube igniter,[38] followed in 1881 and 1882 by two-stroke, Robson-type engines. In 1883 the British Gas Engine and Engineering Co., Ltd., London, was formed to build these engines. Atkinson was appointed the managing director.[39]

Atkinson "Differential Engine"   1885

The "Differential" engine shown at the 1885 Inventions Exhibition in London had a power impulse on each revolution of the crankshaft, but it could not be classed as a two-stroke.[40] Two pistons, operating in an open ended horizontal cylinder, were tied to an overhead shaft, each with its own linkage system, and the combination went through the equivalent of four strokes in a single revolution. (Fig. 11-14, Plate) Since only one of the pistons served as a power piston to actually exert a torque on the shaft, the engine was not a true opposed-piston type. This additional complexity was not the desired end, but the means to do what no other designer has since achieved: an expansion stroke double that of the intake. (The "Miller cycle" as adapted by Mazda partially achieves this effect.)

Heat transfer to the coolant was also reduced by completing the expansion stroke in one-fourth the time of any other engine having the same shaft speed.

There were no cams or eccentric operated slide or poppet valves; all were pressure actuated, except that the governor could override a spring-loaded gas valve. When the power piston reached the end of the expansion stroke it uncovered intake and exhaust ports in the cylinder wall, each backed up by a valve.

A small diameter wrought iron pipe, open at its lower end to connect with the combustion chamber and kept hot by a continuous gas flame, served as an igniter tube. There was a degree of ignition timing as the pump piston covered a small hole through the cylinder wall leading to the tube until compression was at a maximum. The charge then became exposed to the tube hole and started to burn. Average tube life was about 180 hours.[41]

A cycle begins with both pistons close together at the extreme "right" end of the cylinder. (Fig. 11-16). Only a small residual fraction remained in the cylinder from the previous charge. (Not only desirable, but neces-

1. Beginning of Intake Stroke: Both pistons at extreme "right."
2. End of Intake Stroke: "Left" piston has drawn in charge. "Right" piston has covered port.
3. End of Compression Stroke: Both pistons at extreme "left." The "right" piston has caught up to the "left" piston.
4. End of Power or Expansion Stroke: The "left" piston remains stationary. The "right" piston moves to uncover the exhaust port.

Fig. 11-16   Atkinson "Differential" engine. Piston positions at different points in cycle (*Audel's Gas Engine Manual*, 1907)

sary to avoid infringing the Otto patent.) The left, pump, piston moves rapidly away from the power piston to suck in a homogeneous charge (also to avoid Otto) past the spring-loaded valves and through the uncovered intake port. After the pump piston travels a specified distance the power piston begins to move leftward. At this point intake is complete, and the space between the two pistons can be termed the length of the intake stroke. The two now progress together with the power piston gradually catching up to the pump piston to compress the charge. At the end of the compression stroke, with a cylinder pressure of about forty-five psi, the pump piston uncovers the igniter tube port. There it remains almost stationary until the power piston moves rapidly through its expansion stroke, a distance almost double that between the pistons on the intake stroke. The power piston uncovers the ports, comes to a virtual stop, and the pump piston now moves to push out the exhaust past an outwardly opening valve in the exhaust line. Cylinder pressure is about ten psi when the port is first uncovered. When the two pistons are almost together again the cycle is ready to begin anew.

The engine was offered in five sizes from one to eight horsepower. Representative specifications included:[42]

Nominal horsepower	1	4	8
Price, £	90	160	210
Engine speed, rpm	180	160	150
Floor space, ft	2.5x3	3.5x4	4.5x 6.5
Approx. weight, lb	1,200	2,500	4,200

Prof. Robinson tested a two (nominal) horsepower "Differential" engine in 1885 with these results: 2.6 bhp at 148 rpm with a "London" gas consumption of 25.8 cu ft/bhp hr, a creditable figure at that time for a small engine.[43] The thermal efficiency is not known because no heating value was given for the gas.

The "Cycle" Engine – 1886

Less than a year later Atkinson introduced a single-piston engine which still incorporated the desired features of a longer and faster expansion stroke.[44] (Fig. 11-17, Plate) The British Gas Engine Co. built over a thousand between 1886 and when production ended in 1893. Manlove, Alliott and Co., Nottingham, and the Warden Manufacturing Co., Philadelphia, also built the "Cycle" engine, the former from 1889 to 1892, and the latter for about a year beginning in 1889.

A two-bar linkage interposed between the connecting rod and the crank throw took the piston through four unequal strokes in only one crankshaft revolution. (Fig. 11-15, Plate) The intake to expansion stroke ratio was 0.56:1. Intake and exhaust valves placed in a more conventional cylinder head opened and closed under cam and pushrod action. A hot-tube igniter in the head remained exposed to the combustion chamber, but some degree of timing was made possible by adjusting where the flame played on the tube. These engines were relatively insensitive to ignition timing anyway so this was not a problem.

In 1888 the Society of Arts conducted carefully controlled tests on several representative types of gas engines. These London tests provide excellent comparative data between an Atkinson "Cycle" and a Crossley-Otto four-stroke. One of the objectives concerned speed regulation and cyclic variation for electric power generation. The advent of the incandescent lamp magnified an annoying problem already found with arc lights for the early single cylinder four-stroke engine: the new lights flickered even worse as speed fluctuated due to the long time between firing impulses in such slow moving engines. Steam was clearly superior because of its higher speeds and having a power impulse from every stroke. Even with massive flywheels, gas engines as lighting system generators left something to be desired. The Society for the Encouragement of Arts, Manufacturers and Commerce therefore wanted to find out which engine performed best in this troublesome area. The results show the "Cycle" engine to be clearly superior, and Atkinson was awarded the Society's gold medal:[45]

	Atkinson	Crossley
Nominal rating, hp	4	6
Bore-Stroke, in	7.5 x 9.25	8.5 x 14
Engine speed, rpm	131	160
Full load speed variation, %	1.75	6.57
Mean effective pressure, psi	46	68
Brake horsepower	9.5	14.7
Mechanical efficiency, %	85	86
Gas consumption, cu ft/bhp hr* . .	22.6	24.1
Heating value of gas, Btu/cu ft . . .	633	626
Thermal efficiency, %	23	21
Cooling water per hour, lb	680	713
Water temperature rise, °F	50	128

*Includes ignition gas

The above results also demonstrate the reduction in heat rejection to the cooling water. On a Btu per bhp hour basis the loss to the coolant was forty-two percent less than for the Crossley. However, fifty percent of the heat went out the exhaust in the Atkinson as compared to thirty-six in the Crossley.

Atkinson left no doubt that his theories to improve thermal efficiency worked in practice. However, the mechanism adopted did not lend itself to higher speeds or to weight reduction.

When the Otto British patent expired in 1890 a death knell sounded for almost every manufacturer choosing to stick with a two-stroke engine. Atkinson and his British Gas Engine Company were no exception. As more engine builders switched to increasingly simplified four-stroke designs, and competition became more frantic, the selling price of Otto-type engines dropped to as low as fifty percent of the patent protected days.[46] Only the financially strong with proven products survived.

Atkinson made one last attempt to continue with a two-stroke engine, but it did not prevail. The "Utilité", brought out in 1891 was similar to Robson and Fielding, its external distinction being a large, enclosed crankcase. Pumping by the under side of the piston raised this chamber to about five psi to provide scavenge air. Gas under pressure from a separate gas pump was introduced into the air on its way to the combustion chamber. The mixture formed was purposely too weak to ignite so the danger of explosions in passages leading to the combustion chamber was eliminated. Just prior to final compression the necessary additional gas was added to the cylinder.

The end of the British Gas Engine Co. in 1893 did not close out Atkinson's career in this field. Crossley Bros., Ltd. recognized his demonstrated abilities and hired him in July of that year as chief engineer at an annual salary of £600.[47] Among his numerous contributions at Crossley was an induced scavenge system to improve the efficiency of their large four-stroke gas engine. This was one of the first applications of a tuned exhaust pipe to extract more of the residual gases from the cylinder at the end of the exhaust stroke. A special pipe up to sixty feet long, depending on the model, was employed. Atkinson retired from Crossley in 1912 and died two years later.

The Trent Gas Engine – 1888

Another English two-stroke engine, the Trent, deserves mention because of a unique feature.[48] Richard Simon designed a stepped-piston engine that was built by his firm, the Trent Gas Engine Co. of Nottingham. A two diameter piston, reciprocating in a cylinder of similar configuration, used the ring shaped volume above the larger piston diameter to pump scavenge air directly into the combustion chamber over the piston crown. Cam-actuated gas and air valves, piston timed exhaust ports and a hot-tube igniter were other features. Tests measured a compression pressure of thirty-six psi with a peak pressure of only eighty-four psi. Gas consumption was about twenty-eight cubic feet per brake horsepower hour when the engine was developing 6.4 brake horsepower. Clerk commented that the indicator diagram suggested poor cylinder scavenging.[49] The company went out of business in 1894, the engine having ceased production some years before that.

The "Six-Cycle" Engine

Several British engines were neither two nor four-stroke cycle, but "six-cycle." Three revolutions of the crankshaft were necessary to produce one power stroke. The extra turn, interposed between the end of the exhaust stroke and the beginning of the intake on a normal four-stroke, cleaned out the cylinder of essentially all residual exhaust by drawing in air and then shoving it right out again. Even though the mechanical efficiency was five or six percent less than that of a four-stroke, the overall brake thermal efficiency was almost the same. Starting combustion with only an air and gas mixture and not a high percentage of leftover exhaust made this possible. (Owners of automobiles with early — 1960s and 1970s — EGR systems will recall what excessive exhaust gas recirculation for emission control did to fuel mileage!)

Charles Linford, who later tangled with the Otto patent in English courts brought out the first six-stroke engine in 1880.[50] This design had a vertical cylinder containing two, inwardly opposing pistons, each connected to the same throw on a crankshaft by similar rocking levers. The crankshaft was placed on a height level with the pistons' inner position. Added cams allowed scavenge air to be drawn in on a fifth stroke and then expelled through the exhaust valve on a sixth prior to starting the normal intake of gas and air. These engines were built for about a year in sizes of one to five horsepower (at 140 to 200 rpm) by C. Linford and Co. of Leicester, England.[51] (Clerk makes no mention of Linford.)

The Beck six-stroke engine, designed by Arthur Rollason, came a few years later.[52] The Newcastle-built engine had one, single-acting piston which made it comparatively large for a given power. A test in 1888 on a 7.5 inch diameter by 15.02 inch stroke Beck engine gave 5.85 brake horsepower at 163 rpm. Gas consumption was 26.1 cu ft/bhp hr to yield a thermal efficiency of 19 percent from a gas having a heating value of 611 Btu/cu ft.[53]

Concurrently with the Beck was Samuel Griffin's reasonably successful double-acting engine made at Kilmarnock, Scotland, by Dick, Kerr and Co. By having a combustion chamber on each end of the piston a power impulse was delivered every one and a half revolutions. The "Griffin" was sometimes referred to as a "three-cycle" engine. An opposed, single-acting piston version was also brought out by Dick, Kerr. It had separate cylinders like the Beck, each making one power stroke out of the six. This engine was thought of highly enough to be included in the Society of Arts trials with the Atkinson and Crossley engines. Its performance in gas consumption came out slightly below the other two. Michael L. Mery of Chico, California, received U.S. patent 543,157 in 1895 for electric ignition and valving features on his double-acting, six-stroke engine. Several of these still exist.

Oechelhäuser-Junkers Opposed-Piston Engine – 1892

Hugo Junkers (1859-1935) was a many-faceted man: teacher, engineer and entrepreneur.[54] The founder and guiding genius behind Germany's largest aircraft company, he was also for some years a distinguished professor of thermodynamics at the University of Aachen.

An operational diesel engine for large transport aircraft was another of his important contributions. That Junkers did not enter aviation (with the first all-metal plane) until he was past fifty should give heart to those who despair of ever beginning a second career. In 1933 he was forced out of his industrial complex, and his assets were confiscated because of outspoken comments against Hitler. It is unfortunate the Junkers name most often connotes an instrument of war.

From 1889 to 1894 Junkers was an assistant to Wilhelm von Oechelhäuser (1850-1923), manager of the Berlin-Anhalt'schen Maschinenbau AG in Dessau. Oechelhäuser had been investigating gas engine combustion for several years and was granted several patents for this work. Not until joined by Junkers did the breakthrough come on a new design. The two jointly developed an opposed-piston gas engine ultimately capable of burning low heating value blast-furnace gas.[55] The first of these were placed in service in 1896. (Cockerill introduced four-stroke engines using this fuel in 1898 after several years of experimentation.) The gas, a normally wasted byproduct of steel making, had a heating value of about 100 Btu/cu ft, or one-tenth that of natural gas. Engines powered by the gas could either generate electricity for nearby distribution or operate pumps for blowing draft air in the mills.

Junkers had the opportunity to start with a "clean sheet of paper" to apply his thermodynamics expertise on a new design concept. The results were a dramatic improvement over that attainable with the engines then available. His objective was to increase the expansion, or in effect compression, ratio considerably beyond what was currently thought possible. He commented that Otto had "made a retrograde step inasmuch as he decreased the ratio of expansion, which in the atmospheric engine was 10:1, to approximately 2.5:1 and thus increased the fuel consumption per unit."[56]

The chosen configuration (Fig. 11-18, Plate) had two, inwardly opposed pistons operating in a single horizontal cylinder.[57] The piston farther away from the crankshaft carried a yoke on its outer end which was tied to the crankshaft by two long, crosshead-guided rods straddling the cylinder. Thus there were three crank throws, the middle one for the near piston and the end ones to each receive one-half of the outer piston's force. The axially moving rod portions between the yoke and the crosshead guides each passed through a closed-ended cylinder to reciprocate a double-acting piston. One piston pumped air into a receiver, the other gas into the combustion cylinder. The Junkers opposed-piston design permits a light engine structure and has relatively small unbalanced forces.

Uniflow scavenging was adopted. Inlet and exhaust ports at opposite ends of the cylinder were arranged so that first the exhaust ports were uncovered by one piston, and after the pressure dropped the other piston uncovered the inlet ports to scavenge the remaining exhaust products. Air entered the cylinder from the receiver under about five psi. Gas entered in two stages: shortly after scavenging ended and part way up the compression stroke. The double-acting gas piston and two spring-loaded valves controlled the timing. Maximum gas pumping pressure was thirty to forty psi.[58] An electric ignition system fired the charge when the pistons were closest together at inner dead center.

An experimental engine tested in 1892 produced 100 brake horsepower from a cylinder of 200 mm diameter and a stroke of 2 x 500 mm (for the two opposed pistons). Performance comparisons between this engine and a sixty horsepower Deutz engine of 1891 demonstrated the inherent potential of the radical new design:[59]

Fig. 11-1   Sir Dugald Clerk (1854-1932). (The Science Museum, London)

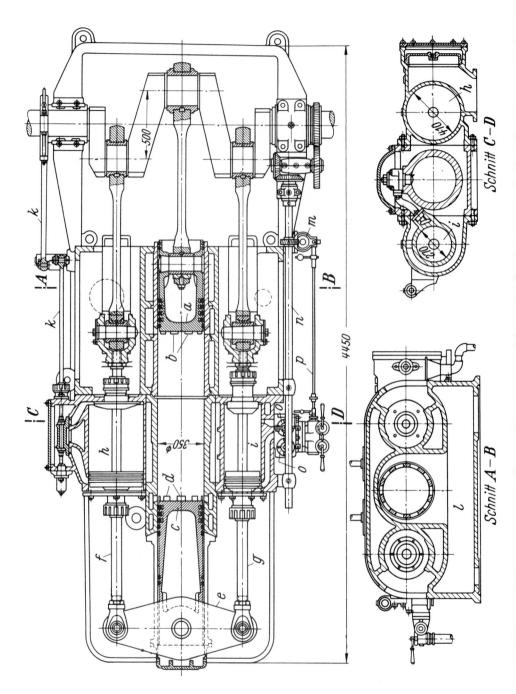

Fig. 11-18   Opposed-piston, two-stroke engine of Oechelhäuser
and Junkers, 1893. It produced 220 hp at 140 rpm on
coal-gas. (Sass, *Geschichte* . . .)

	Oechelhäuser-Junkers	Deutz
Compression pressure, psi	270	36
Peak combustion pressure, psi	970	142
Mean indicated pressure, psi	147	59
Engine speed, rpm	160	140
Gas consumption, cu ft/bhp hr . . .	11.8*	22

*After subtracting for the work required to operate the gas and air pumps.
Both engines used coal gas.

Nothing was said in Junkers' paper about combustion knock. Since the compression ratio was near 10:1 any of his comments on this subject would have been helpful.

The Oechelhäuser-Junkers design was built under license by three firms in increasingly larger sizes. By 1914 these *Grossgasmaschinen* were producing up to 1,500 horsepower from a single cylinder of 1,100 mm bore and strokes of 2 x 1,350 mm. Engine speeds were around 100 rpm. The royalties derived from sales of these engines (and a very popular hot water heater of his invention) gave Junkers the financial strength first to develop large ship diesels and then begin his aviation activity.

Within the span of only a few years we have seen pioneer engine makers devise various, sometimes ingenious, methods of causing a piston to receive a power impulse on each revolution. There were unmentioned others who contributed detail refinements, some workable and some not, to make the "two-cycle" into the reliable machine it is today. In the United States a few additional pioneers were John Charter, Cyrus W. Baldwin and Clark Sintz. In England, Charles G. Beechy (the Fawcett), John Taylor (the Midland) and J.E.H. Andrew (the Stockport) added more names of designers and builders of two-stroke engines actually placed in production. One can only admire the creativity and perseverance of those who competed against the entrenched Otto empire.

NOTES
1. *Proceedings of the Institution of Civil Engineers,* v. 69, London, 1882, p. 220.
2. Harry Ricardo, *Memories and Machines: The Pattern of my Life,* (London, 1968), p. 68.
3. "Obituary, Sir Dugald Clerk," *Minutes of Proceedings, Inst. of Civil Engineers,* 1932/33, Pt. 1, v. 235, p. 507.

4. British patent No. 3,045 of Aug. 1, 1878, and U.S. No. 230,470 of July 27, 1880.
5. "Dugald Clerk Engine Exhibited at Kilburn Show," *Engineering,* June 27, 1879, pp. 574-75.
6. Dugald Clerk, "Cylinder Actions in Gas and Gasoline Engines," *Transactions, The Society of Automotive Engineers,* 1921, Part 11, p. 44.
7. *Ibid.,* p. 44.
8. Based on British patent No. 1,089 of March 14, 1881. The U.S. equivalent was No. 249,307 issuing November 8, 1881.
9. Clerk, "Cylinder Actions. . .," *op. cit.,* p. 46.
10. Dugald Clerk, *The Gas and Oil Engine,* 6th ed., (London, 1896), p. 191.
11. "The Clerk Gas Engine," *American Machinist,* August 5, 1882, p. 5.
12. A.G. Elliott, *Gas and Petroleum Engines,* 2nd ed., (London, 1905), p. 31.
13. Rachel E. Waterhouse, *A Hundred Years of Engineering Craftsmanship, A Short History of ... Tangyes Ltd ...,* (Birmingham, 1957), p. 81.
14. James Robson, *A Brief Memoir of James Robson, the Inventor of the Two-Cycle Internal-Combustion Engine and of the Gas Hammer,* (Birmingham, 1915), 45 p. The author, a son, was at the time "Chief of the Gas and Oil Engine Departments of Tangyes, Ltd., Cornwall Works, Birmingham."
15. *Ibid.,* p. 15.
16. British patent No. 4,050 of 1880.
17. British patent No. 2,334 of 1877.
18. James Robson, *The Development of the Gas Engine,* (Birmingham, ca. 1915), printed lecture, p. 6.
19. British patent No. 4,501 of 1879.
20. Robson, *A Brief Memoir, op. cit.,* p. 27.
21. Waterhouse, *op. cit.,* p. 80.
22. Gustav Goldbeck, *Gebändigte Kraft,* (Munich, 1965), p. 99.
23. German patent No. 6,776 of February 13, 1879; British No. 3,732 of 1879; and U.S. No. 225,778 of March 23, 1880. (The U.S. patent was the first to issue in that country for a two-stroke compression engine.)
24. Hugo Güldner, *Das Entwerfen und Berechnen der Verbrennungskraftmaschinen,* 3rd ed., (Berlin, 1914), pp. 666-671; Bryan

Donkin, *Gas, Oil and Air Engines,* 2nd ed., (London, 1896), pp. 64-65, 476.

25. Friedrich Sass, *Geschichte des deutschen Verbrennungsmotorenbaues von 1860 bis 1918,* (Berlin, 1962), p. 133.
26. *Ibid.,* p. 140.
27. Eugen Diesel, et al., *From Engines to Autos.* (Chicago, 1960), p. 141. Dr.-Ing. Friedrich Schildberger, the author of the section on Karl Benz, was for many years before retirement head of the Daimler-Benz museum at Stuttgart.
28. *Ibid.,* p. 146.
29. Donkin, *op. cit.,* p. 177.
30. German patent No. 22,256 of October 25, 1882.
31. Güldner, *op. cit.,* p. 668.
32. British patent No. 9,949 of July 9, 1884, and U.S. No. 316,868 of April 28, 1885.
33. British patent No. 532 of February 8, 1881.
34. U.S. Patent No. 386,211 of July 17, 1888. (The application was first filed in November 1885.)
35. British patents Nos. 6,410 of April 14 and 9,247 of June 1, both of 1891; U.S. patent No. 543,614 of 1895. Frederick W. Cock, a Day employee, contributed to the Day basic design. His British patent No. 18,513 of October 15, 1892, (U.S. No. 544,210) made further simplifications to Day's design and is the one from which the most Day engines were produced. H. S. Torrens, *The Newcomen Bulletin,* No. 136, Dec. 1986, p. 11, gives Day personal and company information.
36. Dugald Clerk, *The Gas, Petrol and Oil Engine,* v. 2, (New York, 1913), p. 214.
37. *Marine Oil Engine Handbook,* 3rd ed., (London, ca. 1914), pp. 117-18.
38. British patent No. 3,213 of 1879.
39. "Memoirs – James Atkinson", *Proceedings of the Institution of Mechanical Engineers,* May 1914, p. 347.
40. British patent No. 2,712 of February 28, 1885, and U.S. patent No. 336,505 of February 16, 1886.
41. William Robinson, *Gas and Petroleum Engines,* (London, 1890), p. 41.
42. British Gas Engine & Engineering Co., Ltd.; company brochure on Atkinson Engines, 1885, p. 4.
43. Robinson, *op. cit.,* p. 45.

44. British patent No. 3,522 of March 12, 1886, and U.S. No. 367,496 of August 2, 1887.
45. Robinson, *op. cit.*, p. 530, and Donkin, *op. cit.*, pp. 476-78.
46. Dugald Clerk, *The Gas and Oil Engine,* 6th ed., (New York, 1896), p. 271.
47. An Atkinson letter to Crossley, dated July 21, 1893, lists the employment terms. A copy kindly sent to the author by Mr. Frank Beard, Crossley-Premier Engines Ltd.
48. British patent No. 16,183 of November 8, 1888.
49. Clerk, *op. cit.*, p. 290.
50. British patent Nos. 1,500 of April 17, 1879, and 330 of January 24, 1880. The U.S. patent was No. 232,987 of October 5, 1880.
51. William Robinson, *Gas and Petroleum Engines,* 2nd ed., (New York, 1902), pp. 161-62.
52. British patent No. 7,427 of June 2, 1886.
53. Robinson, *op. cit.*, pp. 163-66.
54. Theodore von Kármán, in his autobiography, *The Wind and Beyond: Theodore von Kármán,* (Boston, 1967) has several vignettes about Junkers and their long association. The entire book is highly recommended reading.
55. British patent No. 14,317 of August 8, 1892 and U.S. No. 508,833 of 1893.
56. Hugo Junkers, "Investigations and Experimental Researches for the Construction of my Large-Oil-Engine," translated from the *Jahrbuch der Schiffbautechnischen Gesellschaft,* (Berlin, 1912), p. 3.
57. Sass, *op. cit.*, pp. 305-06.
58. Güldner, *op. cit.*, p. 670.
59. Junkers, *op. cit.*, pp. 3, 4.

Chapter 12

Gas and Gasoline Engines to 1900

A dam of creative ideas burst when the Otto patent no longer formed a barrier. The rate of new developments accelerated, and a competitive market brought attractive prices. Customers were impressed by the improvements in economy and reliability. Most evident was the appearance of higher speed engines vaporizing a liquid fuel to make mobile applications feasible. The dawn of the automobile age was at hand. Refined ignition and carburetion systems, multi-cylinder and immense single cylinder gas engines of many times the power of a few years earlier were placed in service.

New engines bred new applications, and these in turn gave rise to even newer engines. The energy supply was in a similar dynamic state. Fuels adequate in the early 1880s were no longer economically in abundant supply or able to feed the broadening spectrum of diets required by expanding lines of engines. Thus new engines also generated new fuels.

Daimler and Maybach: 1882-1900

Gottlieb Daimler (Fig. 12-1, Plate) left Deutz under strained conditions in 1882, and Wilhelm Maybach (Fig. 12-2, Plate) rejoined him within a few months. For the next five years in the *Gartenhaus* of Daimler's Cannstatt villa near Stuttgart they labored first over engine and then vehicle chassis designs. Their objective was to build a lightweight engine capable of running at speeds three times faster than those they had worked with at Deutz. Daimler knew that if his ideas were to be realized, a minor redesign of the ponderous gas engine was not the answer. A thousand pounds per horsepower and speeds of under two hundred rpm were too far away for a starting base. Not only the engine structures, but the existing "surface carburetors" as used on gasoline-fueled stationary engines, themselves weighing several hundred pounds, were also out of the question.

231

Gasoline was a logical choice for the horseless carriage, one of Daimler's visualized applications, because of transportability and high energy per unit volume relationship. (The latter is a key factor in any consideration of alternative fuels for mobile transportation.) The gasolines of pre-1900 were either so-called natural gasolines or easily distilled top fractions from the new crude oil sources of Russia and the eastern United States. These fuels, a byproduct in the case of refined crude, had almost one hundred percent volatile fractions. The low boiling and flashpoints made for easy starting but were extremely hazardous. This compared to forty percent volatile fractions in the "gasolines made by the processes of Dr. Wm. M. Burton (1865-1954) coming on stream after 1913.[1] (A rapidly increasing demand for gasoline after 1900 could not be met without finding ways to extract more of it per barrel of crude. Burton, a pioneer in the oil industry, pointed the way with his thermal cracking process first installed at Standard Oil of Indiana's Whiting refinery.)

Two basic problems had to be solved by Daimler and Maybach before their 600-800 rpm engine was feasible: to vaporize and mix gasoline and air in the correct ratio in a compact container and then to provide positive ignition at the higher speeds.

A hot-tube igniter heated by a gasoline fed, external flame ignited the charge.[2] Daimler was certainly not the first with such an idea, as evidenced by the narrowness of his United States patent.[3] A single claim pertained only to an insulated combustion chamber and made no reference to the hot-tube igniter. Daimler wanted to initiate combustion from the hot walls and piston, employing forced air cooling only to the lower cylinder portion, but this proved inadequate. He then depended fully on the flame heated tube shown in the patent for the point of ignition. As with other engines using the same method, the tube's red hot inner surface fired the charge at the end of the compression stroke. Timing was not an independent variable; in fact, it was an objective to keep ignition unregulated for simplicity. Daimler continued with his heated tube igniter until the late 1890s even though the open flame was undesirable for boat and automotive applications. Emil Jellinek, a wealthy promoter of Daimler cars (and whose daughter, Mercedes, had her name bestowed on them after Daimler's death) once publicly declared that the hot-tube was a fire hazard. He said his own car had caught fire "innumerable times."[4] Yet the hot-tube, with the burner encased in a sheet metal box, generally was more reliable than the electric systems of Benz and others in the earliest days of automobiles.

Because of the fire hazard and a need for more accurate timing in the high performance engines, Daimler grudgingly adopted a low tension (voltage) magneto system perfected by Robert Bosch (1861-1942). This was fifteen years after Otto had won high honors at the Antwerp Exposition in 1884 for a Deutz gasoline engine equipped with a similar but less refined magneto. The Otto "make and break" design used on the Deutz Model "AB" engines (Chapter 9) was not patented in Germany and gave Bosch an opportunity to develop the reliable magnetos which made him world famous.

Maybach solved the vaporization problem with a surface carburetor containing a float to maintain the gasoline level. (Fig. 12-3) His design, and a similar one by Karl Benz, were almost concurrent developments with that at Deutz. Much reduced in weight, the Maybach carburetor was about the same diameter as the engine cylinder. Vaporization was enhanced by preheating incoming air, the air pipe being routed over the hot-tube igniter flame. A mixing valve placed between the carburetor and the engine adjusted the overall air:fuel ratio. The surface carburetor worked only because of the highly volatile fuel.

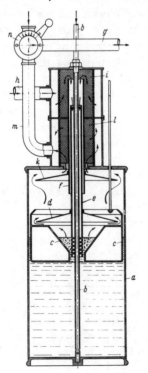

a) Gasoline reservoir; b) feed pipe; c) float; d) baffle moving with float c); e) air supply tube – moves with c) & d); f) stationary tube; g) pipe to engine intake valve; h) tube leading from intake air preheater to the carburetor; i & l) wire gauze filter and flame arrester; k) fixed baffle; m) suction line to mixing valve n); s) housing for hot-tube igniter and burner; t) gasoline container for burner; u) gasoline line to burner.

Fig. 12-3
Maybach surface carburetor with float, 1885. (Sass, *Geschichte des deutschen Verbrennungsmotorenbaues*, 1962)

Gasoline vaporizing techniques were not new to Maybach. He had experimented with primitive carburetors on the Otto and Langen atmospheric engine shortly after his arrival at Deutz. Fires and explosions were commonplace. In his memoirs he tells of holding a gasoline soaked rag at the engine air intake, and with the combustion gas supply shut off, varying the rate of the power stroke by moving the rag either closer or farther from the inlet.[5] This of course was done in conjunction with a gas fired ignition flame! Maybach said that a safety net was finally placed around his test area on the main production floor to protect other workers from occasional flying debris. His last experiments during that time included passing air over gasoline inside a sheet metal can. (It was these tests that brought out the net.) Both Otto and Daimler witnessed Maybach's work, and Maybach said Otto particularly was quite interested in the results.

No patents issued on the Maybach (or Benz) surface carburetors, possibly due to a signed and dated sketch by Eugen Langen in 1876 illustrating the idea (but without the float) that was incorporated in the later developments.[6]

Daimler and Maybach evolved a series of engines from a basic design built in 1883.[7] (Fig. 12-4, Plate) The first vehicular one of 1885 (Fig. 12-5) was in a motorcycle[8] followed by a larger model the next year in a modified horse drawn carriage. This family of engines was dubbed the *standuhr* or "upright clock" as they resembled a small, free standing mantel clock. (Figs. 12-6 and 12-7, Plates) The motorcycle engine reduced the weight per horsepower by a factor of four from contemporary stationary engines. The little air cooled engine developed one-half horsepower at 600 rpm from a cylinder bore and stroke of 52 mm by 100 mm. Total weight of the engine was less than 200 pounds.

Valve operation differed from standard practice. Suction opened a spring-loaded inlet valve on the piston downstroke. An exhaust valve, directly under and axially in line with the inlet, opened into a passage common with the inlet. The exhaust valve was actuated by a face cam, a circular, grooved track cut in an end face of the vertical flywheel. A sliding shoe, free to pivot about its center and fastened to the lower end of the exhaust push rod, followed in the groove. In two flywheel revolutions the cam motion was translated into one vertical displacement of the exhaust valve. (Fig. 12-8) The groove formed a continuous path, but like a simple pretzel, was folded over to appear to be two concentric circles crossing each other at one point. The inner path served as the base circle, the outer as the lift and the crossing segments the ramps. The long, sliding shoe was shaped to travel through the crossovers on the desired track.

A third valve was located in the piston crown. (Fig. 12-9) Its function, in combination with a crankcase pressurized by the pumping action of the piston, was to aid in expelling residual exhaust from the cylinder after the exhaust valve opened. Maybach designed the valve to open when the piston neared bottom center by having the underside of the valve spring cage hit a stop as the piston continued descending. A more complete and deliberate removal of the residual fraction by pressure scavenging also

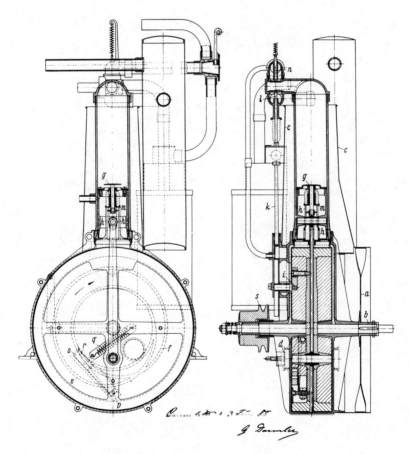

Fig. 12-5   Daimler and Maybach engine for the first motorcycle, 1885. (Sass, *Geschichte . . .*)

avoided infringement of the first three claims of Otto's basic patent. However, the performance benefit accruing from the piston valve was enough for it to be retained several years after invalidation of the patent.

A scaled up motorcycle engine and a four wheeled carriage were combined in the first Daimler automobile. (Fig. 12-10, Plate) Its earliest

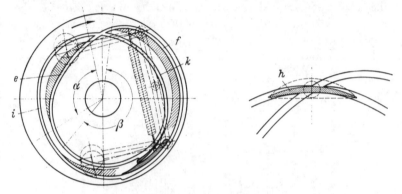

Fig. 12-8   Flywheel face cam grooves and pivoting follower shoe to actuate exhaust valve, *Standuhr* engine. (Sass, *Geschichte* . . .)

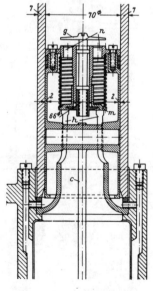

c) Connecting rod; g) Valve plate; h) Valve stroke limiter; m) Spring plate; n) Bore for valve seat.

Fig. 12-9   Section through *Standuhr* engine showing piston scavenge valve. (Sass, *Geschichte* . . .)

travels in September of 1886 were around the garden paths of Daimler's property. The now water-cooled engine developed 1.1 horsepower at 650 rpm from a cylinder of 70 mm by 120 mm. To carry away the increased heat load Maybach designed a water jacketed casting containing the clearance volume above the piston, a common intake and exhaust passage and the valve housings. The unit assembled over the top of the cylinder.

Between 1886 and 1889 Maybach perfected and Daimler promoted both the engine and the automobile. The lightweight design made possible many mobile power applications besides the auto: small boats, fire engine pumpers, street cars and industrial locomotives.

Even a non-rigid airship (blimp) was powered by a Daimler engine before 1890. A second major development was a seventeen degree vee, two cylinder engine of 0.565 liters displacement[9] (Fig. 12-11, Plate) The narrow vee, in conjunction with both connecting rods being on the same crank throw, timed the power strokes almost exactly one revolution apart and was one of the patented features. From a bore and stroke of 60 mm by 100 mm the engine produced 1.5 horsepower at 600 rpm.[10] A dynamometer test in 1961 of an early twin-vee engine gave an output of 1.65 horsepower at 920 rpm.[11] Maybach next designed a completely new chassis and power train to take the vee engine. This second "Daimler" auto was more than just a modified horseless carriage. (Fig. 12-12, Plate)

A marine engine conversion was placed in several motor launches beginning in 1886. Demonstrations with the boats generated as much, if not more, tangible interest than did the automobile. Greater thought was given to these installations than merely bolting an engine onto its bed. A complete system was worked out incorporating a reversing gear, engine cooling and an integral bilge pump.[12]

A major sales thrust was made in the automotive market. Through Daimler's promotional efforts, the "vertical clock" engine became the powerplant for the pioneering French car builders. Daimler's representative in France was the same Edouard Sarazin who was a principal with Deutz in Compagnie Française des Moteurs à Gaz. Daimler reasoned Sarazin had no conflict of interest because Deutz had only stationary engines while his went into mobile or portable applications.[13] Sarazin attracted Emile Levassor (1844-1897), an engineer and partner of Panhard and Levassor, to the new, high-speed engine. As a result Panhard and Levassor built a test chassis not long after Daimler drove his own first car.

Sarazin died in 1887 leaving his business affairs in the hands of his young but able wife. She continued her husband's relationship with Daimler even though they had no formal agreement. Daimler was not sure he wanted to commit his future engine prospects in France to a woman, but Madame Sarazin finally won him over. Levassor tidied up the situation by marrying his good friend Sarazin's widow whom be had begun courting, and not only acquired a bride but rights to an engine.[14] Unfortunately, the marriage was not destined to last long because Levassor died several years later from injuries suffered in a race car accident.

Panhard and Levassor built a Daimler twin-vee engine in 1890 for Armand Peugeot (1849-1915), the first French automobile manufacturer, and then started their own car production the following year with the same engine. (The Daimler licensing agreement continued until 1900.) On July 22, 1894, Peugeot cars captured second, third and fifth (behind a winning steam car) in what turned out to be the world's first automobile race. Billed as a reliability trial, competitive instincts prevailed to turn the seventy-eight mile round trip between Paris and Rouen into a race. A Panhard finished fourth to make a clean sweep for Daimler-designed gasoline engines. A Benz automobile came in sixth.

English rights to the Daimler patents were granted to Frederick Richard Simms (1863-1944) in 1893. Three years later he formed a company to build the Daimler car. (A fierce parliamentary struggle that year resulted in the repeal of an 1878 law which had prevented for all practical purposes the use of an automobile in England. The law required a person to walk at least fifteen yards in front of a self-propelled road vehicle.) Thus the Daimler Motor Company Ltd. in Coventry became a founder of the English auto industry and has continued to be a respected car name.

A similar situation almost developed across the Atlantic in the United States. Daimler signed a contract in 1888 with the piano maker, William Steinway. Beginning in 1891, engines for the Daimler Motor Co. of New York City were produced on the site of the old Underwood Works in Hartford, Connecticut. Daimler industrial, marine and automotive engines stimulated great interest at the 1893 Columbian Exhibition in Chicago, but with the issuance of the Selden patent in 1895 and Steinway's death in 1896, sales of Daimler automobiles were thwarted.[15] The engine itself continued to sell well.

Daimler accomplished for the high-speed gasoline engine what Deutz did for the stationary gas engine: the establishment of an international organization building to a common design under license.

All did not go smoothly for Daimler and Maybach, however. The need for expansion capital brought in two new partners with the formation of Daimler-Motoren-Gesellschaft in November 1890. Trouble started almost immediately. Maybach had been promised the position of Technical Director by Daimler, but the new partners with the controlling interest denied him this. Maybach left the company and with personal funds began development work under his own name for the first time.

Daimler also was extremely frustrated as he, too, saw an impossible situation staring him in the face. The new management had little understanding about the complexities involved in producing precision machines. Daimler himself finally quit all active participation in the company in 1892, remaining only on the board of directors because of his stock interest, and started working again full time with Maybach. It was almost as in the *Gartenhaus* days, but now in an old Cannstatt hotel. Daimler supplied the challenge and direction, and it was left to Maybach's inventive genius and engineering talents to bring forth a workable result.

Out of this newest phase of their long association poured advanced ideas. Because of their success the controlling partners at Daimler-Motoren-Gesellschaft were forced to accept them back into the company in 1895 almost on their own terms. Daimler had the say over engineering, manufacturing and marketing matters, and Maybach at last became Technical Director.

The hiatus away from D-M-G gave Maybach a golden opportunity to shine in his own light. All of his ideas now resulted in patents issuing in his name. Maybach was a free agent, but Daimler was still under contract to D-M-G which prevented him from following past practice of having his and Maybach's ideas patented in his name. While it is not intended to imply that all of Daimler's early patents were based on Maybach inventions, numerous original sketches by Maybach did end up protected under the Daimler name. (Company histories offer many instances where an employee, the true inventor, did not share fully in the fruits of his ideas. Yet, without the job, the facilities and the encouragement or coercion by a banker or a boss, that idea might never have been born. The "wrong" man sometimes having his name on a patent might not be such a terrible injustice after all.)

Just before the founding of Daimler-Motoren-Gesellschaft, Maybach designed the first in line, four-cylinder engine for marine and industrial markets. (Fig. 12-13, Plate) Its initial rating of five horsepower at 620 rpm came from cylinders of 80 mm by 120 mm, and the specific weight was reduced to thirty kilograms per horsepower. Two connecting rods were paired to a single elongated crank journal making it a two throw crankshaft but with power strokes every half revolution. The engine retained the hot-tube igniters and had a single surface carburetor located over a short output shaft between the flywheel and a clutch. About this same time Maybach experimented on an automobile with a tubular cooling pipe, the forerunner of a modern radiator.[16]

From the "Hotel Hermann" days came another of Maybach's important contributions, the 1892 "spray" carburetor. This was the first carburetor to direct the fuel spray from an orifice into the *center* of an air stream (Fig. 12-14, Plate) A small float in its own chamber maintained the liquid level at the jet by opening and closing a needle valve in the supply line to the float chamber. A reduced diameter air passage at the jet increased velocity and thereby reduced pressure to improve the spray characteristics. All of the basic elements of a modern carburetor were present.

England[17] and France granted Maybach a patent, but the English one was later ruled invalid because of Edward Butler's 1887 patent.[18] In the Butler spray carburetor fuel entered the mixing section as a thin cylindrical sheet of liquid surrounding the air stream in the central core of a venturi. The mixture control was less effective as compared with Maybach's, but Butler's broadest patent claim did not specify either method, thus anticipating Maybach. Butler devoted many years to carburetor and engine design as well as to writing two textbooks on these subjects.[19]

The spray carburetor was incorporated into the new "Phönix" in line, two-cylinder engine that same year. (Fig. 12-14, Plate) The name was chosen because D-M-G owned the Daimler name rights for engines. One of the most famous of the pre-1900 gasoline engines, it set the trend for future engine design: fully water jacketed multicylinders cast in a single block, a multi-cylinder head with all cast passages, etc. Hot-tube ignition continued. The first models developed two horsepower at 760 rpm from cylinders of 67 mm by 108 mm bore and stroke.

A round trip race from Paris to Bordeaux in 1895 brought glory to the Phönix engine. Panhard and Levassor built a special two-seater car, and Levassor drove it the entire 1,183 kilometers in an elapsed time of less than forty-nine hours. Levassor's Phönix developed 4.2 horsepower at 800 rpm as compared with the latest Daimler-Motoren-Gesellschaft twin-vee output of 3.5 hp at 720 rpm. Weight per horsepower had been reduced to twenty kilograms.[20] Dirt buildup on some external linkage caused the only mechanical problem; Maybach and Daimler had proved beyond any doubt the reliability of an automobile engine.

A recitation of Maybach's engineering triumphs reads like a capsule history of the early automobile. After Daimler's untimely death in 1900, Maybach assumed all technical leadership at D-M-G. The unbeatable thirty-five horsepower Mercedes racing cars, introduced almost immediately after Daimler died, were mostly Maybach's creation, both in engine and chassis design. Wilhelm Maybach, who left D-M-G in 1907, and his equally talented son Karl (1879-1960) founded Maybach-Motorenbau-Gesellschaft at Friedrichshafen in 1909 to build Zeppelin and aircraft engines. The deeds of this venture, plus the Maybach automobile, high performance diesels, etc., are a captivating story in themselves.[21] Regardless of era, a Maybach design translated beauty into form and function, the final test of an engineer's total capability.

The Benz Automobile Engines: 1886-1900

Karl Benz (Fig. 12-15, Plate) built motorcars. Engines designed under his direction had but one job: to power automobiles and commercial vehicles. To Benz a chassis and an engine were part of an integral whole, a philosophy quite different from Daimler who viewed the high-speed engine as a power source for any mobile application. While Benz cannot compare with the Daimler-Maybach team in the number of differing engine models produced, his contributions to early automobile design and manufacturing place him in the front rank of car pioneers. By 1899 Benz & Cie, Rheinische Gasmotorenfabrik AG had turned out over 2,000 automobiles, more than any other builder.

The engine in Benz' first automobile bore little resemblance to the "vertical clock" of Daimler and Maybach. (Fig. 12-16, Plate) A horizontal cylinder and flywheel were placed high and in the rear of the vehicle so that the flywheel on the underside of the engine was in the same plane as the driver's floor. (Benz had some concern about a possible gyroscopic action of a flywheel rotating in a vertical plane and affecting steering control.) The complete vehicle weighed only 263 kilograms including an engine weight of 96 kilograms. Because of steering problems not yet solved to Benz' satisfaction, a tricycle arrangement was adopted. The car that first ran on a public road in July of 1886 looked remarkably like the drawings shown in a German patent granted to Benz in January of that year.[22] (Fig. 12-17, Plate)

Almost identical in weight to the earliest Daimler, the Benz engine turned much slower and developed less than half the power. Its original rating was two-thirds of a horsepower at 250-300 rpm from a cylinder bore and stroke of 90 mm by 150 mm. (A laboratory test in 1940 gave 0.88 hp at 400 rpm.)[23]

Vaporization of the gasoline occurred in a surface carburetor having the liquid level controlled with a float and needle valve (Fig. 12-18). The gasoline was heated by piping part of the exhaust through the bottom of the carburetor tank.

Ignition came from an improved spark plug based on the design used in the Benz stationary engines. The vibrator on a Rühmkorff induction coil maintained continuous sparking at the plug as long as breaker points in the coil secondary circuit were separated by a cam. (Fig. 12-19) The condition of the battery determined the spark strength. It also limited the distance a car could travel before it weakened to the point where recharging or exchanging was needed. The "buzzer-type" system was safer than a flame heated hot-tube, but was susceptible to the vagaries associated with batteries of that day.

A water tank on the top side of the cylinder formed part of an evaporative cooling system. As the water on the jacket walls next to the

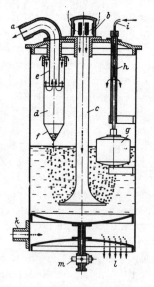

a) Suction line to engine; b) wire screen; c) air supply; d) & e) vapor extractor; f) funnel; g) float; h) guide for float valve; i) gasoline conduit; k) heated gas entrance; l) heated gas exit; m) drain cock.

Fig. 12-18　Benz surface carburetor with float control, 1886. (Sass, *Geschichte . . .*)

combustion chamber turned to steam, the bubbles rose into the tank. The level in the tank provided enough hydraulic "head" to keep sufficient water in the cylinder jacket, but frequent replenishment of the tank was a necessity. One Benz customer reported on this after a long distance tour of 583 miles in 1894. The trip required the addition of 1,500 liters of coolant. (Total gasoline consumption was 140 liters or at a rate of about 15.7 miles per U.S. gallon.)[24] A variation on his system became known as "hopper cooling" in the United States and was used very satisfactorily on thousands of small stationary engines.

The motion to actuate a slide intake and an exhaust poppet valve came from a single, half-speed cam. The intake slider moved by eccentric action from a rod free to swivel about a pin projecting from the end face of the conventional radial exhaust cam.

A few words about the vehicle powertrain are appropriate. A flat belt was driven from a pulley on the camshaft. The belt ran forward over another pulley forming half the housing of and driving a differential gear assembly. The other housing half acted as an idler pulley onto which the belt was slid when the operator wanted to disengage the engine from the rear wheels. The output shafts of the transversely mounted differential each had a sprocket on their outer ends to chain drive independently turning rear wheels.

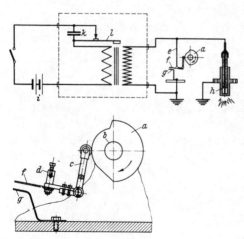

a) Control surface of cam; b) camshaft; c) angle lever with terminal contact d); e) secondary circuit; f) & g) leaf spring contacts; h) spark plug; i) battery; k) condenser; l) vibrator arm.

The condenser k) and the coil with the vibrator arm were contained in a portable box. The circuit breaker f-g) was in the secondary circuit. Afterwards, Benz put the breaker in the primary circuit to reduce battery drain.

Fig. 12-19   Ignition system for the Benz automobile engine of 1886. (Sass, *Geschichte . . .*)

Benz began advertising his three wheeled automobile in 1888 (Fig. 12-20, Plate), but the results were dismally poor. Even though several exhibits and magazine articles gave the car good publicity, not a single sale was made in Germany.[25] Again it was the French who became the first customers.

In 1893 Benz introduced the four wheel "Viktoria" model using his patented knuckle steering system[26] and a larger three horsepower engine. A suction-actuated poppet valve and a spray-type carburetor were added, with mixture and timing adjustments made handy to the driver. Journal bearing lubrication on the exposed crankshaft came from oil and grease cups. The belt drive was retained, but a "hill climbing" ratio was provided by adding another pulley onto the countershaft. Several hundred Viktorias were built in the 1890s.

Engine speeds increased to 450-500 rpm on the lightweight "Velo" of 1894, the most popular of the Benz line. Engine and transmission improvements came fast, and by 1895 the first Benz buses entered service. The most powerful engine built before 1900 was the horizontally opposed, twin cylinder "Kontra" appearing in 1897. (Fig. 12-21, Plate) Used until about 1902, the output was first five, then nine and finally fourteen horsepower.[27] The earliest version had a bore and stroke of 100 mm by 110 mm with a total displacement of 1.72 liters. Maximum engine speed was 900 rpm. The last of the series was "oversquare" at 135 mm bore by 130 mm stroke, a radical departure at the time, and anticipating modern practice for compact engines.

Karl Benz encountered difficulties similar to Daimler's as a result of less farsighted business partners. The men who had backed Benz in the launching of his horizontal, two-stroke engine became increasingly concerned about a profit drain from this line into what appeared to them to be a poor risk on the automobile. Finally, in 1899, new backers were found who bought out the old, and the company was incorporated as "Benz & Cie., Rheinische Gasmotoren-Fabrik AG".

Automobile sales continued upward for two more years, and new products, including gas producers, enhanced the stationary engine line. A disastrous slide in orders began with the introduction of the Mercedes racing car by Daimler-Motoren-Gesellschaft in 1901. The crisis was eventually weathered by the addition of the first Benz cars designed from the wheels up as racers. Until this time Benz personally had steadfastly refrained from active racing participation by producing basically touring cars. However, many Benz cars were raced before 1901 and earned a good reputation for reliability, if not for outright speed. The

first race in the United States on November 28, 1895, ended with only
the winning Duryea and a Benz crossing the finish line. A fifty-two mile
course between Milwaukee and Chicago required ten hours and twenty-
three minutes for the winner with the second car coming in twenty-four
minutes later. In an earlier heat on November 11 of ninety-two miles
the Benz won at an average speed of about 10 mph. A Duryea, the only
other entrant, went into a ditch and failed to finish.

A recognition of the airplane as a potential military weapon fostered
rapid developments in high output engines, and with the new race car
experience, Benz & Cie. became a major supplier of aircraft engines
in World War I. The rivalry between Daimler and Benz on the race
courses is legend, but competition ended when these two pioneering
companies consolidated in 1926. The heritage left by Benz, Daimler
and Maybach has been proudly upheld, although to most the name of
a car distributor's daughter — Mercedes — is better known.

Siegfried Marcus

Any list of gasoline engine pioneers should include Siegfried Marcus
(1831-1898), a prolific Viennese inventor. Although better known for
his automobile (Fig. 12-22, Plate) because of still-persistent Austrian
partisans, Marcus was nevertheless a man of numerous interests. Early
experiments with telegraphy and electricity led him into magneto ignition for gas and gasoline engines. His concurrent carburetor developments were known to Deutz as these had been brought to Otto and
Langen's attention by Reuleaux. The Deutz inventory of June 30, 1875
lists "a gas appliance from Vienna.[28]

The Marcus automobile was a subject of some concern during the
Otto patent trials because it was purported to have run as early as 1875
with a four-stroke engine. However, the date, based on evidence
researched by the Vienna Technical Museum (Technisches Museum für
Industrie und Gewerbe in Wien) where the car is on display, is "about
1888". Though much later than Otto's competition had hoped (in vain)
the construction is nevertheless impressive. The four-stroke engine has
a low-tension magneto ignition system and a wick-type carburetor, both
features predating Daimler and Benz.

Electric Ignition 1885-1900

Technology from the infant field of electrical engineering was
quickly applied to ignition systems on I-C engines. The basic idea of
electric ignition was not new, for Barsanti, Lenoir and Robson had

made engines run using a spark igniter. Lenoir even reached the stage of selling such a system, albeit often to his customer's chagrin. Twenty years later spark ignition advocates could take advantage of the rapidly broadening knowledge of electricity and its application to everyday practical uses. By the mid-1880s men on both sides of the Atlantic had already demonstrated that electric ignition held promise. By 1900 spark igniters were making obsolete the popular hot-tube. Yet, as late as 1896 Dugald Clerk wrote:[29]

> Electric methods of ignition are objectionable whether used in gas or oil engines; so objectionable, indeed, that no gas engine at present manufactured in Britain uses an electric igniter. ... [I]t has always been the author's opinion that any engine with an electric igniting device, even if good in other respects, would not attain extended use in Britain.

He went on to add that "curiously enough" these objections did not sufficiently bother the "Continental public" or the "American public." Two electrical systems offered promise: the "jump spark" with separated, fixed electrodes (as used by Benz) and the "make and break" having momentarily contacting electrodes. Either a battery or low voltage magneto supplied the electrical energy.

The jump spark system (to use the terminology of the day) usually employed a timed contact breaker in the circuit. Benz' first system located a breaker in the secondary circuit of the induction coil, but in order to reduce battery drain, it was moved into the primary so that current only flowed when the breaker was closed. In the original placement there was the battery drain both when the points were open with sparking across the plug gap and when the points were closed to complete another circuit in the secondary. All of the earlier jump spark systems had a vibrator or trembler in the coil primary circuit. With the circuits closed, sparks jumped the plug gap at the same rate as the opening of the vibrator contacts. Although mechanically simple, the jump spark method was highly sensitive to dampness and carboning of spark plug electrodes. Frequent plug cleaning was a necessity.

The Simplex Igniter — 1884

One engine with a jump spark managed to avoid the spark plug fouling problem. The "Simplex," a French four-stroke gas engine first produced in 1884, did this by placing the plug in an antechamber sealed off from the cylinder except when the piston was near top center of the compression stroke. At that time the continuously sparking plug in the firing chamber was connected to the combustion chamber by a port in a slide-valve. (Fig. 12-23) Just before the slider port indexed the two chambers, a small vent hole leading from the firing chamber to the outside opened momentarily (about 1/150 of a second). A portion of the compressed cylinder charge then blew out enough residual exhaust gas left from the previous cycle to ensure positive ignition on the next. Because of the reduced heat load on the slide-valve as compared to the contemporary Otto gas flame ignition, the designer said that "with ordinary attention it will work for more than a year without any repairs."[30]

It was the Simplex engine, designed by Edouard Delamare-Deboutteville (1856-1901) and Léon Malandin, which helped to break the Otto four-stroke patent in France. Otto brought infringement proceedings against the makers after its introduction, but the French court's decision finally went against Otto in 1888. (The Lenoir four-stroke engine had already been declared not to infringe in 1885.)

The Simplex engine went on to enjoy an excellent reputation for reliability and performance in both Europe and England. (Fig. 12-24, Plate) Built by Matter et Cie. of Rouen and John Cockerill of Seraing, Belgium, it was the first French engine to burn producer gas and then blast furnace gas. By 1900 a single cylinder of 1,300 mm bore and 1,400 mm stroke developed 600 bhp at 90 rpm on blast furnace gas.[31]

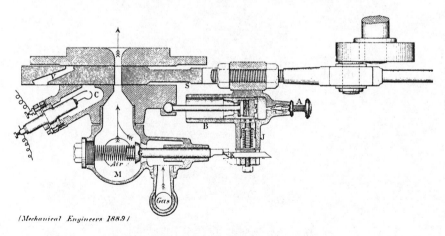

[Mechanical Engineers 1889]

Fig. 12-23   Remote-located spark plug and air governor, Simplex gas engine, 1889. (*Proc., Inst. Mech. Engrs.*, 1889)

247

Make and Break Ignition

Reliability improved with the "make and break" system through its reduced sensitivity to misfiring from poor insulation. The system was also readily adaptable to the low tension magnetos making their appearance in the late 1880s. (Fig. 12-25) A fixed and a movable electrode combining both breaker and igniter functions were located directly in the combustion chamber. The electrodes came together by a "hammer" action from swiveling one electrode against the other (Fig. 12-26) or by

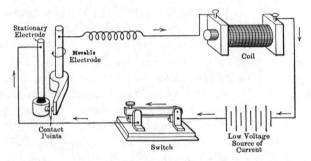

Fig. 12-25 Schematic diagram of low-tension "make and break" ignition system. (Hirshfeld, *Gas Engines for the Farm,* 1914)

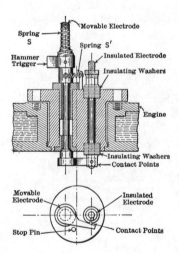

Fig. 12-26 Typical construction of a "make and break" igniter block as installed in an engine. (Hirshfeld, *Gas Engines for the Farm,* 1914)

248

a "wiper" movement from a rotating electrode rubbing over a spring leaf, fixed electrode. Numerous variations on the above were built, but they fell into either the hammer or wiper categories.

The wiper method claimed the advantage of less impact loading plus a self-cleaning action at the contacts. Both had the problems of seals and lubrication where the movable electrode passed through the cylinder wall or head into the combustion chamber.

The complete circuit consisted of the battery, a disconnect switch, the insulated fixed electrode, the grounded movable electrode, a reactance or "sparking" coil, and then back to the battery. The reactance coil was simpler than an induction coil which required two sets of windings, as only one set of windings went around the iron core.

Operation of a make and break system was as its name implied. just prior to ignition the circuit was closed ("made") to allow a current flow. This was by the hammer or wiper making contact through either cam or eccentric action. When the electrodes were quickly separated again, under the snap action of a spring in the case of the hammer, a reactance-generated spark arced across the developing gap to ignite the charge.

Daniel S. Regan of San Francisco is credited with building the earliest make and break system in the United States. His gas engine patent of 1885[32] showing such a method became the genesis of a sizeable I-C engine industry in the San Francisco Bay Area by 1900. Regan utilized piston motion to time the breaking of the circuit; a rod or "finger" projected from the piston crown to open the contacts at top center by pushing one electrode away from the other. The contacts then closed and remained so until the piston came up again. Since the engine worked on the four-stroke cycle, a spark was also generated and wasted" at the end of the exhaust stroke. Regan did not yet have the make and break where the contacts were together for only a small portion of the total cycle, but the effect was the same.

A further improvement, patented by Regan in 1889[33] changed the mechanism so that the piston projection was the grounded (and obviously movable) electrode. At top center it struck a leaf spring set in an insulated plug in the cylinder head. Except for still wasting a spark on every other revolution, a true make and break was achieved. This patent formed the basis of a tangled infringement/assignment suit in San Francisco between Regan, his Regan Vapor Engine Co., and Mora M. Barrett, a former partner and principal in the Pacific Gas Engine Co., *(47 Fed Rep. 511)*. Regan won on appeal in 1892 *(49 Fed.*

Rep. 68), but it was the Pacific Gas Engine Co. which had the greater commercial success. Barrett added his own ignition ideas, incorporating them in the "Pacific" and "Union" gas and gasoline engines. One of the first changes was a redesign of the valve cams plus an interrupter to allow the grounded piston electrode to generate a spark only at the end of the compression stroke.[34] A Pacific seven horsepower gasoline engine powered a freight boat on San Francisco Bay as early as 1888, and in 1890 a fifteen horsepower engine was installed in a stern wheeler running on the Eel River north of San Francisco.[35] These engines had a form of surface carburetor, and a battery was the source of electrical energy. The Pacific became the Union Gas Engine Co. after 1890 (and finally the Union Diesel Engine Co.). By 1893 the company was selling twenty-five horsepower, two-cylinder V-type and inline marine engines.[36]

In the late 1880s John Charter adopted a make and break ignition on his two-stroke gas and gasoline engines. His patent of 1887 describes a cam-operated rocker lever lifting one electrode away from the other.[37] The point of contact was in an inlet port located in the upper cylinder wall.

The Charter Gas Engine Co. of Sterling, Illinois, built gas, gasoline and kerosene engines till well after 1900. John Charter's son, James, also designed a gasoline engine, the "Caldwell-Charter", that was built in Chicago by H.W. Caldwell and Son. In 1893 James Charter and his project moved to Fairbanks-Morse at Beloit, Wisconsin, putting that company in the internal-combustion engine business. The engines introduced by Fairbanks-Morse the same year were all of four-stroke design.

Nicolaus Otto, meanwhile, had developed his low tension magneto (Fig. 9-13). It mounted directly under the end of the camshaft where a cam finger tripped a spring loaded lever not only to rotate the magneto shaft through part of a revolution (enough to generate the momentary voltage), but also to snap a hammer contact away from a fixed, insulated contact point in the cylinder. As the contacts separated, the magneto coil developed the required high voltage reactance or "back emf" to cause a spark to jump the gap. (Fig. 12-27)

A nephew of Eugen Langen, working as a research engineer at Deutz, was granted a German patent in 1887[38], describing the basic elements of a "high tension" magneto ignition system. Paul A. N. Winand's main claim is so broad it bears quoting:[39]

In a magneto and electric generator ignition apparatus, the arrangement of a second secondary winding on the armature, the field magnet, or both, in which at the interruption of the primary current a secondary current of high voltage, the ignition voltage, becomes induced.

Through lack of interest, Deutz allowed the Winand patent to lapse in 1890 by choosing not to pay the annual tax. They thought that with the low voltage magneto and the hot-tube igniter there would be little need to perfect a third ignition system.[40] (Gottlob Honold, a Robert Bosch engineer, later saw the merit of Winand's original thinking and added his own innovations. The resulting magneto introduced in 1902 by Bosch became world famous as the heart of automotive and aircraft ignition systems.)

Discouraged by the turn of events at Deutz, Winand left in 1888 and went to work for Schleicher, Schumm at Philadelphia. The proof of his activity while there can be seen in the five U.S. patents granted to him for engine improvements. One of the most important of his American projects was the design work on gasoline engines for U.S. Navy submarines. (After abandoning steam engines in submarines, the Navy selected only Otto Gas Engine Co. power.[41]) Winand went to a Deutz branch in Russia in 1898 and finally returned to the main plant in 1902. He was involved with the design of submarine engines and torpedoes for the German Navy before his death in 1912.

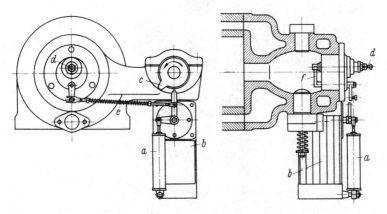

Fig. 12-27 "Make and break" ignition system, Deutz gasoline engine of 1885. (Sass, *Geschichte* . . .)

The Simplex Carburetor — 1884

Since every engine builder had his own idea as to the best way of vaporizing gasoline, there were literally dozens of carburetors and atomizing designs used before 1900. Delamare-Deboutteville was no exception with his unique variation of a surface carburetor for the gasoline-fueled version of the Simplex engine. It was used only on engines of up to six horsepower.

The Simplex carburetor (Fig. 12-28) dripped gasoline from an overhead canister down a cylinder containing a spiraling hair brush. Surrounding the brush-filled cylinder was a jacket through which circulated hot water from the engine. A portion of the incoming water (at about 50°C)[42] was diverted to enter the top of the brush-filled cylinder along with the gasoline. The water and gasoline mixture discharged into a lower tank where the almost totally vaporized gasoline separated from the water and passed to an air mixing valve. The gasoline was of around 0.65-0.70 specific gravity.[43] The water level in the lower tank was main-

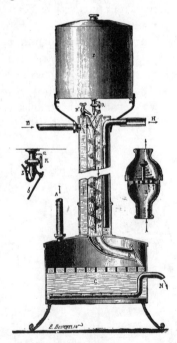

Fig. 12-28   Simplex gasoline and hot water carburetor for small
engines. (Robinson, *Gas and Petroleum Engines*,
1890)

tained by an overflow pipe drawing the water from the base of the tank. A check valve in the exiting vapor line prevented an engine backfire from causing an explosion in the carburetor itself. The designer claimed that an advantage of his vaporization method was the complete absence of engine deposits resulting from residue in the fuel since these were carried out with the overflow water.

While surface and spray carburetor development has been emphasized, another method tried with modest success on a few early German gasoline engines should at least be mentioned. This involved a small plunger pump to spray fuel under pressure from an orifice into the air stream of the intake pipe. The popular gasoline engines of Johannes Spiel, built beginning in 1884 by Halleschen Maschinenfabrik, Halle, used such a "pressure carburetor" for about ten years.[44] John Charter in the U.S. also employed a cam actuated "injector pump" and rocker lever. The pump action could be stopped when governed speed was exceeded; the force from a flyball governor lifted a roller cam follower on the lever away from the lobe.

Engine Speed Controls

Of equal importance with good ignition and fuel delivery is the ability, in many engine installations, to maintain a relatively constant speed regardless of the load imposed. The most demanding application of this requirement is the generation of electric power where speed regulation, i.e., deviation from the specified, may be as little as one or two percent full-load to no-load. If the engine should be left unattended there is an additional safety consideration for an overspeed control to prevent a "runaway". (Those who have worked with diesels and their fuel systems know the value of guarding against this happening!) The first gas engines with a slide-valve for intake and ignition probably would not have had a runaway tendency because of severe air port restrictions which caused high pumping losses and marginal breathing characteristics (volumetric efficiency). Also restricting engine speed was the inability of the gas flame ignition system to keep up with any significant increase beyond the normal operating range.

Since essentially all of the early gas engines were stationary prime movers for driving machinery or simple electric generators there was a specific need for adequate speed control. But governing of gas engines presented a problem not found with steam. It was first thought that the gas valve could be governor modulated to control the energy portion of the combustible mixture as did the steam engine with its flyball

253

governor to regulate the supply of "power" into the cylinder. The Lenoir and Hugon engines did just this and pointed out the difficulty of borrowing the concept. By varying solely the fuel supply already adjusted to provide a lean mixture for minimum consumption, any further reduction quickly changed the mixture to exceed a lean burn limit. The charge then failed to ignite, with the gas in that charge being wasted. Governing was accomplished, but at a price. Throttling the air and fuel after they had combined to form a burnable mixture was not attempted for many years. (Hindsight causes us to wonder why it took so long to adopt this logical solution, but a partiality to the slide-valve for intake, and for many years ignition, precluded. and probably inhibited thinking about such a desirable change.

An alternative to the gas waste at or above governed speed was to have the governor simply cut off the gas supply for however many revolutions were needed to allow engine speed to drop. This was descriptively referred to as "hit and miss" governing. The massive flywheels smoothed out the impulse fluctuations sufficiently for most applications, but electric lighting generators continued to be a problem. Cyclic variation control here was already marginal because of the relatively long interval between power strokes on the slow turning, single cylinder engines. Magnifying this was the governed speed cut out immediately followed by a more powerful impulse on the first firing after re-application of the gas. (Clerk attributed the better combustion after a gas shutoff to a cleaning out of residual exhaust during the overspeed cycles when air only was inducted.)

The most common methods adopted to shut off the gas for speed control were to use either the force from a centrifugal governor or the inertia of the operating mechanism itself to disconnect the gas valve from its actuator. Typical of the flyball governor control was that for Deutz engines beginning on the first production models of 1877. (Fig. 12-29, Plate) The actuating cam for the gas valve was simply slid axially along its shaft and away from the follower lever. In a few other engines the shifting occurred in several stages to permit some modulation of the gas supply before total cutoff.

One form of an inertia or pendulum governor consisted of a weight hanging downward from a rod pivotally mounted on a pin projecting from the slide-valve. A lightweight, thin finger, attached to the pendulum rod and positioned parallel to the slider, acted directly upon the gas valve stem. The inertia of the pendulum mass was adjusted so that below governed speed the pendulum and the slider acted as a unit to let the finger open the gas valve. Above the governed speed the inertia of the pendulum caused it to lag, or relative to the slider, remain momentarily stationary. This imparted a rotating motion to the pendulum and finger so that the latter dropped away from the gas valve stem and shut off the gas supply. When the engine speed lowered, the finger repositioned itself on the stem end to reopen the gas valve at the next inward slider movement.

The Simplex engine, full of unique but practical features, was no exception when it came to speed control. On the smaller models an air governor" maintained the fixed speed. (Fig. 12-23) An air pump, whose piston was attached to the stationary slide-valve cover, reciprocated in a cylinder mounted on the slider. As the cylinder moved back and forth over the piston, air was sucked in and out past a bleed port sized by an adjustable needle valve. At a right angle to the air cylinder was a spring-loaded plunger acting against the air cylinder pressure. A knife-ended rod, retained in the outer end of the plunger was positioned to push axially against a groove in one end of the gas valve stem. In operation, the needle valve was set so that below governed speed the air bleed rate kept the pump cylinder pressure below that required to lift the plunger off its seat. The sharp-ended rod thus opened the gas valve upon its making contact with the stem toward the end of the slider travel. If speed increased above the desired maximum, the rate of pressure buildup in the cylinder was more than the bleed port could accommodate, causing the spring-loaded plunger to move outward and in turn to thrust the rod away from the gas valve stem.

Larger Simplex engines employed a pendulum-type governor whose weight pivoted about a *stationary* pin. (Fig. 12-30) The period of the pendulum was accurately set by moving a balance weight on a rod to conform to the desired horizontal velocity of the ignition and intake valve slider. The rod portion below the weight was notched to catch a pawl-like finger whose opposite end made contact with the gas valve stem toward the end of the slider travel. Pushed by the pawl, the pendulum traveled through approximately a forty-five degree arc from the vertical position. The finger pivoted about its middle from a pin on the slider and was acted upon by a torsion spring. This served to keep the pawl end in the notch of the pendulum rod. Below governed speed the fall of the pendulum could keep up with the speed of the gas valve actuating finger. If speed increased beyond that desired, the pawl velocity exceeded that of the notch and pulled away from it. This allowed the torsion spring to rotate the finger slightly so that the end normally

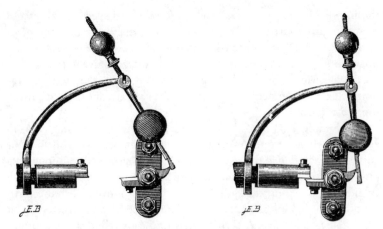

Fig. 12-30 Pendulum-type inertia governor as used on large
Simplex engines. (Robinson, *Gas and Petroleum
Engines,* 1890)

making contact with the gas valve now missed it entirely and thus prevented gas from entering the combustion chamber. When engine speed dropped, the pendulum notch once again captured the pawl and in turn repositioned the opposite end to act on the gas valve.

Other methods of controlling engine speed included either holding open the exhaust valve or keeping it closed. Quite popular in the United States, particularly for small, inexpensive gasoline engines, was another "hit and miss" governor whereby the electric ignition was cut off above governed speed. When combined with the "make and break" ignition that was simple to interrupt, the price of the initial system outweighed the minimal cost of the inexpensive, wasted fuel.

Compound Gas Engines

It soon became an accepted fact that the efficiency of an I-C engine was a direct function of its gas expansion ratio. But how to increase the expansion within the limits imposed by material and fuel technology of the late nineteenth century? Atkinson had shown one way through mechanical alteration of stroke lengths. The larger triple and even quadruple expansion steam engines beckoned another and more enticing alternative. Thus for a time, compounding, i.e., additional expansion taking place in a second cylinder, appeared feasible. Several men actively experimented with such engines including Daimler (1879),

Clerk (1882), Crossley (1888) and Butler (1890), but all ultimately faced the same realization that steam had more desirable thermodynamic properties for compounding than did the gas engine. What made it attractive at all was a late burning characteristic of those gaseous fuels having a lower heat value. A pressure as high as forty to sixty psi remained in the cylinder at the time the exhaust valve opened.[45] Countering this advantage, however, in compound engines heat transfer to the water jackets from the additional connecting passages and cylinder reduced the potential for further energy extraction by as much as forty percent.[46] Furthermore, the increased complexity and cost, balanced against the availability of relatively cheap fuel, made it uneconomical to try to harness part of that thirty percent energy waste going out the exhaust pipe.

Daimler, while still at Deutz, tried compounding an Otto engine. His engine exhausted alternately from two, high pressure cylinders into a third, low pressure cylinder. (Chapter 9) Dugald Clerk made a two-stroke engine having a double-acting pumping cylinder. One end of the cylinder was for the usual air pumping and the other for expanding the exhaust from the main power cylinder.[47] Crossley modified its two-cylinder, four-stroke engine by making the cylinders double-acting and exhausting alternately into the inner (crankshaft) end of one from the outer end of the other. For his second attempt (1890) Butler publicly demonstrated in London a three cylinder four-stroke engine. Two outer cylinders fed an inner one, similar to Daimler. Butler claimed that compounding added thirty percent more power than when the inner piston was disconnected.

The Burt Acme-Compound engine (somewhat of a misnomer) had a fuel consumption comparing favorably with conventional four-stroke engines.[48] Two horizontal and unequal size cylinders were directly connected by a cross port at their head area. The piston in the smaller cylinder drove a crankshaft that was geared to, and turned at, half the speed of the main crankshaft driven by the larger piston. Exhaust ports were located about seventy percent down the stroke of the smaller cylinder. By the action and timing of the added, slower moving piston, a greater expansion to intake ratio was achieved. The engine had no cams; intake was through a suction operated valve, and a hot-tube igniter, uncovered by the smaller piston (which slightly led the larger at that point), set off the charge. A test of a twelve nominal horsepower engine in 1892 gave a fuel consumption of 19.3 cu ft per bhp hr. The smaller cylinder had a bore and stroke of ten inches by eleven inches and the larger eleven and a half inches by twenty inches. The engine produced thirteen bhp at 160 rpm. Burt and Co., Glasgow, also built a six horse-power model.

Hamilton's Pressure Scavenging

John Henry Hamilton (1858-1932) believed yet another way to improve engine performance was by completely scavenging the residual exhaust. His correct conclusion came from experiences while working as a design engineer under Arthur Rollason on the Beck six-stroke engine. (Chapter 11) Four years later, in 1890, Hamilton applied for a patent on a more conventional engine which accomplished just that.[49] He and Rollason entered into a partnership the same year with the five Wells brothers at Sandiacre, Nottingham, to build a four-stroke engine incorporating his new pressure scavenging concept.[50] (With the expiration of the Otto patent, 1890 was an exciting year for many engine builders.)

The "Premier" engine, introduced not long after by "Wells Bros., Engineers," had a differential (stepped) piston whose larger diameter pumped air from its annular chamber into the combustion chamber after the exhaust valve opened. Essentially all of the residual gas was flushed out by the blow down from the pumping chamber. When the piston started outward on the intake stroke, a gas valve opened to allow the gas to mix with the air being drawn into the cylinder. The design was changed several years later to a double piston arrangement where a larger diameter pumping piston acted as a crosshead for the smaller. A fixed rod tied the two pistons together. Scavenge and combustion air entered the space between the two pistons and the combustion chamber on the piston's outstroke via a flap valve in the engine base. Gas admitted by the gas valve at the power cylinder inlet mixed with the air being drawn into the cylinder the same as with the stepped-piston design. A cam-actuated, poppet intake valve to admit air from the pumping chamber was located vertically on top of the horizontal cylinder.

The volume of the pumping chamber was sized to limit the buildup of scavenge air pressure to about five psi. On the Premier engines having only one combustion chamber the pumping piston went through a wasted cycle, that is, on the compression and power strokes the scavenge chamber air was compressed and then expanded again. About 1895, with the demand for increased power, another combustion cylinder axial with the construction just described utilized this wasted pumping cycle. These "tandem" engines were built in sizes up to 200 horsepower. (Fig. 12-31, Plate)

Fig. 12-2   Wilhelm Maybach (1846-1929). (MTU, Friedrichshafen)

Fig. 12-1   Gottlieb Daimler (1834-1900). (Daimler-Benz Museum)

Fig. 12-4 Daimler 1883 gasoline engine with hot-tube igniter and grooved face cam. (Daimler-Benz Museum)

Fig. 12-6   Daimler and Maybach Standuhr (Vertical Clock)
gasoline engine for first automobile, 1886. 1.1 Hp at
650 rpm; 70mm by 120mm bore and stroke
(Daimler-Benz Museum)

Fig. 12-7 Original print of 1886 model *Standuhr* engine showing
cylinder head with cast passages. (Daimler-Benz
Museum)

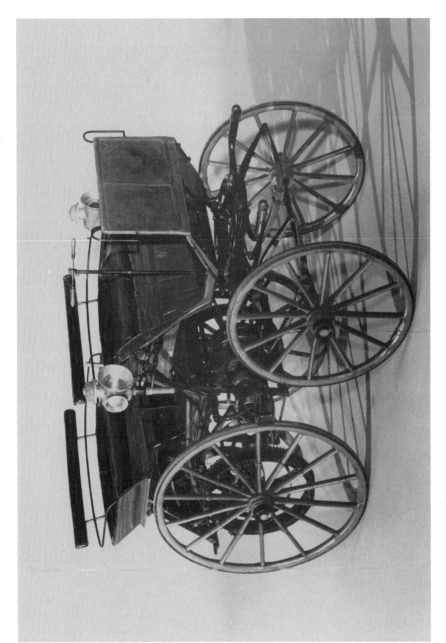

Fig. 12-10   First Daimler automobile with chassis modified from a horse-drawn carriage, 1886. (Daimler-Benz Museum)

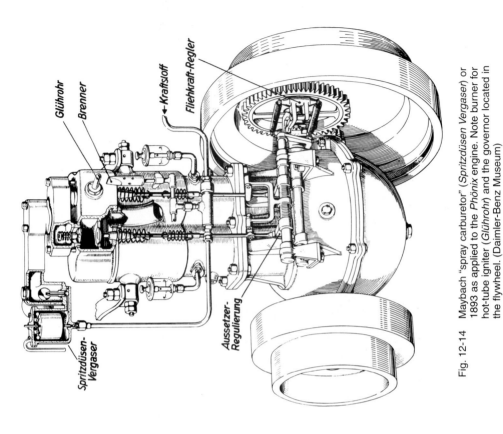

Glührohr

Brenner

←Kraftstoff

Fliehkraft-Regler

Spritzdüsen-Vergaser

Aussetzer-Regulierung

Fig. 12-14   Maybach "spray carburetor" (*Spritzdüsen Vergaser*) or 1893 as applied to the *Phönix* engine. Note burner for hot-tube igniter (*Glührohr*) and the governor located in the flywheel. (Daimler-Benz Museum)

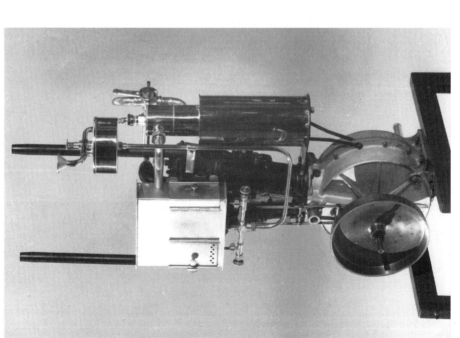

Fig. 12-11   Daimler "Twin-Vee" engine, 1889, with hot-tube ignition and surface carburetor. 1.5 Hp at 600 rpm; 60mm by 100mm bore and stroke; 0.565 liters displacement.

Fig. 12-12 Maybach-designed chassis of the second Daimler auto, 1889. The *Stahlrad* (Wire Wheel) model. (Daimler-Benz Museum)

Fig. 12-13   Daimler-Maybach four cylinder in-line engine for
stationery and marine application, 1890. Introduced
with 5 hp at 620 rpm; 80mm by 120mm bore and
stroke. (Daimler-Benz Museum)

Fig. 12-15   Karl Benz (1844-1929). (Daimler-Benz Museum)

Fig. 12-16   First Benz automobile engine, 1886. 0.67 Hp at 250 rpm.
(Daimler-Benz Museum)

Fig. 12-17   First Benz automobile, 1886. (Daimler-Benz Museum)

Fig. 12-20   Cover page of first Benz auto catalog, 1888.
(Daimler-Benz Museum)

81312

Fig. 12-21   Benz flat, opposed-piston *Kontra* engine, 1897.
Introduced with 5 hp at 900 rpm and 100mm bore by
110mm stroke; 1.7 liters displacement. (Daimler-Benz
Museum)

Fig. 12-22   Siegfried Marcus automobile, 1888, in the collection of the Vienna
Technical Museum. (Technisches Museum für Industrie and Gewerbe)

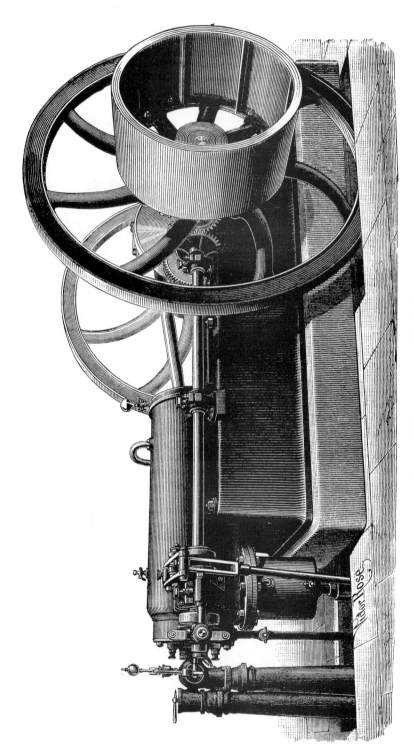

Fig. 12-24   Simplex 100 hp gas engine, 1889, the largest engine of its day. 22.6 in. bore by 37.4 in. stroke. 100 bhp at 107 rpm. (Robinson, *Gas and Petroleum Engines*, 1890)

Fig. 12-29   Governor control, Deutz "A" Model engine, 1877. Cam
is shifted away from gas valve actuating linkage. Note
manual gas valve (located on top of governor valve) to
regulate full power mixture. From the collection in the
Henry Ford Museum. (Author photo)

Fig. 12-31   Wells Brothers (Premier) tandem, scavenging engine.
60 Bhp at 160 rpm; 12 in. bore by 18 in. stroke.
(Robinson, *Gas and Petroleum Engines,* 1890)

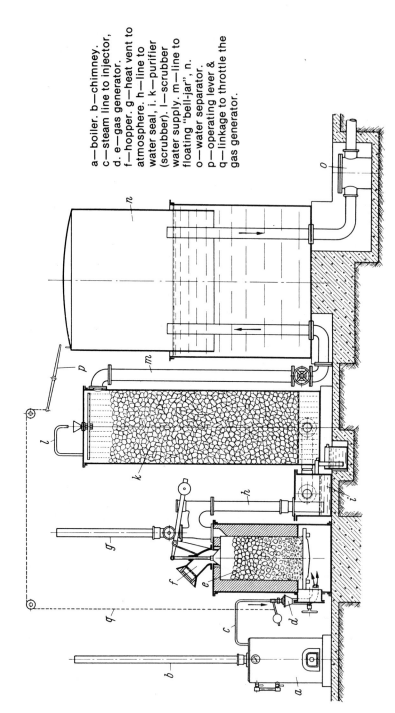

a—boiler. b—chimney.
c—steam line to injector,
d. e—gas generator.
f—hopper. g—heat vent to
atmosphere. h—line to
water seal. i. k—purifier
(scrubber). l—scrubber
water supply. m—line to
floating "bell-jar", n.
o—water separator.
p—operating lever &
q—linkage to throttle the
gas generator.

Fig. 12-32   Dowson coal-gas producer, 1887, as made under
license by Gasmotoren-Fabrik Deutz. (Sass,
Geschichte . . .)

A differential piston configuration similar to the first Premier, was substituted for the double pump and power piston assembly, and output was increased to 650 indicated horsepower by about 1900. Two years later the concept was further developed when double tandem units burning blast furnace gas produced 2,000 indicated horsepower at ninety rpm. The cylinders had a thirty-eight inch bore and a forty-eight inch stroke. The reliability of these engines was enviable. Specifications for one installation required that they be stopped for less than ten hours once every two weeks. The engines had no trouble meeting this stipulation, with some going from four to six weeks without a stop.

A test on a sixty bhp Wells tandem engine in 1895 showed a brake thermal efficiency of almost twenty percent.[51] In 1908, a modified 150 horsepower Premier engine reached a forty percent thermal efficiency.[52] (One change was a reduction in cylinder diameter from twenty to sixteen inches.) The efficiency was not specified as brake or indicated efficiency, but even if it were the latter the result is still remarkable. It must be remembered, however, that the scavenging itself improved fuel consumption by probably no more than five percent. Most of the gain in overall efficiency came as a result of higher compression ratios, an increase made possible to a great degree by removing the residual exhaust which could cause premature ignition and consequent knocking.[53]

The Hamilton system became the dominant method of exhaust scavenging, particularly in Britain. It was so successful that Atkinson's scavenging by a long, tuned exhaust pipe was abandoned by Crossley in favor of Hamilton's way. When Wells Bros. became the Premier Gas Engine Co., Ltd. in 1898 Hamilton was chief engineer. The following year he succeeded Rollason as managing director. One of his contributions while chief engineer was the direct coupling (rather than through belts) of the large, slow speed gas engines to A-C generators.

Up to then it was considered that the repeated shock loading from the relatively infrequent firings would cause insulation failures in the generator. Hamilton was able to disprove this by the mid-1890s. His continued creativity kept Premier in the forefront of the British stationary engine industry for many years. In 1936, six years after Hamilton retired at the age of seventy-two, Premier was absorbed into Crossley Bros. Ltd. Premier had been bought by Crossley in 1919 and run as a separate company.

Bánki High Compression Engine — 1894

Professor Donát Bánki (1859-1922) of the Budapest Technical University has received little recognition for his unique high compression, four-stroke gasoline engines built by Ganz & Co. in Budapest. They were among the most advanced of the pre-1900 era. Beginning in 1894 Ganz sold Bánki gasoline and then oil and gas-fueled engines in sizes of up to 50 hp. With compression ratios of about 6.5:1 they produced brake thermal efficiencies of twenty-eight percent!

Bánki and his collaborator Jánossal Csonka circumvented the fuel-imposed limitations on compression ratio by spraying water into the intake air upstream of the valve. The water was usually introduced upstream of the fuel (gasoline, oil or gas). As the charge temperature rose during compression, the inducted water vaporized to cool the charge enough to allow the high compression ratio.

A hand adjusted, vertical needle valve for each liquid throttled the fuel and water sucked into the intake passage. The needles' conical tips extended into passages in the intake housing casting that were filled with fuel and water. Float valves maintained fixed liquid levels. A drilled hole in each needle connected the tip with a horizontal orifice opening into the center of the air passage.

A hot-tube igniter fired the charge in an untimed manner. Waste heat from the torch "lamp" for the hot tube warmed the intake port in order to improve fuel and water vaporization during starting and light load operation.

Speed regulation was by a "leaf spring" governor set in the driven gear of the eccentric opening the exhaust valve. Governor linkage overrode the exhaust valve mechanism at maximum speed and held open the valve. This reduced intake air vacuum and in turn the fuel and water sucked from the needle orifices.

Independent data on Bánki *benzin* engines in 1899 confirm the efficiency and the quantity of water vaporized. Both engines had a bore and stroke of 250 x 400 mm:[54]

	Meyer	Jonas
Speed, rpm	211	209
Brake horsepower	25.2	26.4
Brake sp. fuel consumption, g/bhp hr	242	221
Brake sp. water consumption, kg/bhp hr	18.4	13.6
Water:fuel ratio	5.3	4.8
Brake thermal eff., %	25.3	28.0

Adding the charge cooling water made combustion noise sound normal at peak cylinder pressures of up to 40 atm, but "there were violent explosions" when it was shut off. The high water consumption undoubtedly deterred a wider acceptance of the engine.

Gas Producers: 1880-1900

The inevitable demand for larger and larger gas engines focused attention on new coal gasification processes for power fuel. Ordinary town or illuminating gas of the early 1880s was too expensive a fuel for gas engines larger than fifteen to twenty horsepower. It still cost less to run a higher horsepower steam engine burning cheap coal in its boiler than a comparable size gas engine on the gas made from higher grade coal for lighting. Regardless of the other advantages enjoyed by gas power, the large steam engine remained a fierce competitor until this fuel picture was altered.

Fortunately, a gas engine could tolerate a variety of gaseous fuels. It liked the hydrogen rich town-gas that burned with the desirable yellow flame for lighting,* but it ran equally well (with adjustments) on more carbon based fuels giving off a blue flame. The capability promoted an increasing effort in the 1880s to develop commercial processes to manufacture such gases.

An unexpected incentive helped this search along. With the advent of the incandescent electric light, the gas lighting industry appeared doomed to a quick death, but an Austrian chemist, Baron Carl Auer von Welsbach (1858-1929), saved it with his gas mantle. This little piece of chemical-soaked gauze, so familiar to campers, increased light output from about three to over twenty candlepower per cubic foot of gas per hour.[55] Important to the gas power user, the mantle was not restricted to ordinary illuminating gas, and the way opened to build more efficient, large gasification plants. Welsbach's mantle, patented in the mid-1880s came into general use about 1890. The advent of cheaper, manufactured domestic gas then allowed its use for home cooking. Instead of passing out of existence, the gas industry was given a rebirth; it also had a new product, the gas stove, to sell.

The average English town gas of 1880, made from bituminous-type coal, produced a gas having a higher heating value averaging over 600 Btu per cu ft, but at a plant efficiency of less than twenty-five percent.[56]

---

*The "illuminants" came from a small percentage of what were then called "heavy hydrocarbons." These compounds have the names "ethylene" (C_2H_4) and "butylene" (C_4H_8).

By 1900 a "Mond" gas producer extracted as much as seventy percent of the energy locked in the same or even cheaper grades of coal, giving off a gas of about 150 Btu per cu ft. This efficiency figure was for the total system, after deducting the energy required to generate the steam used in the process.[57] Dr. Ludwig Mond (1839-1909), a German chemist who became a naturalized British subject, began his experiments in 1879 and built the first full scale plant in 1893. It was practical solely for major city-size installations.

Specifically needed for the gas engine was not only an efficient producer, but one available in sizes small enough to supply economically a single engine. Joseph Emerson Dowson (1844-1940) announced his answer to these requirements in a paper read in 1881 to the British Association for the Advancement of Science.[58] The Dowson gas producer became the most widely used and copied gasifier of the late 1800s. It had an efficiency almost equaling the Mond (sixty to seventy percent), but it required anthracite coal, or at the least, high grade coke. The higher heating value of the gas, sometimes referred to as "semi-water gas," was likewise similar to that from a Mond producer (150 Btu per cu ft). Average Dowson gas included about nineteen percent hydrogen and twenty-five percent carbon monoxide. Methane and the hydrocarbon illiminants amounted to less than two percent.

Without delving too deeply into chemistry, the Dowson process went as follows. A mixture of steam and air was forced through a bed of red hot coal or coke. (Fig. 12-32, Plate) The steam (H_2O) dissociated into its two components as it passed through the incandescent carbon. The oxygen ultimately combined with the carbon to form carbon monoxide, while the hydrogen remained free. About six percent of the carbon dioxide, formed as part of the intermediate reaction, failed to reduce to CO and appeared as an end product. By using forced air, a high volume (about fifty percent) of free nitrogen was also in the gas. This was the reason for its low heat value as compared with town gas made in a closed retort.

The chemistry of the gasification had been known for some time. Sir William Siemens (1823-1883) built a gas producer as part of his steel making processes in the mid-1860s using a similar technique. However, the hot, dirty gas that his "regenerative furnace" could tolerate gave a gas engine a serious case of indigestion. Dowson not only designed a continuous gas maker, but he also incorporated the coolers and "scrubbers" to remove solid impurities in a package size reasonable to house and maintain.

One benefit of the new producer gas was an improvement in engine performance. The "weaker," lower heat value gas required a higher compression ratio to assure positive ignition. Because maximum allowable cylinder pressures were limited by slide-valves, the Dowson provided the final incentive to dispense with them. Hot-tube igniters and poppet inlet valves were phased in near the time of full acceptance of the Dowson gas producer. Combustion knocking caused by the high hydrogen content of illuminating gas placed another limitation on compression ratios. The ignition rate of a hydrogen rich fuel is faster than for that of a high carbon base. For this reason the permissible compression ratio with producer gas is as much as two full ratios higher (from 5:1 to 7:1) than for illuminating or town gas. Dowson thus offered engine builders a gift of greater efficiency through the opportunity for increased expansion. Adding the Hamilton or Atkinson scavenging systems further increased the power potential and improved the ignition of the lower heat value gases.

A subsequent refinement of the Dowson process was the "suction" gas producer. Instead of forcing the air through the coal or coke bed, the piston, on the engine's intake stroke, pulled the air through. This allowed a simplification of the gas making equipment. Most of the large engine builders, including Crossley, Deutz and Tangyes, had licenses to build both the conventional Dowson and the suction gas plants. These were sold as a package with the engines.

The mention of natural gas up to now has been conspicuous by its absence for the reason that virtually none was available except in limited areas of the United States. About 1880 a small gas line network was opened in parts of Pennsylvania, New York and West Virginia. The Indiana fields supplied natural gas to Chicago, beginning in 1891, through two, parallel, eight inch lines about 120 miles long. These fields were exhausted by 1907 and manufactured gas returned.

Blast furnace gas was another major source of fuel to be tapped for power. Oechelhäuser and Cockerill (Chapter 11) built engines capable of running on the fuel, starting in the late 1890s. The potential aggregate power of this normally wasted gas was enormous. B.H. Thwaite, the first Englishman to make an engine run on blast furnace gas, stated that for each ton of pig iron produced per hour the equivalent of 480 electrical horsepower could also be continuously generated[59] (after deducting for the mill's own requirements). Unfortunately, the gas had such a low heating value, 80 to 90 Btu per cu ft, it was not a good fuel for steam generation. Blast furnace gas became a viable fuel after solving the problem of partially cleaning the gas before it reached the engine, and then making the engine itself live with the remaining impurities and grit.

First in Germany and then the United States (England followed somewhat later on a more reduced scale), the immense horizontal engines burning blast furnace gas came into their own. They not only drove pumps for blowing air over the molten mass in the furnaces, but also generated electricity for the factory and nearby areas. Thwaite, impatient with the slow progress of utilizing the wasted energy, said that "the great clouds of dust issuing from the stacks of our furnaces which are now polluting the atmosphere would be prevented"[60] if England would adopt greater use of the gas for a power fuel.

In 1905 Emil Capitaine (See Chapter 13) designed a suction gas producer-engine combination for his sixty foot, twin screw yacht. The four cylinder engines had a bore and stroke of 8-1/4 x 11 in. Output was 75 hp at 300 rpm. Thornycroft in England built the boat and engines.[61]

The rapid proliferation of gas and gasoline engine power spawned by Otto's success is a complete story in itself. Sadly, only the highlights can ever be considered for inclusion in an overall history of the engine. What was once a tinkerer's art had at last become a respectable subject of study for engineers and scientists.

NOTES

1. F.C. Mock, "The Fuel Question from the Driver's Viewpoint," *Transactions, Society of Automotive Engineers,* 1917, Part 1, p. 347. (The entire paper, which includes discussions by Burton and Harry L. Horning, is an excellent historical document.)
2. German patent No. 28,022 of December 16, 1883.
3. U.S. patent No. 313,922 of March 11, 1885.
4. Eugen Diesel, et al., *From Engines to Autos,* (Chicago, 1960), p. 251.
5. *Lebenslauf Maybach,* January 12, 1921, pp. 99-101 of a typed abstract from Maybach's handwritten memoirs in the Deutz Archives.
6. Friedrich Sass, *Geschichte des deutschen Verbrennungsmotorenbaues von 1860 bis 1918,* (Berlin, 1962), p. 94.
7. German patent Nos. 28,243 of December 22, 1883, and 34,926 of April 3, 1885, issued to Daimler.
8. German patent No. 36,423 of August 29, 1885.

9. German patent No. 50,839 of July 9, 1889; U.S. No. 418,112 of December 24, 1889.

10. Sass, *op. cit.,* p. 171.

11. *The Annals of Mercedes-Benz Motor Vehicles and Engines,* 2nd ed., Daimler-Benz, (Stuttgart, 1961), p. 40.

12. German patent No. 39,367 of 1886.

13. H.O. Duncan, *The World on Wheels,* (Paris, 1927), p. 413. From a letter to Madame Sarazin, February 4, 1888.

14. Duncan, *op. cit.,* p. 414.

15. *The Annals of Mercedes-Benz, op. cit.,* p. 44.

16. Sass, *op. cit.,* p. 181.

17. British patent No. 16,072 of August 25, 1893.

18. British patent No. 15,598 of November 15, 1887, and U.S. No. 423,214 of March 11, 1890.

19. Edward Butler, *Carburettors, Vaporisers, and Valves,* (London, 1909) and *The Evolution of the Internal-Combustion Engine,* (London, 1912).

20. Jacques Ickx, "The Great Automobile Race of 1895," *Scientific American,* May 1972, pp. 102-11.

21. See: *50 Years of Maybach 1909-1959;* Maybach-Motorenbau GmbH, (Friedrichshafen, ca. 1960) and M.G.W. Metternich, *The History of the Maybach Automobile,* Verlag Automuseum Nettelstedt, ca. 1967.

22. German patent No. 37,435 of January 29, 1886, and British Patent No. 5,789 of April 28, 1886.

23. *The Annals of Mercedes-Benz, op. cit.,* p. 26.

24. Eugen Diesel, et al., *From Engines to Autos,* (Chicago, 1960), p. 162.

25. *Ibid.,* p. 154.

26. German patent No. 73,515 of February 28, 1893.

27. Sass, *op. cit.,* p. 269.

28. Gustav Goldbeck, *Gebändigte Kraft,* (Munich, 1965), p. 75. See also: Lynwood Bryant, "Origin of the Four-Stroke Cycle," *Technology and Culture,* VIII, April 1967, pp. 188-93, for more on Marcus' life.

29. Dugald Clerk, *The Gas and Oil Engine,* 6th ed., (New York, 1896), p. 462.

30. Edouard Delamare-Deboutteville, "On Gas Engines, With Description of the Simplex Engine," *Proceedings, Institution of Mechanical Engineers,* July 1889, p. 513.

31. William Robinson, *Gas and Petroleum Engines,* 2nd ed., (New York, 1902), p. 298.

32. U.S. patent No. 320,285 of June 16, 1885 (Filed December 6, 1884). A second Regan patent issuing that year, No. 333,336, combined gas valving features with the make and break ignition.

33. U.S. patent No. 408,356 of June 6, 1889, reissued as No. 11,068 on April 1, 1890, with three more claims (six total). A British patent in Regan's name, No. 15,488 of October 27, 1888, was also granted.

34. U.S. patents 430,504, 505 and 506, all of June 17, 1890.

35. Charles A. Winslow, *Historical Development of Internal Combustion Engines on the West Coast.* A paper presented before the Society of Automotive Engineers, June 11, 1946, in San Francisco, p. 3.

36. Albert Spies, "Modern Gas and Oil Engines," *Cassier's Magazine,* v. 4, October 1893, pp. 440-41.

37. U.S. patent No. 370,242 of September 20, 1887.

38. German patent No. 45,161 of April 13, 1887.

39. Sass, *op. cit.,* p. 161.

40. Goldbeck, *op. cit.,* pp. 224-25.

41. William Hovgaard, *Modern History of Warships,* (London, 1920), reprint 1971, p. 292, and F.A. Talbot, *Submarines, Their Mechanism and Operation,* (Philadelphia, 1915), p. 28.

42. Delamare-Deboutteville, *op. cit.,* p. 521.

43. William Robinson, *Gas and Petroleum Engines,* (London, 1890), p. 75.

44. Sass, *op. cit.,* p. 217; "Spiel's Petroleum Engine," *American Machinist,* January 15, 1887, p. 3.

45. Edward Butler, *Evolution of the Internal-Combustion Engine,* (London, 1912), p. 56.

46. *Ibid.,* p. 65.

47. *Ibid.,* p. 58.

48. Clerk, *op. cit.,* p. 338.

49. British patent No. 6,015 of April 21, 1890. Two other patents, Nos. 21,120 and 24,384 of 1893 show additional improvements to the basic idea.

50. H.J. Gibbons, *John Henry Hamilton and His Work,* A Herbert Akroyd Stuart Lecture (Nottingham, 1947), pp. 4-5. (Most of the biographical material was obtained from this source.)

51. Clerk, *op. cit.,* p. 346.

52. Gibbons, *op. cit.,* p. 21.

53. Clerk, *op. cit.,* p. 379.
54. Hugo Güldner, *Das Entwerfen und Berechnen der Verbrennungs-motoren,* (Berlin, 1905), pp. 123-24, and Bryan Donkin, *Gas, Oil, and Air Engines,* (London, 1911), pp. 512-16.
55. G. Stewart, *Town Gas, Its Manufacture and Distribution,* (London, 1958), p. 47.
56. William Robinson, *op. cit.,* p. 609.
57. *Ibid.*
58. Report of the British Association for the Advancement of Science, 1881.
59. B.H. Thwaite, "The Blast Furnace as a Center of Power Production," *Cassier's Magazine,* v. 33, November 1907, p. 35.
60. *Ibid.,* p. 40.
61. "Suction Producer Gas Motor Yacht 'Emil Capitaine'", *The Practical Engineer,* (England), Sept. 15, 1905, pp. 431-33.

INTERNAL FIRE

Chapter 13

Oil Engines: An Interim Solution

The oil engine was a product of both legislation and availability of a new fuel. By the Petroleum Act of 1879, Britain decreed that all oil for burning in lamps had to have a flash point* above seventy-three degrees Fahrenheit. Earlier laws had already specified how the more inflammable fractions were to be transported and stored. Other European countries passed similar, but in general less restrictive legislation. The United States lacked a nationwide law, although several states had requirements ranging from exacting restraints to the allowance of almost any fuel. Coupled with these varying degrees of legal controls, newly obtainable kerosene-type lamp oils made that worth considering as a fuel. "Oil for the lamps of China" likewise meant fuel for the engines of the West.

The decade of the 1890s saw the introduction of the oil engine, a workable but albeit interim answer to a safe, liquid-fueled powerplant. It was less efficient and often more temperamental than its contemporary gas and gasoline engines. M. Durand, a French gasoline engine builder stated a point of view common to many on the Continent when he said it was "a mistake to attempt to distill the oil in the engine itself, when a mineral essence, already distilled [gasoline] can be obtained."[1] Many of the German and French engines were produced in gasoline and kerosene fueled versions because both were acceptable to the customer and his government. While it was not illegal in Britain to burn gasoline in engines, the handling impositions and prohibitive insurance premiums made its use less than attractive. As a result, the British had the "carrot" of availability in an alternate fuel as well as the "stick" of the law to influence the thrust of their developments. A success of the British designs brought them to the United States and the Scandinavian countries.

---

*Flash point, i.e., the lowest temperature at which vapor arising from the fuel can be ignited in air by an open flame.

Perfecting engines compatible with the less volatile fuels was a slow process. New problems, unknown in the gas engine, took years to effectively solve, and by the time they were, improved refining processes made gasoline an accepted fuel. The diesel engine also arrived on the scene. Nevertheless, the low compression oil engine filled an important need, and its final demise did not take place until well after 1900. (Higher compression "semi-diesels" were a development later than the time frame of immediate interest.)

The thermal efficiency of the pre-1900 oil burning engine rarely, if ever, reached that of a good quality gas engine, but its inherent safety and constantly improving reliability made it an acceptable product, especially for marine and remote applications. Much of the technology derived from experience with the four-stroke oil engine was later adapted to the diesel engine. Examples of the problems encountered included: ignition sensitivity to the broad-range fuels; carboning of valves, vaporizers and combustion chambers; incompatibility of gas engine lubricants with the liquid fuels; and idiosyncrasies of fuel spraying nozzles.

In the period 1885 to 1895 three broad classifications of oil engines appeared and in the following order:

1. Oil was sprayed into an external chamber, vaporized and mixed with the full charge of air prior to entering the combustion chamber. Ignition was by either electric spark or hot tube;

2. Oil was injected as a liquid into a vaporizing chamber which was connected to, and formed part of, the combustion chamber, and mixed with air separately drawn into the cylinder. Ignition started from the hot, inner surfaces of the vaporizing chamber;

3. The oil portion of the total charge was vaporized in a small, external cavity and drawn into the combustion chamber at the same time as, and separately from, the major portion of the air. Ignition usually came from a hot-tube or the vaporizer itself acting as a hot-tube. Engines having this type of fuel preparation were of second generation design.

Two Englishmen, William Dent Priestman (1847-1936) and Herbert Akroyd Stuart (1864-1927), and a German with a French name, Emil Capitaine (1861-1907), were the earliest and most influential in the development of practical four-stroke oil engines. The work of these three subsequently figured in an often times heated controversy over what Rudolf Diesel had actually invented. Nationalistic philosophies and rival personalities were to bring forth great exercises in semantic hairsplitting.

Priestman's Engines

Born and raised near Hull, England, of Quaker parents and educated in a Quaker school, W.D. Priestman (Fig. 13-1, Plate) served an apprenticeship at Sir W.G. Armstrong and Co., Newcastle-on-Tyne. He opened a business in 1870 at the Holderness Foundry in Hull with the help of his father. A small yard surrounded on three sides by the foundry was his allotted area. When later joined by Samuel Priestman the firm became and remained Messrs. Priestman Brothers, Hull. (Samuel's name was included on almost all of the engine patents.) Their principal initial product, a special bucket for dredges, proved to have a limited market, and attention turned to potential internal-combustion engines.

Experiments before 1880 centered on gasoline fueled engines, reportedly based on features found in an 1881 engine patent of the Frenchman Eugène Etève and Charles Lallement.[2] The Etève construction describes a Lenoir-type engine employing air pressure to force gasoline from a tank and spray it into the working cylinder as the piston moved down the intake/power stroke. Ignition was electric, also based on Lenoir. Little is actually known of the early Priestman developments, except that presumably for reasons of the danger and the high cost of insurance for having gasoline on the premises, the efforts in this direction were abandoned before commercial introduction.

Two elements from these days and the Etève patent were retained: spraying fuel from a tank pressurized by air and an electric spark for ignition. It was not until almost the end of Priestman engine production that a form of hot-tube ignition was adopted.

The decade of the eighties was spent in perfecting an oil burning engine. (Fig. 13-3, Plate) Priestman soon discovered the gross fallacy in the casual statements by numerous patent holders about the ease of substituting heavier fuels for the highly volatile gasolines. Those were frustrating days, and an insight of the man facing up to his problems is offered in a later tribute from an employee:

> I sincerely believe that the source of his inspiration, energy and courage was contained in the minute copy of the New Testament which he always carried in a small metal box in his waistcoat pocket. How well I remember the occasions when we were up against difficulty and disappointment, he would bring out this little box and say, "Never mind, this is the only thing that really matters," and we would proceed to tackle our next job with renewed strength.[3]

Documented evidence of Priestman's labor appears with his first patent granted in 1885.[4] Its title refers to the "...Working of Motor Engines Operated by the Combustion of Benzoline or other Liquid Hydrocarbons." These fuels would have been either "paraffin" (kerosene), the common stove and lamp oil, with a specific gravity of about 0.8 or the specifically mentioned Benzoline, an English name for petrol (gasoline) before the coming of the automobile. The oil terminology for fuels is often confusing. For example, before 1900 an "oil" engine could have been any engine burning a liquid fuel, either gasoline or kerosene. A clue as to which might come from its specific gravity, under 0.75 being a reasonable indication of a more volatile fuel. The flash point, however, was the positive determinant.

Priestman's single claim from his first patent states "The improved method of preparing the mixture constituting the inflammable charge by compressing the air approximately to the pressure at which the charge is to be used in the working cylinder and then permeating the same with liquid hydrocarbon."[5] An 1886 patent[6] shows that Priestman was really trying to perfect a Clerk two-stroke cycle engine. The difficulties soon caused him to go to the four-stroke and pay license fees under the Otto patent to Crossley Brothers until it expired in 1890.[7]

The problem still remained as to how best to ignite the less volatile oils in a low compression engine. Most of Priestman's efforts were devoted to this area for the next fifteen years and his numerous patents trace the continued refinement and sometimes dead-ended failures. Two separate elements were combined to prepare the fuel-air charge prior to its introduction into the cylinder: a pressurized atomizer and a heated vaporizer chamber. These devices, first shown in patents of 1886 and 1887[8] distinguish the Priestman engine.

An air pump, driven by an eccentric on the crankshaft, pressurized a fuel tank in the engine base to something under fifteen psi. Lines leading from the top and bottom of the tank carried air and fuel under pressure to an atomizer attached to one end of the vaporizing chamber. By directing the air flow into the fuel coming from its orifice, a breakup of the fuel droplets was assured. (Fig. 13-4) The air from the "spray maker" constituted only a small fraction of that needed for the combustible charge, the remainder being drawn through a spring-loaded valve opening by suction on the engine's intake stroke. (Fig. 13-5) This larger volume of air entered the vaporizer past a conical plate perforated with small holes. The exit from the atomizer was located on the axis of the cone so that its discharge passed through the second source of incoming air. Fuel spraying was continuous.

Integral with a shaft actuated by a governor were both a plug valve and a butterfly valve. (Fig. 13-5) When engine speed exceeded the desired, the shaft was turned slightly to restrict an oil supply passage through the plug valve as well as the air entering past the spring-loaded valve. By throttling both air and fuel the engine fired a charge under all

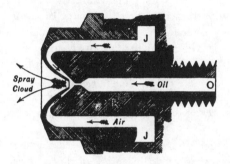

Fig. 13-4   Priestman engine fuel spray nozzle. (Robinson, *Gas and Petroleum Engines,* 1902)

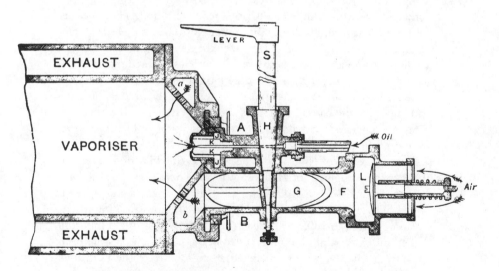

Fig. 13-5   Priestman engine fuel and air controls. (Robinson, *Gas and Petroleum Engines,* 1902)

load conditions. This was a radical departure from the "hit and miss" governing when only the fuel was reduced often to the point of misfire, or was shut off entirely. A penalty was paid with a high part load fuel consumption due to the very reduced cylinder compression pressures (an inherent disadvantage of any engine having its intake throttled).

The vaporizer consisted of an exhaust-jacketed chamber whose exit led to the engine cylinder past another spring-loaded valve. (Only the exhaust valve was cam actuated.) The volume of the chamber and the cylinder were proportioned so that the charge of air and fuel sucked into the cylinder was retained in the chamber through a complete cycle to enhance mixing and vaporizing. Vaporizer temperatures had to be kept under 300°F. If the charge overheated, the oil vapor began to distill into an oil gas whose residue left a tarry deposit which accumulated in the engine.[9] A heating lamp, fueled from the pressurized tank, heated the vaporizer prior to starting. This procedure required several minutes.

The extent of fuel vaporization in the heated chamber was of necessity somewhat less than total. Regardless of the atomizer effectiveness, for which Priestman deserves great credit, the higher boiling point fractions in the kerosenes of that day, and the relatively low chamber temperatures, prevented complete vaporization. The unvaporized fuel, along with a portion of what had vaporized in the external chamber, condensed on the cylinder walls prior to combustion. These heavier fractions acted as an excellent lubricant and obviated the need for supplementary lubrication.[10] Unfortunately, the glaze-like carbon deposits tending to form around the spark plug electrodes required that the plug have sometimes more than just occasional maintenance. The spark, generated by a battery and coil system, was not always the "hottest", particularly as the battery neared its time for recharging. If a constant, magneto-generated spark had been used the ignition problems resulting from carboning would have been considerably lessened.

Toward the end of 1886 articles began appearing in periodicals about the Priestman engine.[11] In 1888 Sir William Thompson (Lord Kelvin) ran tests at the Priestman factory, and that same year the engine was successfully exhibited at the Royal Agricultural Show. An "improved" version, released in 1892, provided greater accessibility to the vaporizer and atomizer. A hand pump was added to build up tank pressure prior to starting. (Figs. 13-6 and 7) External appearance of the horizontal cylinder engines remained little changed over the next ten years. (Fig. 13-8, Plate)

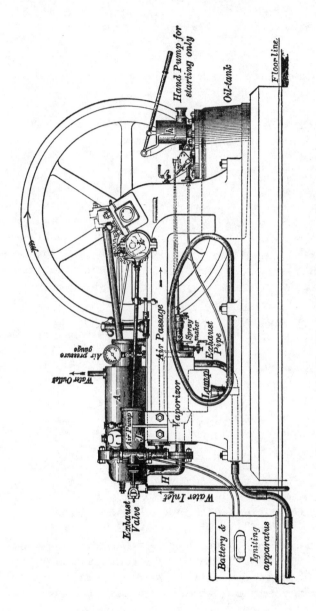

Fig. 13-6   Priestman engine of 1892. (Donkin, *Gas, Oil and Air Engines*, 1896)

275

Tests by Prof. W. Cawthorne Unwin, the first in 1890 and the next two years later, illustrate not only the improvements in performance on the same size engine, but the effect of different fuels:

	1890	1892	
Cylinder bore, in	8.5	8.5	
Stroke, in	12	12	
Engine weight, lb	—	4,030	
Fuel trade name	Broxburn	Daylight	Russoline
Fuel specific gravity			
(60 °F)	0.81	0.79	0.83
Fuel flash point,°F	152	77	86
Fuel heating value,			
Btu/lb	19,700	21,490	21,180
Indicated horsepower	5.24	9.37	7.41
Brake horsepower	4.50	7.72	6.76
Test speed, rpm	180	204	208
Compression pressure,			
psi	—	35	28
Peak cyl. press., psi	—	151	134
Mean effective press.,			
psi	34	53	41
Exhaust valve opening			
press., psi	—	35	34
Brake sp. fuel consumption,			
lb/bhp hr	1.24	0.84	0.95
Brake thermal eff., %			
(Calculated)	10	14	13

Broxburn Lighthouse, a Scottish shale oil from an area a few miles west of Edinburgh, was distilled from what was then called "petroleum peat." First experimentally made in 1850, Scottish oils formed an important source of petroleum for the British Isles. (Crude oil production was over fifty million gallons in 1885.)[12] Royal Daylight, an American product, and Russoline, from the Baku fields in Russia, were popular and readily available kerosene-type burning oils. A problem associated with most of these early fuels when used in engines was that even though they met the legal specifications for the flash point, they frequently contained volatile as well as heavier fractions. The more volatile end of the fuel necessitated low compression pressures to avoid

PORTABLE PETROLEUM ENGINE, BY MESSRS. PRIESTMAN BROTHERS, LIMITED, HULL.

Fig. 13-7   Priestman portable engine of 1892. *(Engineering,* 1892)

preignition, while the opposite end caused engine deposits. The first Priestman engines could only tolerate a compression ratio of two to one, a basic shortcoming resulting in almost no compression at part throttle settings. (Fig. 13-9) It was customary to refer to and sometimes specify a fuel by well or refinery location and not by a generic name. As the demand increased for gasoline and other products either left in the lamp oils or simply wasted, it became economic to recover them and in turn offer a more standardized kerosene. However, the oil trust battles between Rockefeller, the Rothschilds, the Nobels, and Marcus Samuel's Shell Transport & Trading kept prices in a state of flux, and engines often had to be adaptable to the fuel that was available.

In 1891 Priestman Brothers introduced a two cylinder, vertical engine for marine applications. That the builders had sufficient confidence in the reliability of their product to enter this field speaks well for its reputation. These double-acting engines were made in two sizes: thirty brake horsepower at 300 rpm and sixty-five bhp at 250 rpm. (Fig. 13-10, Plate) The larger was double-acting with a bore and stroke of

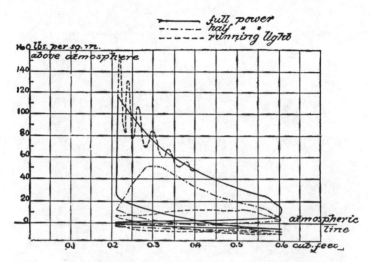

Fig. 13-9   Priestman engine, full load and part load pressure-volume diagrams. (Goldingham, *Oil Engines,* 1900)

fourteen and a half by sixteen inches. It stood over eight feet from its crankshaft centerline and weighed about seven and a half tons. (Above a cylinder diameter of fifteen inches it was found that water cooling the piston became necessary.)

In 1895 a Priestman service engineer sailed in two fishing boats with these engines. His voyages of 500 to 700 miles from port often gave him exciting times in the engine room. Packing glands sealing the piston rods at the lower combustion chamber were a major problem. Increased cooling water flow made seals last longer but caused more rapid spark plug sooting. The engineer later wrote that plugs might be changed with the engine running, but because of the "danger of a flash" it was "advisable to keep one's face as far away as possible." The seals could not be changed in rough seas or when hurrying to port with a catch of fish. He recalled sleeping with "one ear open listening for the crack of flames down the rods."[13]

Marine engines formed an important part of the Priestman business, and they were used as auxiliaries in sailing vessels as well as the main power in tugs and barges.

Since there appeared to be little threatening competition, a branch factory, Priestman and Co., was established in Philadelphia about 1892. Albert Priestman, one of the brothers, was its manager.[14] In principle, the American version was identical to the British, but the construction was considerably altered. The most noticeable difference were the two flywheels, acting as cheeks for the single throw crankshaft, and supported between outboard main bearings. (Fig. 13-11) The rationale for this unique, built-up crankshaft design was that the flywheels acted to absorb the shock of the firing impulse. These engines, advertised as late as 1900, were offered in four sizes from five to twenty indicated horsepower.[15]

Encroaching competition by other oil engine builders who had less expensive designs gradually cut into Priestman sales. Compression ratios one half that of the new entrants also meant engine sizes were disproportionately larger. (Beginning about 1895 water was sprayed directly into the cylinder to forestall preignition in an attempt to increase output.) Engine production ceased before 1905, and the company fell back again on the manufacture of its dredging equipment. Of all the oil engine pioneers, only Priestman perservered to transform his own ideas into commercial hardware and then stick with those ideas until their time had passed.

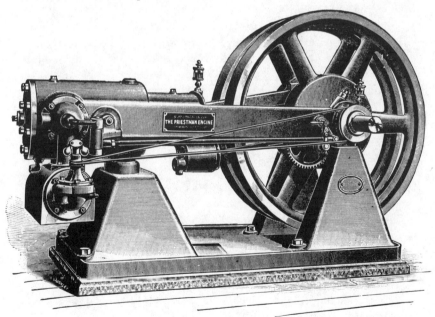

Fig. 13-11   American design of Priestman engine. (Hiscox, *Gas, Gasoline and Oil Engines,* 1900)

Herbert Akroyd Stuart

Akroyd Stuart's activity with oil engines spanned a period of less than ten years. (Akroyd was the maiden name of his mother who came from a prominent Halifax family.) For reasons not fully known, he turned his back on a promising opportunity and moved half a world away. Stuart, (Fig. 13-2, Plate) the son of an inventive Scotsman, was born in Yorkshire at Halifax and raised in Bletchley, Buckinghamshire. His father ran the Bletchley Iron and Tin Plate Works which was more of an experimental shop to build and work with the ideas of his choosing. It was a not-for-profit concern financed through his own independent means.[16]

Young Stuart received some technical education after grammar school, but where and for what length of time is not certain. At some point he did act as an assistant in the Mechanical Engineering Department at the City and Guilds of London Technical College and was connected with the Mechanical Engineering Department at Finsbury Technical College. (William Robinson, who was associated with the London College at the time, became well acquainted with Stuart.) Stuart then joined his father at Bletchley where he began experimenting with engines. He was twenty-two when his first patent on improvements to a Priestman-type engine issued.[17]

Five years passed before Akroyd Stuart struck off in a direction different from that pursued by Priestman and others. Based on the several patents granted to him during this period, he is seen exploring new methods of vaporizing fuel (gasoline and kerosene), scavenging the exhaust and improving speed control. All but the initial patent list Charles Richard Binney, a financial backer of the engine developments, ahead of Stuart's name. Beginning in 1890 the order is reversed. There is no record of "Colonel" Binney having contributed any ideas to the Stuart engine.

It is the patents of 1890 (and after) that are of most interest. Two granted in that year describe for the first time a vaporizing chamber connected to the working cylinder via a small throat.[18] From this point on, all Stuart-related engines had such a distinguishing characteristic and became the most notable example of the "second" type of oil engine listed earlier in the chapter. In future years these came to be referred to as "hot-bulb" engines. "Semi-diesel", another popular name coined later, was an unfortunate choice, both for the confusion and the rancor on the part of some English oil engine boosters.

The earlier 1890 patent, No. 7,146, shows a suction-operated air inlet valve opening into the vaporizer. (Fig. 13-12) Air was drawn into the cylinder through the vaporizer, compressed, and then near the end of the compression stroke a measured fuel charge was sprayed onto the walls of the hot chamber where it was quickly vaporized and set on fire. The burning and expanding charge proceeded through the contracted passage and into the cylinder to force the piston outward on the power stroke. The poppet exhaust valve, acting through a rocker lever, was opened by a cam turning at half engine speed.

A cam-actuated plunger pump, at floor level, drew the kerosene fuel from the tank past a spring-loaded check valve having an adjustable opening pressure. The cam lifted the plunger on the fill stroke, and a tension spring pulled the plunger down on the delivery stroke to pump

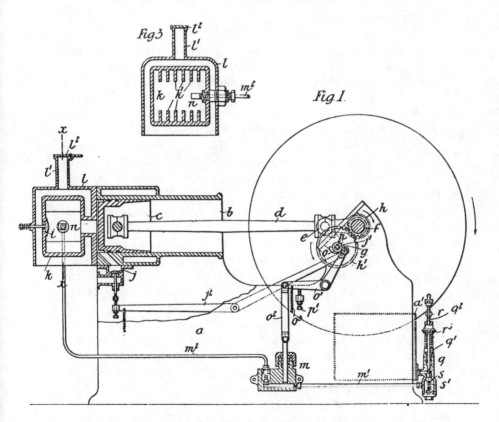

Fig. 13-12 Akroyd Stuart engine of 1890 with air intake through vaporizer. (From the drawings of his British patent No. 7,146 of 1890)

the charge, past a check valve, into the vaporizer. The pump plunger had a fixed, cam-determined stroke. In order to reduce the fuel delivered per stroke, the governor or hand throttle overrode the valve in the suction line and opened it as needed so that on the delivery stroke of the plunger part of the pumped oil was returned past the suction line valve and back into the tank. The displacement of the plunger for a six horsepower engine of 1890 design is given as 0.015 cu in.[19]

A chronic problem with the initial design, and one existing until Stuart relinquished control of his patents, was that the fuel spray action was "soft" and did not end sharply which caused nozzle "after dribble." Making the condition worse were too frequently leaking check valves. The result caused rapid carboning up of the spray nozzle necessitating frequent nozzle cleaning.

Stuart's second 1890 patent, No. 15,994, added a new dimension to the oil engine and provided the essential features found in the production engines. In this disclosure changes were made in the time of fuel delivery into the red-hot vaporizer and in the location of the air inlet valve. No longer was the air drawn through the vaporizer; it now entered directly into the working cylinder. The fuel charge was sprayed onto the ribbed vaporizer walls during the air intake stroke. (Fig. 13-13, Plate) Ignition did not occur at this time because of insufficient oxygen in the vaporizer to begin combustion. Instead, the fuel vaporized and "cooked" until the air from the cylinder began entering the hot-bulb on the compression stroke. By the end of the stroke the residual gases in the vaporizer had been diluted and a combustible mixture generated so that ignition could take place.

Much of the experimental work leading up to the ideas disclosed in Stuart's 1890 patents was performed on a Spiel gasoline engine in the Bletchley shops.[20] Several of his pre-1890 patent drawings, in fact, show an engine having Spiel's inverted, vertical cylinder configuration.[21] With the hazards of gasoline becoming more apparent, Stuart and his assistants looked for a means of burning the "heavier" paraffins. As an interim step, the test engine was started on gasoline and then, when the combustion chamber parts had become sufficiently heated, was switched to kerosene. (A story, originated by Prof. Robinson, is told of how in his early experience Stuart accidentally spilled lamp oil into a hot tinning pot and observed at almost too close a range the explosive characteristics of vaporized kerosene when the spilled fuel was ignited by the hot surface.[22]) In order to achieve self-ignition on the experimental Spiel engine the water jacketing of the cylinder was gradually reduced to a point where self-ignition occurred with any load. From these crude tests evolved the germ of the idea for the cylinder-connected vaporizing chamber.

It is not clear if Stuart's intention was to go into the business of selling his engines or to find a buyer of his ideas. Before the end of 1890 some dozen engines sized from one to six horsepower were built in London by Messrs. G. Wailes & Co. According to one source, four were sold and several sent out "on approval."[23] The engine was also exhibited in London at the Islington Agricultural Hall before Christmas of 1890.

In April of the following year Prof. Robinson performed at Bletchley the earliest test on which data can be relied. From a cylinder having a 9.25 inch bore and a 16 inch stroke the engine produced 7.6 brake horsepower at 216 rpm. The compression pressure was close to 35 psi and the indicated mean effective pressure was given as about 36 psi. The fuel consumption was one pound of 0.85 specific gravity oil per bhp per hour.[24] The fuel pump plunger had a diameter of slightly less than 3/32 inch by a 1/2 inch stroke. The vaporizer was air cooled but offered no problem from causing too-early an ignition.[25]

The Hornsby-Akroyd Engine

Messrs. R. Hornsby and Sons Ltd., of Grantham had been searching for an internal-combustion engine to build upon the expiration of the Otto patent. They learned of Stuart's engine, and in the first part of 1891 entered into negotiations with him. In business since 1815, Hornsby enjoyed a reputation as a machinery and steam engine builder who had the manpower, the facilities and the money to do what was needed. It was no wonder that Stuart considered an arrangement with them. After a thorough investigation of the engine (the above test by Robinson is believed to have been part of this program), a contract was signed on June 26, 1891, whereby Hornsby acquired world rights to all Stuart engine patents. Hornsby management, still unsure of the engine's future, gave no money to Stuart at that point; he would profit through future royalty payments. Fortunately, the enthusiasm of Chief Engineer Robert Edwards, provided Hornsby with the confidence to go ahead with the engine.[26] From then on the engine was known as the "Hornsby-Akroyd."

Numerous design changes were made by Hornsby prior to production. (Fig. 13-14) While the Stuart engine showed good promise in the evaluation tests, it was by no means ready to hand over to a customer. Significant modifications instituted by Hornsby, and the reason for them, included:[27]

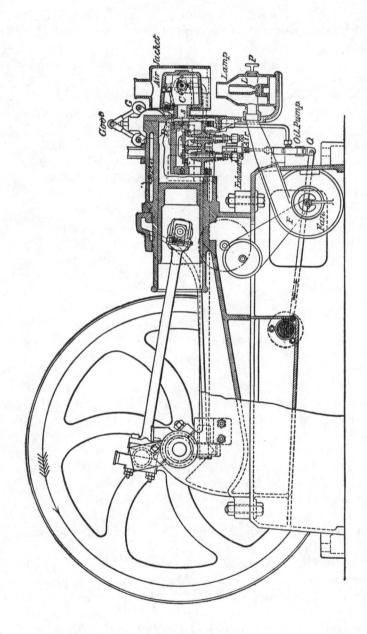

Fig. 13-14   Hornsby-Akroyd engine, section view. (Donkin, *Gas, Oil and Air Engines*, 1896)

— A redesign of the fuel pump. The clearances in the pump were reduced and the delivery stroke was made cam-actuated to assure faster and sharper spraying into the vaporizer. Carboning of the nozzle and the vaporizer was thereby reduced.

— A change in the governor control of the valve. Previously, at part load conditions the governor-controlled valve in the suction line would sometimes open so quickly as to cause a sudden reversal of flow and break the column of oil in the long suction line; the engine consequently stopped, and the supply line had to be primed again. The Hornsby design used the governor to open a bypass valve located at the spray nozzle. With the spill off now in the pressurized line, the pump had no trouble with air. Further, placement of the bypass valve at a high point in the line gave a convenient means to bleed off air before it entered the nozzle. (Fig. 13-15, Plate) A check valve was later added in the nozzle as were two ball check valves in series in both the suction and discharge lines at the pump.

— Nozzle cooling. The nozzle was water jacketed to lessen carboning due to overheating.

— A mechanically actuated intake valve. To provide a more uniform and accurately timed supply of air, the valve was made cam operated. Without this, the time of ignition varied since it was a function of the compression pressure.

— An air blower to aid in cooling the vaporizer.

After the engine had been running under a load for a short while the vaporizer became hot enough so that the starting lamp could be extinguished. Ignition then depended entirely upon the temperature inside the vaporizer. This self-ignition of the fuel may be likened to the "after-running" or "dieseling" of a modern spark ignition engine that continues to run after switching off the ignition. The heat of compression, i.e., the Diesel principle, was in no way a factor for ignition with the Hornsby engine.

According to Prof. Robinson, control over the temperatures within the vaporizer chamber was vital. If it was too cool ignition stopped or required the use of a lamp (a particular problem on light load governing); if it became too hot the chamber filled up with carbon. At the same time excessively high ambient chamber temperatures reduced the overall volumetric efficiency and in turn the power.[28] Another important consideration was the length and diameter of the neck connecting the vaporizer with the cylinder. The wrong proportions meant the difference between an engine's success or failure. This was a vital factor in scavenging enough the residual gas in the vaporizer to prevent too early charge ignition. Premature ignition problems almost caused an early abandonment of the engine by Hornsby.[29]

The high operating temperatures inside the vaporizer casting also brought about a frustrating metallurgy problem. It took several years to find a suitable cast iron which offered reasonable life expectancy.

Stuart had proposed a water jacket surrounding the neck area in one of his last engine patents in 1892,[30] but because of frequent cracking at the juncture of the cooled and uncooled metal the idea was never adopted. The final solution, at least the one that could be lived with, was to band with a water jacket the half of the full diameter of the vaporizer next to the neck and not the neck area. (Fig. 13-16) The rear half was a separate casting into which the fuel was sprayed from the water cooled nozzle. This refinement of 1896 was used on all engines of five horsepower and over. Its effect was such that the compression ratio of the sixteen horsepower engine, for example, could be increased to allow a new rating of twenty horsepower.

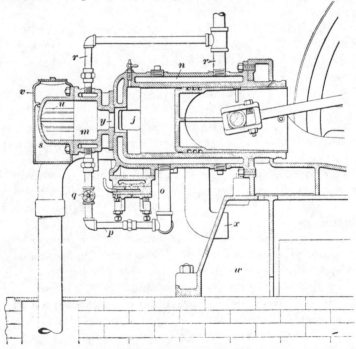

Fig. 13-16   Section view of Hornsby-Akroyd engine with a water-cooled vaporizer. (The Smithsonian Institution)

When the Hornsby-Akroyd engine was introduced in 1892 it became an almost instant success. Offered sizes ranged from one and half to sixteen brake horsepower. The lack of an electric ignition system was a large plus in its favor. The engine was also less sensitive to fuel variations. There were still problems of nozzle, vaporizer and cylinder carboning which meant a certain maintenance schedule had to be followed, but performance was reliable and consistent if this was carried out. Hornsby sold other of its products to farmers, so the company knew the value of building a machine that could still function even if all was not in perfect condition.

Although not the most efficient of the oil engines offered in the mid-1890s, the Hornsby was recognized as one that met the requirements of simplicity and the lack of need for a skilled attendant. The engine consistently won prizes at agricultural fairs on these points. The following results of tests at Cambridge in June 1894 by the Royal Agricultural Society give a good comparison of engines from Hornsby and the two newer entrants of Crossley and Premier:[31]

	Hornsby-Akroyd	Crossley	Premier
Bore & stroke, in	10 x 15	7 x 15	8.25 x 15
Weight, lb/bhp*	523	519	633
Time req'd. to start, min	8	16	21
Engine speed, mean, rpm . . .	240	201	160
"Explosions" per min.**	120	75.3	72.2
Brake horsepower	8.6	7.0	6.5
Mechanical efficiency, % . . .	83	88	89
Oil consumption, lb/bhp hr .	0.98	0.82	1.04
Brake thermal eff., %	14	16.7	—

Oil used: Russoline

*Calculated from given data
**A remarkable figure if true. This indicated there were no misfires when the governor reduced the fuel to maintain speed.

The time to start the Hornsby from a cold condition seems lengthy by today's standards, but because it was so much less than its rivals and so even in its running, that these became major factors in its winning the medal at the Cambridge show.

Another test on a Hornsby-Akroyd rated at 25 horsepower in January 1898 gives a good illustration of performance improvements during the intervening three and a half years.[32] At the end of the day's test, the 14.5 in. by 17 in. cylinder actually was able to produce 39 bhp, or a fifty percent overload.

Load factor	Full	Two-thirds	One-third	No load
Speed, rpm	202	202	203	201
Explosions per min	101	101	100	100
Brake horsepower	26.7	18	9	0
Ind. mean effective press., psi	45	31	18	6
Mechanical efficiency, %	82	80	69	
Fuel consumption, lb/bhp hr	0.74	0.91	1.3	—
Compression pressure, psi	60	—	—	—
Peak pressure, psi	168	150	95	—
Brake thermal efficiency, %	18	—	10	—

Note that even at part throttle conditions there was no misfiring in order to maintain the governed speed.

Beginning in 1895 Hornsby began building two-cylinder, vertical marine engines of about ten horsepower. These grew in size and horsepower, and in 1903 Hornsby supplied the British Admiralty with a four-cylinder, 400 horsepower engine with cylinders of 25 in. bore and 13.5 in. stroke to provide a low profile and higher operating speeds.[33]

Very few contemporary sources ever bothered to tell of the lubricants used. We are indebted, therefore, to John W. Young, who was with Hornsby at the start of their oil engine program, for describing the lubrication situation at that time.[34] Steam engine practice was followed generally except for cylinder lubrication, but here the I-C engine builders ran into a problem. About the time the gas engine industry began there was a switch by steam operators from animal and vegetable "fatty" oils to the mineral oils reaching the market. (Above seventy-five or eighty psi steam pressure the non-mineral oils tended to decompose under the action of wet steam and released an acid which attacked the cylinder.) It was natural that the first gas engines to add cylinder lubrication adopted the mineral oils. Unfortunately, these oils contained certain "resinous bodies" which formed varnish deposits on the cylinder walls. When the engine cooled down the varnish hardened, and the piston often "locked so firmly that a screw-jack was frequently needed

Fig. 13-10
Priestman 1894 2-cylinder,
double-acting kerosene
fueled marine engine;
14^1/$_2$ in. bore x 16 in.
stroke; 65 hp at 250 rpm.
(James D. Priestman
collection)

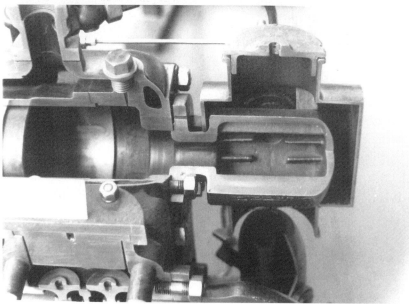

Fig. 13-13   Cutaway of air-cooled vaporizer antechamber on the
Hornsby-Akroyd engine in the collection of the
Deutsches Museum, Munich. 4 Bhp at 250 rpm.
5.5 in. by 10 in. bore and stroke. (Author photo)

Fig. 13-15   Hornsby-Akroyd engine in the collection of the
Science Museum. (The Science Museum, London)

Engineers (VDI) in 1888. It stated that in contrast with conventional practice an engine's economy could be improved by shortening the stroke and increasing the cylinder diameter. This reduced piston speed in relation to what he referred to as the speed of gas expansion.[38] Engine speeds could in turn be raised and the weight and cost be reduced. Capitaine's engines most always had a stroke equal to the bore and turned up to several hundred rpm faster than the standard engines of similar application. Higher speeds were certainly not unknown at that time because Daimler's automobile engines, even though of much smaller size, were also being promoted.

Novelty best describes Capitaine's experimental, four-stroke oil engine of 1885 built by the Berliner Machinenbau-AG. The "upside-down" configuration had a horizontal crankshaft on top like the older Körting designs so that its conical cylinder head pointed at the base. The cylinder water jacket was formed by the outer structure wall and a "wet sleeve" cylinder liner sealed at its top and bottom to the outer wall. The head was uncooled. A suction (and inertia) operated intake valve opened downward from the center of the piston crown, and an exhaust valve was actuated by a cam on a stub shaft turning at half crank speed. A plunger fuel pump operating from the exhaust valve pushrod forced the oil charge into a stationary, vertical tube extending from above the cylinder liner down into the piston skirt area. When the piston was "up" and the exhaust valve started to open, the fixed tube telescoped into a slightly larger diameter tube fastened to the piston and leading to the intake valve port. The fuel charge was then deposited onto the head of the closed intake valve, and sufficient heat for vaporization was transferred to the fuel before the intake valve opened. A hot-tube igniter attached to the conical surface of the cylinder head pointed toward the intake valve. Ignition began when the charge was sufficiently heated by the hot-tube and the increased compression, hopefully at the end of the compression stroke. Reported power from the 100 mm bore and stroke engine was 1.5 hp at 600 rpm.[39]

From about 1888 onward Capitaine's engines were of more conventional construction: vertical cylinders with an enclosed crankcase in the base. A second stage of fuel vaporizer design appeared on a series of what still must be viewed as semi-experimental engines. Called an internal bypass vaporizer, it consisted of a horizontal, U-shaped tube whose ends projected into a cylindrical portion of the combustion chamber directly under the intake valve. (Fig. 13-17) The external, rounded section both received the fuel charge and heat from a "lamp."

A baffle plate in the space under the intake valve diverted part of the incoming air into the upper tube-end of the vaporizer. Thus the fuel sprayed into the vaporizer by a plunger pump was mixed with air, heated and then drawn into the conical shaped part of the combustion chamber under the action of air passing through the tube on the intake stroke. At the end of the compression stroke the same heated tube became the igniter of the mixture. There was a possibility of ignition

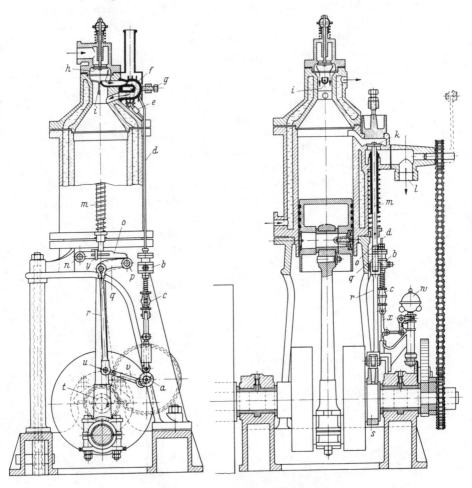

Fig. 13-17   Capitaine engine with internal bypass vaporizer –
1888. (Sass, *Geschichte des deutschen
Verbrennungsmotorenbaues,* 1962)

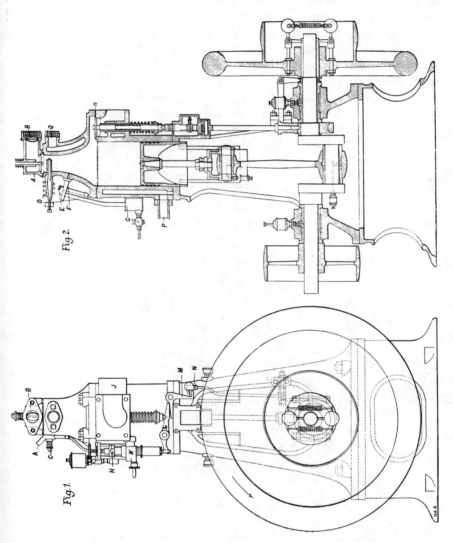

Fig. 13-18   Capitaine engine of 1891 (*Engineering, 1892*)

too far ahead of top center, but the higher than average speeds reduced the risk. During a start this early ignition was only a nuisance rather than a problem because the hand crank was designed to prevent a kick-back into the arms of the man holding it.[40]

Grob & Co., Leipzig, built the bypass vaporizer engine and intro-duced a superceding design in 1891. (Fig. 13-18) Shortly thereafter Capitaine transferred his patents to Swiderski, also in Leipzig who, with a successor company, continued to produce the engine almost unchanged until after 1900.[41] (There appears to be an overlapping time when both were making it.) Combined sales of Grob and Swiderski were said to have been over 3,000 engines by 1894.

The third and final phase of the Capitaine engine saw the vaporizer again redesigned to modify its principle of operation. The engine became one of the earliest to adopt a small, externally heated vaporiz-ing chamber into which only a small fraction of the air was admitted with the fuel entering the combustion chamber. (Fig. 13-19) The method was typical of the third classification of oil engines mentioned at the beginning of the chapter. During the exhaust stroke the fuel

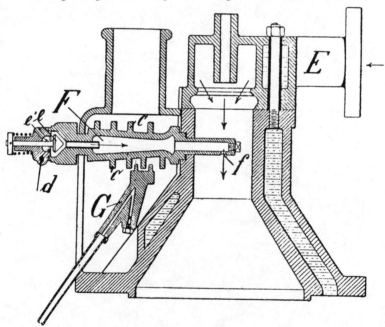

Fig. 13-19 Vaporizer/igniter on Capitaine engine of 1892.
(Lieckfeld, *Oil Motors,* 1908)

charge was sprayed into the flame-heated cavity where it turned into a vapor. A fuel pump plunger was actuated by the same eccentric mechanism which opened the exhaust valve. As the piston movement caused the suction-operated inlet valve to open, the same vacuum also lifted a small air bleed valve on the outside end of the vaporizer so that the fuel vapor could be drawn into the combustion chamber directly in the path of the incoming air. At the end of the compression stroke, the by now homogeneous charge was ignited by the vaporizer tube which performed the additional function of a hot-tube igniter. Until 1891, when it was realized that ignition did in fact occur in the vaporizer, a separate igniter tube was installed. (Fig. 13-18)

A series of performance tests on kerosene burning engines were run in 1894 with the previously mentioned Cambridge test being held almost concurrently with ones at Berlin and Meaux, France. For the most part data from these tests may be trusted, although a few unbelievable fuel consumption figures, both low and high, are best disregarded. The three test series, supervised by engineering professors, afford a comparison of over twenty makes of English, French and German oil engines. The following are results of a Capitaine design built by Grob (Meaux) and by Swiderski (Berlin):[42]

Manufacturer	Grob	Swiderski
Bore and Stroke, in	7.4 x 7.4	6.6 x 7.0
Engine speed, rpm	263	315
Brake horsepower	6.2	4.0
Fuel consumption, lb/bhp hr	0.92	0.96
Fuel specific gravity (Russoline) . .	0.80-.82	0.80-.82
Fuel, Btu/lb	19,870	19,480
Brake thermal efficiency, %	13	13

While the efficiency is not as high as the best of the English engines at Cambridge, a comparison with them on horsepower vs. size shows the effect of a shorter stroke and higher speed:

	Bore-Stroke, in.	Hp	Cu in./ hp
Capitaine-Grob	7.4x7.4	6.2	51.3
Capitaine-Swiderski	6.6x7.0	4.0	59.9
Hornsby-Akroyd	10x15	8.6	137
Crossley	7x15	7.0	82.5
Premier	8.25x15	6.5	123.4

Grob-Capitaine engines were exhibited at the 1893 Columbian Exposition in Chicago, but no American manufacturer received a license to build them. (Fig. 13-20) In England the engines were sold through Leo Tolch from 1891 until about 1904. Tolch subsequently made four-cylinder marine engines on the Grob system. The predominant period of Capitaine's patent activity in Britain and the United States was between 1888 to 1892 although he was a co-inventor with others as early as 1885; these were based on patents issued in his own country. A gas producer bearing his name appeared on the market after 1900.[43]

Fig. 13-20   Grob-Capitaine engine of 1893. (*Scientific American*, 1893)

Capitaine was to become a bitter foe of Rudolf Diesel. He tried to prove that Diesel had pirated his ideas and to have Diesel's basic German patent declared invalid. A Frankfurt court decision in April of 1898 upheld all of Diesel's claims, but until Capitaine's death in 1907 he remained a thorn in Diesel's side.[44] One of Capitaine's admirers in England, Arthur F. Evans, went so far as to write in 1930, without offering proof, that Capitaine "probably sold his invention to Diesel and to remove any ambiguity he [Evans] will put this forward as an historic fact."[45] In 1944 Evans said, in a discussion following a paper on Priestman, "I have it on excellent authority that Capitaine made the first Diesel engine and that the engine is stowed away in some museum in Germany, but... I have not been able to verify it."[46] No one but Evans ever went so far in his comments about Capitaine and Diesel. There is in the literature, nevertheless, a broad spectrum of conclusions offered by others on the subject of English oil engines and their being a forerunner of Diesel's engine to the point of nationalistic overkill.

Kjelsberg Paraffin Engine

Another early kerosene engine was the Kjelsberg made by the Lokomotivfabrik Winterthur in Switzerland and by Nobel Brothers of St. Petersburg.[47] When introduced in 1889, its power train resembled the inverted Körting engine. (Fig. 13-21) Like the Priestman, the fuel and all of the air passed through an external vaporizing chamber. Oil was sprayed onto the walls of the flame-heated vaporizer during the intake stroke. The resulting vapor mixed with the air entering the vaporizer past a suction-operated valve on the intake stroke. Linkage connecting the oil pump and a second intake valve at the entrance to the combustion chamber were actuated off the same cam. A hot-tube igniter, placed between the heating flame and the vaporizer set off the charge in the cylinder at the end of the compression stroke. Above normal speed a governor caused the exhaust valve to be held open and a rod acting on the intake valve and oil pump to be disengaged.

At the Meaux trials a Kjelsberg engine produced 5.2 bhp at 226 rpm and had a fuel consumption of 0.84 lb/bhp hr. Brake thermal efficiency was 14 percent. The bore and stroke of the test engine was 6.3 in. by 9.4 in. About 800 engines had been made by 1895.[48] Possibly because the Kjelsberg followed the basic Körting configuration which Lieckfeld had designed, it was included in his authoritative text as one of the significant early oil engines.

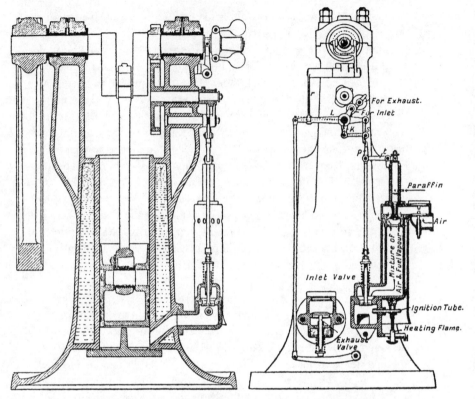

Fig. 13-21   Kjelsberg 1889 engine, section view. (Lieckfeld, *Oil Motors,* 1908)

Other British and European Oil Engines

Oil engines proliferated between 1890 and 1895, both in England and on the continent, with Priestman and Stuart having few imitators. Most followed the pattern of Capitaine, i.e., a small vaporizer containing only a fraction of the combustion air.

Crossley introduced a line of oil engines in 1891 using a bypass air vaporizer and, borrowed from its gas engine, ignition by a timed opening to a hot-tube igniter. Reporting on the Crossley exhibit at a show in 1892 *Engineering* commented:[49]

> In the pleasant days of monopoly it could never be alleged against them that they sat with folded hands indifferent to possible improvement; it is well known that during the

entire period covered by the Otto patent they were continuously at work in perfecting their engine. Now, with so
many competitors at the Show, it is incumbent on them to
demonstrate their right to be still considered at the head of
the gas engine industry.

The Griffin (1892) did, like the Priestman, mix the fuel and all of the
air in an external vaporizer; a hot-tube igniter was employed. The
Robey (1892), licensed under the Richardson and Norris patents, had
a modified Hornsby approach to fuel preparation. Oil was sprayed
against a cylindrical insert spaced inside, and closely concentric to, the
combustion chamber walls above the piston; its self-ignition characteristics were similar to the Hornsby.

Space does not permit more than a brief listing of other English oil
engines of the 1891-1895 period. A number were first attempts which
subsequently saw drastic modifications.

Manufacturer	Patentee	Year first introduced
Weyman & Hitchcock, "Trusty"	Knight	1891
Roots	Roots	1892
Penney & Co., "Safety"	Weatherhogg	1892
Rob't. Stephenson & Co., "Rocket"	Kaselowski	1893
Fielding & Platt, "Fielding"	—	1894
Clarke, Chapman & Co.	Butler	1894
Campbell Gas Engine Co.	—	1894
Wells Brothers, "Premier"	—	1894
Britannia Co.	Gibbon	1895
Tangye	Pinkney	1895

The "Britannia," later built under license in the United States by
John A. Holmes of Philadelphia, was called the "Facile" and operated as
a two-stroke.[50]

Although most French liquid-fueled engines tended toward the gasolines, several heavier oil (kerosene) burners compared favorably in performance with the English and German. Two, the Merlin (1894) and
the Niel (ca. 1893) competed at Meaux, with the Merlin having the
highest brake thermal efficiency of all at sixteen percent.

Built by M.M. Merlin et Cie., the engine resembled the Grob with its single vertical cylinder and vaporizing-igniting method. At governed speed not only was the exhaust valve held open, the oil pump stopped and the intake valve left closed, but the water pump also ceased circulating coolant in order to retain heat in the cylinder. A necessity to maintain a hot engine at governed speed was crucial with all oil engines because if allowed to cool there would be no ignition upon a drop in speed unless a wasteful heating lamp was left to burn continuously. This problem was particularly true at lighter loads. The Merlin at Meaux had a 6.7 in. by 6.7 in. bore and stroke and developed 4.8 bhp at 283 rpm.[51]

The Compagnie des Moteurs Niel oil engine was based on its successful gas engine of conventional configuration. Oil dropped into an external vaporizer from an overhead tank whose level was maintained by a float. The vaporizer was heated off the same burner that kept an untimed tube igniter at temperature. All of the air entered the vaporizer past a suction-operated valve, mixed with the vaporizing fuel and then passed on into the cylinder through a cam-actuated valve. The Niel produced 6.4 bhp at 177 rpm from a cylinder of 7.17 in. by 14.17 in. bore and stroke.[52]

Capitaine was not the only one in Germany working on oil engines. Deutz in 1891 or 1892 introduced a series quite similar to that of the Crossley. (It was probably a joint effort between the two companies.) By 1900 about 1,700 Deutz oil engines of various designs had been built. Daimler eventually modified the hot-tube igniter gasoline engine to burn kerosene. For the most part, the German manufacturers did as the French and supplied engines capable of running on both gasoline and kerosene.

The Mietz and Weiss Two-Stroke Engine
The only pre-1900 American development in oil engines to reach modest success was the Mietz and Weiss. Built to the patents of Carl W. Weiss in the factory of August Mietz, the engines resulting from this partnership had a production run of twenty years. The Mietz and Weiss Engine Co. of New York City was formed in 1894.

Weiss, born in Sophienthal, Germany in 1834, came to the United States in 1876 to visit the Centennial Exposition and stayed.[53] He was an inventor first and foremost, and patents sold to the Dayton Cash Register Co. helped finance his work on engines. The first of these was for a hot-air and a gas engine patented in 1890.[54] Other ideas followed, with two patents for gas and kerosene burning engines in 1897 being the basis for the designs on which the company began production.[55]

Simplicity was this two-stroke engine's virtue. Crankcase compression (by pumping action from the underside of the piston) loop-scavenged the combustion chamber after the piston uncovered first exhaust ports and then intake ports connected to the crankcase.

A tank on top of the crankcase fed kerosene to a metering pump which discharged through a spray orifice screwed into the cylinder wall. (Figs. 13-22 and 13-23) The nozzle directed the fuel charge against a projecting lip on the end of a "hot-bulb" opening into the combustion chamber. Weiss' 1897 patent drawing showed his original idea for injecting fuel directly into the main combustion chamber rather than into an antechamber vaporizer like the Hornsby.

The Mietz and Weiss engines were well received because of their compactness and low first cost. A 1900 catalog listed nine models

Fig. 13-22   Mietz & Weiss two-stroke engine of 1898. (Hiscox,
Gas, Gasoline and Oil Engines, 1900)

301

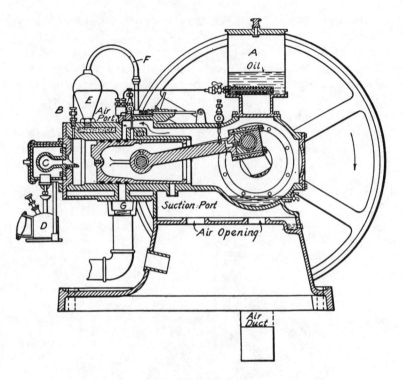

Fig. 13-23   Mietz & Weiss. Two-stroke engines, section view.
(*Cyclopedia of Engineering,* 1916)

ranging from one to thirty horsepower in the single, horizontal cylinder configuration. Occupying a floor space of only thirty by thirty six inches, the one horsepower version weighed, including tank, 600 pounds; its speed was 500 rpm. By 1915 four cylinder, inline engines of 200 horsepower were offered. Mietz died in that year, and because of a disagreement with his executrix over royalties paid to Weiss, the surviving partner left the company. Engine production stopped shortly thereafter.[56]

Advocates of the oil engine were dedicated and faithful to its cause, but were not blind to its limitations. The advantages of safety, access to a suitable fuel and a reasonable reliability were offset by a nuisance of up to a ten to twenty minute delay in starting, a reliance on external heating devices and a serious tendency to fill with carbon. Neither could its inherently poorer efficiency than the gas engine, imposed by the low compression necessary to avoid preignition, be ignored. (Not until the coming of improved fuel systems allowing a later time for injection could compression ratios be raised.) Thus, with the announcement of an engine reported to more than double the work extracted from the same fuel, oil engine builders became vitally interested in Diesel's new invention.

The oil engine served its transitory purpose by preparing the way for a new offspring in the family of internal-combustion engines.

NOTES

1. Bryan Donkin, *Gas, Oil and Air Engines,* 2nd ed., (London, 1896), p. 346.
2. French patent No. 142,877 of May 16, 1881; British No. 3,113 of July 16, 1881, and U.S. No. 272,130 of February 13, 1883.
3. Harry Shoosmith and Philip D. Priestman, *William Dent Priestman and the Development of the Oil Engine,* Diesel Engine Users Assoc., (London, 1944), p. 15. From a letter by E.R. Hillier included in the discussion of the paper.
4. British patent No. 10,227 of August 28, 1885, in the names of W.D. and Joshua Priestman. No drawings.
5. *Ibid.*
6. British patent No. 1,394 of January 30, 1886, to W.D. and Samuel Priestman.
7. Shoosmith, *op. cit.,* p. 16.
8. British patent Nos. 16,779 of December 21, 1886, and 5,255 of April 9, 1887. The latter refers to another patent No. 1,464 of February 1, 1886, to J.J.R. Humes, who was trying to accomplish the same end. Priestman's and Humes' approaches are quite different from each other.
9. Donkin, *op. cit.,* p. 310.
10. J.W. Young, "Notes on the Practical Development of the Oil Engine," *Transactions, The Newcomen Society,* v. XVII, 1936-1937, (London, 1938), p. 112
11. "A New Petroleum Engine," *Scientific American,* November 20, 1886, p. 328.
12. *The Encyclopedia Britannica,* 9th ed., v. XVIII, (Chicago, 1892), p. 243.
13. Shoosmith, *op. cit.,* pp. 3,5. See also: W. McL. Dann, "Early marine oil engines," *The Marine Engineer,* Oct. 1939, p. 308, for

the quoted experiences, and C.L. Cummins & J.D. Priestman, "William Dent Priestman, oil engine pioneer and inventor – his engine patents 1885-1901," *Proceedings, Inst. of Mech. Engrs.,* 1985, Vol. 199, No. 133. The family archives of James Dent Priestman (died 1999), a grandson of W.D.P., provided much new material.

14. Coleman Sellers, "The Priestman Engine from an American Engineering Standpoint," *Engineering,* (London), July 22, 1892, p. 105.

15. Albert Spies, "Modern Gas and Oil Engines," *Cassier's Magazine,* April 1893, p. 439. *Boyd's Philadelphia Business Directory* shows 1901 to be the last year for a company listing.

16. T. Hornbuckle and A. K. Bruce, *Herbert Akroyd Stuart and the Development of the Heavy Oil Engine,* Diesel Engine Users Assoc., (London, 1940), p. 1.

17. British patent No. 9,866 of July 31, 1886, granted to Stuart, "Mechanical Engineer, Bletchley Iron Works."

18. British patent Nos. 7,146 of May 8 and 15,994 of October 8, both of 1890. These two must be considered as a part of a package. Each refers to the other.

19. Wm. Robinson, *Gas and Petroleum Engines,* 2nd ed., v. 2, (London, 1902), p. 694.

20. Hornbuckle and Bruce, *op. cit.,* p. 3.

21. British patent No. 14,076 of October 1, 1888, for example.

22. Hornbuckle and Bruce, *op. cit.*

23. S. Mitton, *Spitalgate and Internal Combustion: 1892-1914,* p. 2. A short tract covering Akroyd Stuart and Hornsby history, given to the author by Mr. Ray Hooley of then Ruston-Paxman Diesel Ltd., Lincoln, England, 1972.

24. Hornbuckle and Bruce, *op. cit.,* p. 8.

25. Robinson, *op. cit.,* p. 694.

26. Young, *op. cit.,* p. 114. Young was an assistant to Edwards at the time and provides a first-hand account of Hornsby's early experiences with the Stuart engine.

27. *Ibid.,* p. 117.

28. Robinson, *op. cit.,* p. 705.

29. Young, *op. cit.,* p. 120.

30. British patent No. 3,909 of February 29, 1892. Another patent of the same year, No. 22,664, had to do with a compressed air starting means. By the end of 1892 Stuart had been granted eight British engine patents.

31. Robinson, *op. cit.,* p. 704.
32. Robinson, *op. cit.,* p. 710.
33. R.A.S. Gimson, "From Hornsby-Akroyd to Ruston AO: 78 years of Medium-Speed Engine Production," *The Motor Ship,* April 1970, p. 27.
34. Young, *op. cit.,* p. 121. See also: Shell Oil Company, *An Outline History of the Oil Engine and Its Lubrication,* (1961), pp. 57-70, for a good historical account of the development of lubricating oils.
35. C.J. Hind, *Akroyd Stuart and the Oil Engines of Lincolnshire,* Diesel Engine Users Assoc., (London, 1963), p. 1. This story, reported in several sources, came from T.H. Barton, founder of Barton Transport Ltd., who was employed by Hornsby at the time.
36. G. Lieckfeld, *Oil Motors,* (London, 1908), p. 34.
37. Gimson, *op. cit.,* p. 27. In 1940 Ruston and Hornsby became part of Davey, Paxman and Co., then as Ruston-Paxman Diesel Ltd. The company has gone through several mergers and takeovers since.
38. Donkin, *op. cit.,* p. 186, from the *Zeitschrift VDI,* v. xxxiv.
39. Friedrich Sass, *Geschichte des deutschen Verbrennungsmotorenbaues von 1860 bis 1918,* (Berlin, 1962), p. 221.
40. Donkin, *op. cit.,* p. 381.
41. Lieckfeld, *op. cit.,* p. 29.
42. Donkin, *op. cit.,* pp. 484-87.
43. Lionel S. Marks & Samuel S. Wyer, *Gas and Oil Engines and Gas Producers,* (Chicago, 1908), part II, p. 35.
44. Eugen Diesel, *Diesel: der Mensch, das Werk, das Schicksal,* (Hamburg, 1937), pp. 300-305.
45. Arthur F. Evans, *The History of the Oil Engine,* (London, ca. 1930), p. 50. The quote originally appeared in a paper Evans delivered to the Institute of Marine Engineers, Nov. 26, 1929, in London. With the exception of his blind spot in regard to Capitaine, Evans does provide an authoritative account of "oil" and diesel engine development. His comments, however must often be viewed as one man's remembrance of the depicted events.
46. Shoosmith and Priestman, *op. cit.,* p. 46.
47. Lieckfeld, *op. cit.,* p. 28.
48. Donkin, *op. cit.,* pp. 486-87.
49. "The Warwick Show," *Engineering,* June 24, 1892, p. 773.
50. Gardner D. Hiscox, *Gas, Gasoline and Oil Engines,* 3rd ed., (New York, 1900), pp. 267-69.

51. Donkin, *op. cit.,* pp. 484-85.
52. Donkin, *op. cit.,* p. 353-54.
53. Weiss' obituary in *The Gas Engine,* April 1915, p. 196, says he came to the U.S. in 1859. Company history gives the later date.
54. U.S. patent Nos. 419,805 and 806 of January 21, 1890.
55. U.S. patent Nos. 592,033 and 034 of October 19, 1897. The former was for a gas engine and the latter the oil.
56. "The Men who Made the Industry," *Diesel Power,* May 1947, p. 73.

Chapter 14

Rudolf Diesel: The End
of the Beginning

Rudolf Christian Karl Diesel (1858-1913) fathered a child of technology and science. After a near fatal birth his new engine suffered through a perilous infancy. Adolescence brought strength but little acceptance. Now, more than a century after conception, its life cycle continues to unfold and in maturity to manifest a promise of even greater achievement.

Why was Diesel's invention unique? His was the first heat engine to directly evolve from the science of thermodynamics. The "Book of Carnot" became a part of his Bible. Diesel analyzed and proved to his satisfaction the engine would work before a single piece of metal was touched. That he later had to revise part of his original thesis or that it eventually required the better part of eight years to develop a marketable engine cannot detract from the visionary concept of his "Economical Heat Motor."

Diesel (Fig. 14-1, Plate) had but one goal for his engine: it must burn less fuel per unit of power than any other prime mover yet devised. His manuscript, written early in 1892 to outline such an engine, closes with a comment on his analysis deeming it "the only way feasible to approach the objective to improve the exploitation of the calorific value of our fuels."[1] Diesel's obsession in the late nineteenth century has become part of a collective and essential dogma in the beginning of the twenty-first.

The changing politics of Europe greatly influenced Rudolf Diesel's life. Although of German parents, he was born in Paris and lived there until his family fled to London in 1870 at the start of the Franco-Prussian War. (If Bavaria, the Diesels' original home, had not joined with Prussia, they could have remained in Paris with Rudolf becoming a French citizen.) The struggle to support a family in London proved even more difficult for Diesel's father, a leather goods maker, than it had been in France. Within a few months it was decided to send twelve year old Rudolf alone to live with a cousin of his father's in Augsburg. Instead of a short stay until the war was over and the Diesels returned to Paris, Rudolf remained for five years with the cousin and her husband, a mathematics professor.

Young Diesel was a brilliant student and the educational opportunities now opened to him were not wasted. His frequent visits to the technical museums of Paris and London aroused in him an intense desire to become an engineer. The sensitive boy was often misunderstood in this by his father who strongly opposed such a career. A first step toward his cherished goal was to enroll in the Royal District Trade School *(Königlichen Kreis-Gewerbsschule)* in Augsburg where his cousin's husband taught.

Diesel visited his parents several times in Paris while he attended the school, but because of their almost dire financial straits and his father's opposition to his taking the time to become an engineer, these were not happy occasions. His cousin's home in Augsburg was a welcome haven, and after three years Diesel completed his studies at the trade school. He became the youngest to graduate from there and did so with highest honors.

One piece of demonstration apparatus that made an indelible impression on Diesel while there was a glass-walled version of the ancient Chinese "firestick." (Fig. 14-2) Operating like a tire pump, a piece of tinder was inserted in the end opposite the plunger. With a rapid inward stroke, the tinder could be observed to ignite under the heat of compression. In later life Diesel used to describe how his engine worked by relating the action of the air pump.

Fig. 14-2   Pneumatic tinder igniter from the school Diesel
attended in Augsburg. (M.A.N. Werk-Archiv)

Because of his outstanding academic record at Augsburg, Diesel was admitted to the Munich Technical School *(Technische Hochschule München)* where he planned to work toward a diploma degree in mechanical engineering. Diesel had to be completely self-supporting during his Munich school days. He was fortunate to receive student grants which he supplemented by giving private tutoring lessons. It was while in Munich, when he turned nineteen, that he became a naturalized German citizen.

He contracted typhoid fever just before his final exams. Although recovering with apparently no ill effects, he had to wait for almost a year before the exams would be given again. One teacher in particular who had befriended the handsome scholar came to his aid during this interim. Prof. Carl von Linde (1842-1934), a renowned expert on heat engines and refrigeration, secured a job for him at Sulzer Brothers in Winterthur. Linde, whose ice making machinery was made by the Swiss firm, enjoyed a close relationship with them. Diesel received his first industrial experience with the famous company. From solving problems using calculus to the filing of a screw thread! However, this traditional apprenticeship procedure gave the new engineer a better understanding of machine tools and their capabilities, a vital bit of knowledge to serve him during his trials of engine development. Diesel took his Munich exams the next year and received the highest marks the school had ever given.

With the coveted diploma in hand, an opportunity soon arose for Diesel to go to Paris to assist in the installation of a large ice plant by a company holding the French sales license for Linde's Sulzer-built products. Thus in 1880 he returned to his native city, but as a German citizen and a man brimming with new ideas.

The world seemed within Diesel's grasp on arriving in Paris at age twenty-two. Within one year he was made manager of the Paris Linde company and given financial security. Two years later he married Martha Flasche, a beautiful German girl who was the talented governess for a French family Diesel had come to know. Three children were born, his business prospered, and more germane to our story, his mind turned to inventing a more efficient heat engine. He often wrote during this period "that it was his aim to create an engine which would eclipse the steam engine."[2] Such a new engine had been a latent, but recurring dream stemming from his university days.

Because of his experience with ammonia as a refrigerant, it was only natural he should first investigate using that as the fluid for a closed-cycle steam engine. His objective was to increase the efficiency over a conventional water based steam engine by highly superheating ammonia vapor in order to obtain a greater temperature differential during the expansion portion of the cycle. (Carnot's principle.) Although Diesel devoted every spare minute and franc for several years on the ammonia engine without success, the knowledge gained from that failure became the genesis of a new engine.

Early in 1892 he outlined in a handwritten manuscript the steps of a transition in his thinking which led to this. Diesel calculated that regardless of the vapor used, either ammonia or water, there was a

> necessity for high pressure because only a great pressure difference will permit the utilization of a steep temperature gradient during expansion... . This gave me the idea to consider the vapour as a gas... . In so doing I discovered that there is practically no difference between vapour and gas, in other words that I might also use gas or air while retaining the high pressure and temperature used in the previous investigation [with ammonia and water]. With high temperature, however, advantageous utilization of a normal combustion process was not feasible. This suggested combustion in the highly compressed air itself. The pursuance of this idea led ... to the concept of the engine.[3]

This statement was omitted from a small book Diesel later published based on that manuscript.[4] Therefore, the essential kernel of his reasoned thinking remained hidden, and what others assumed to be the basis of his invention focused on more restrictive theories.

Diesel was living in Berlin when he formalized the proof of his high compression engine, having moved there in 1890 after accepting an offer from Prof. Linde to manage one of the latter's engineering offices in that city. Diesel regretted leaving Paris and its cosmopolitan atmosphere, but an increasingly uncomfortable French business attitude toward his "German-made" products had become frustrating to him. (Actually, the Linde machinery was manufactured by Sulzer.)

Diesel's Engine Patent of 1892

There is more to the paradox about what Diesel invented and what others thought he invented. The important shade of difference between his manuscript and the subsequent book was compounded by a further omission in his first engine patent claims. The two broadest claims, as filed in his application of February 28, 1892,[5] were "abandoned" when the second petition was sent by his attorney to the German Patent Office two months later; it was a requirement not requested by the patent examiner. These several deletions giving a broader interpretation to his invention would have eliminated or at least alleviated, if they had become general knowledge, much of the personal criticism later directed at him. A proud and yet sensitive man, Diesel suffered great mental anguish over these attacks on his cherished work as well as the aspersions cast on his own integrity.

The patent contained most of the analysis found in the yet unpublished manuscript. He proposed five possible cycles of combustion, the three most important being:

— combustion at constant pressure
— combustion at constant volume
— combustion at constant temperature

His choice, the last, was isothermal combustion, which proceeded along the lines of Carnot's teaching.[6] This proved unfortunate because in practice such a cycle was unworkable and, with the necessary change to a cycle approaching that of constant pressure, critics said neither he nor his licensees, were then building to his patent.

Diesel outlined his constant temperature cycle as follows: adopt the four-stroke cycle, draw in a charge of pure air and compress it to 250 atmospheres. (He speaks in his book of fixing the highest pressure limits at "200 to 300 atmospheres," or about 2,900 to 4,300 psi![7]) With the air heated to 800 to 1,000°C at the end of the compression stroke, fuel would gradually be added as the piston started on its outward stroke. The rate of fuel admission was such "that the produced heat is entirely or partly absorbed by the increase of the volume ... so that the prescribed maximum temperature [due to the heat of compression alone] is not surpassed, and that finally during this combustion no heat is led away to the outside."[8] By the process, cylinder gases theoretically cooled down to near atmospheric, and the cylinder walls needed no external cooling. According to Diesel, indicated thermal efficiencies as high as seventy to eighty percent could be achieved. On paper all looked well, but a serious restriction inherent in this analysis required a major shift in Diesel's thinking when actual development work began.

The abandoned patent claims of Diesel's application, numbers one and two in the original draft copy, substantially read:

> 1. Avoiding the mixing of air and fuel — meaning only air was to be inducted;
> 2. Compressing the combustion air to a pressure high above the level hitherto used, in such manner that the compression temperature rises far beyond the fuel ignition temperatures.[9]

If these two claims had been combined to include no mixing of fuel with air *and* to compress the air to the specified high pressure, it is very likely such a claim would have been allowed. The Examiner himself reinstated the sense of what they disclosed, using it as prefaces in claims covering the constant temperature combustion process and in doing so altered what was meant by a Diesel engine. Claim number one of Diesel's British patent (identical in meaning to the German) illustrates the reduced impact by the combining:[10]

> 1. The method of working combustion motors consisting in compressing in a cylinder by a working piston, pure air, to such an extent, that the temperature hereby produced is far higher than the burning or igniting point of the fuel to be employed; (curve 1-2 ...) [Fig. 14-3] whereupon fuel is supplied at the dead center gradually, that on account of the outward motion of the piston and the consequent expansion of the compressed air or gas the combustion takes place without essential increase of temperature and pressure (curve 2-3 ...) whereupon, after the admission of fuel has been cut off, the further expansion of the body of gas contained in the working cylinder takes place (curve 3-4 ...)... .

Whether or not Diesel's patent attorney, one of the best in Berlin, had concern over possible prior patenting by Akroyd Stuart of the broad compression-ignition claims is not known. Claim 2 of Stuart's British patent No. 7,146 of 1890 reads: "In an engine operated by the explosion of a mixture of combustible gas or vapour and air, forming the said mixture by introducing the combustible gas or vapour into a charge of air under compression, substantially as described." The "charge of air under compression" required a secondary heat source (the vaporizer ante-chamber) to raise the temperature high enough for ignition. (See Chapter 13) This was the essence of Stuart's invention and not the

312

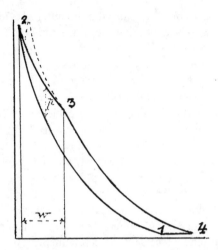

Fig. 14-3 Pressure-volume diagram of an isothermal combustion
cycle as shown in Diesel's German patent No. 67,207
of 1892)

deliberate employment of highly compressed air for maximum expansion and efficiency.

There is a possible explanation for Diesel's acceptance of the isothermal expansion cycle of Carnot in the patent rather than what made that cycle feasible in the first place. Both Prof. Linde, and another highly respected teacher from his Munich alma mater, Prof. Moritz Schröter, enthusiastically accepted the ideas put forth in his manuscript. Diesel had to assume that if experts were so sure of the cycle's practicality, who was he to change his mind and decide that it might not be the best one for his high compression engine. For whatever reason, personal pride or a wish not to embarrass his mentors, Diesel never publicly admitted until it was too late that his engine could not and did not run on a modified Carnot cycle. While Diesel was still defending his earlier-held beliefs, the great academicians who had reinforced him in such thinking remained silent.

A true engineer, Diesel used analytical techniques for problem solving. Some said he was too theoretical and impractical, yet consider the realm of his work. He was advancing the state of the art by a quantum leap with his unheard of cylinder pressures. No one but a highly competent engineer could have intelligently tackled the problems to be faced. Being forced to lower his objectives and modify his theories

313

should not discredit him. Anyone who is willing to extend the frontiers of the possible has experienced failure and rethinking, and come out the better for it.

Heinrich von Buz and Maschinenfabrik-Augsburg

With the filing of his pioneer patent Diesel could now seek someone to develop and build his engine. His first choice, Prof. Linde's firm, had no interest. He then turned to Heinrich Buz (1833-1918), the director of Maschinenfabrik-Augsburg A.G. with whom he had had some deal-ings while still in Paris. Founded in 1840, the company was world famous for their high-speed printing presses and triple expansion steam engines. Diesel contacted them because of their expertise in building refrigeration machinery. Maschinenfabrik-Augsburg A.G. was to merge with Maschinenbau A.G. Nürnberg in 1898. The name of this amalga-mation was shortened in 1908 to Maschinenfabrik Augsburg-Nürnberg A.G., or M.A.N. AG. (Today the diesel division of MAN AG is MAN B&W Diesel AG, the name assumed when MAN fully assimilated Burmeister & Wain, the Danish diesel company in 1984.)

M.A.N. became the birthplace of Diesel's engine, and to Heinrich von Buz must go the recognition of making that birth possible. Buz (Fig. 14-4, Plate) could see in Diesel's proposals both a future threat to his company's steam engine business as well as the promise of a new power source. At first Buz rejected entering into the project because of the extremely high compression pressures involved, but after Diesel calculated the engine should still work at a much lower pressure the director's interest was kindled. In his original letter to Buz, Diesel had already reduced the pressure from 250 to 150 kg/cm². Diesel had come to realize no one would accept even the lower figure, so after another analysis the new workable pressure became 44 kg/cm² or 626 psi.

On April 20, 1892, Buz wrote Diesel that Maschinenfabrik-Augsburg would build an experimental engine to determine if the combustion system Diesel proposed was viable. It was to be a step by step evaluation and development; efficiency considerations were of secondary importance. An agreement was signed the following February 21st with one of the terms being that Diesel would receive a twenty-five percent royalty. Diesel meanwhile had published his manu-script and was able to interest Krupp in sharing the developmental costs with M.A.N. It was only through Buz's personal enthusiasm over the potential of the new engine that the Krupp directors finally signed a contract with Diesel. This document, formalized on April 10, 1893, specified that not only would development costs (and later profits) be shared between the two companies, but it also stipulated Diesel was to receive an annual sum of 30,000 marks during the trial period. With a very comfortable income assured he could devote full time to the engine. All work was to be done in Augsburg.

Constant Pressure Combustion

Diesel had begun to have serious doubts about the practicality of his isothermal combustion cycle before the tests started. Several authorities had questioned that, if the cylinder temperature was to remain constant as the fuel entered and burned, the derived power would as a consequence be extremely low. (Only about fifteen percent of the air was expected to be utilized for combustion.) Yet to increase the work extracted per cycle would mean more fuel had to be added and the concept of isothermal combustion abandoned. Diesel made a thorough reanalysis of his original calculations, this time incorporating a parameter of maximum potential power as well as maximum efficiency. In notes of mid-1893 entitled "Supplements to the Theory of the Diesel Engine" he concluded that:[11]

1. Combustion at constant temperature is out of the question.
2. Combustion under constant pressure is the only process to be adopted.

This was total rejection of the Carnot process being ideally suited to the I-C engine. However, even with the shift to a constant pressure combustion cycle (not to be confused with Brayton's continuous combustion process) there remained an opportunity to at least double the thermal efficiency of a gas engine, still a major accomplishment. Why Diesel waited almost twenty years to make public his reversal in thinking remains an unsolved mystery. Nevertheless, the "Diesel cycle" of constant pressure combustion became a term in the engineer's lexicon alongside that of the Otto (or Beau de Rochas) and Clerk. The worry over potentially low power outputs ended, and Diesel went ahead with the tests although he had preknowledge the uncooled cylinder would have to be changed.

The First Development Engines: 1893-1894

The initial test engine (Fig. 14-5; Fig. 14-6, Plate) completed in July of 1893 never ran under its own power. It pointed out a myriad of problems, but proved to Diesel's satisfaction that a charge of fuel injected at the end of the compression stroke could be ignited solely by the heat of compression.

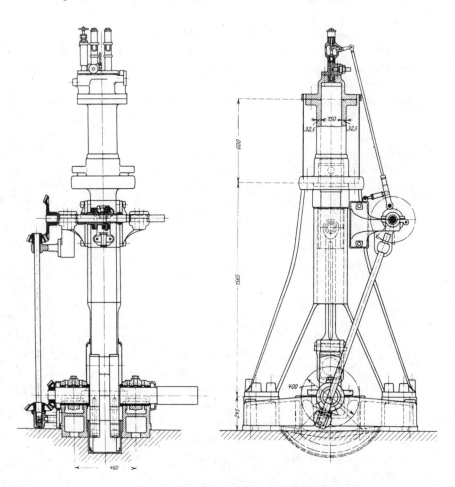

Fig. 14-5   Elevation and partial section views of Diesel's first experimental engine of 1893. Note in the end view the sheet metal encasing to form a cylinder waterjacket. This was not added until later. (Diesel, *Die Entstehung des Dieselmotors*, 1813)

Several misconceptions exist about Diesel's first engine, one being that it ran on coal dust. Diesel chose or was urged to choose liquid fuels from the outset, and not until after acceptance tests held in 1897 did he spend any time on powdered coal as a fuel. These coal tests covered only a relatively short period at M.A.N. (One of Diesel's assistants, Rudolf Pawlikowski, continued with the development of such an engine at other companies until 1940.) Another traditional tale relates that this engine was badly damaged in an explosion the first time fuel was added. (What actually happened will be seen shortly.) All of the early diesel* engines after the very first depended upon high pressure air to blast the fuel charge into the cylinder. "Air injection" was a necessary crutch until technology was created to avoid the problems associated with high pressure hydraulics and "solid injection." Diesel did not yet know all that lay ahead of him in this area, and had assumed a plunger pump and needle-type injection valve would suffice. The initial system was a failure; poor and undependable spray characteristics, because of varying and too low injector pressures, caused incomplete or no combustion. It was a desperation move to finally add the air blast for fuel delivery.

Many features of the Augsburg design were unique to contemporary gas and gasoline engine practice.[12] A vertical, uncooled cylinder of 150 mm bore and 400 mm stroke was mounted on an A-frame base, a common construction for large steam engines. (Fig. 14-7) A long, ringless piston (Diesel referred to it as a "plunger piston") was sealed at the lower end of the cylinder by a thin, U-shaped bronze band forced it against by oil pressure. This also served as a piston lubricant. The seal proved a failure, and after many intervening designs a built-up piston with rings evolved. (Fig. 14-8) A deep, cylindrical pocket formed in the crown of the piston contained most of the combustion chamber volume at the time of ignition.

The cylinder head was filled with valves: a combined intake and exhaust valve having a double seat; an adjustable safety valve vented into an external compressed air tank; an outward opening pintle valve in the fuel nozzle; and a timed valve also opening to the air tank. This last valve initially had two functions: it acted as an air starting valve to admit tank air into the cylinder to turn over the engine; then after the engine was running on its own the tank was supposed to be recharged by taking a portion of the air from each compression stroke when the air valve was opened by a cam. A separate compressor was required to pump up the tank initially or to make up for any recharging difficulties.

*The author has chosen not to capitalize "diesel" when it is used in the generic sense.

a) "Plunger" piston
b) Piston sealing ring
c) Safety valve
d) Starting and tank charging valve
e) Fuel needle valve ("solid" injection)
f) Combined intake and exhaust valve

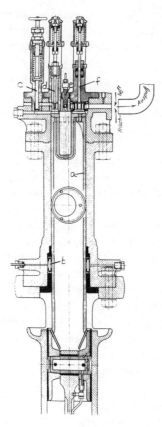

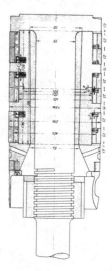

Fig. 14-7
Section view of cylinder and head
of first Diesel experimental engine,
1893. (Diesel, *Entstehung . . .*)

Fig. 14-8
Piston construction of 1894 engine.
(Diesel, *Entstehung . . .*)

The first twenty days of the test were spent in "running in" the engine
to correct lubrication and machining deficiencies as well as to determine cylinder compression pressures. No fuel was added. Initially
the maximum attainable pressure reached only eighteen atmospheres
(265 psi) which was far short of the designed forty-four atmospheres.
Stopping various leaks past seals and valves raised the pressure to about
thirty-three atmospheres, but the remaining cause of the compression
loss eluded them. Diesel finally discovered that irregularities in the
combustion chamber and a larger than designed-for piston cavity had

increased the clearance volume by sixty percent.[13] When this situation was corrected the actual testing could begin, and on August 10, 1893, the first charge of fuel, gasoline(!), was injected. The resulting combustion generated an estimated pressure of eighty atmospheres, blasting pieces of the indicator mechanism valve between Diesel and his friend Lucien Vogel (1855-1915), a chief engineer of another major department at M.A.N. It was a dramatic announcement by the engine to herald its future.

Inherent design deficiencies appeared as testing proceeded. The maximum indicated power developed by the engine was only a little over two horsepower, or far less than enough for it to run by itself. The fact that sufficient compression pressures, eight to ten times other I-C engines, could be generated and that fuel could be injected into the cylinder at those pressures to start any kind of combustion at all is in retrospect an accomplishment, but at the time the enthusiasm in Augsburg was not overwhelming. Thirty-eight days from the first cranking over the tests were terminated.

New tests began the following January on an engine incorporating the changes found to be necessary from the first series.[14] Separate exhaust and intake valves were added, with the exhaust valve containing a small, pilot valve which opened before the main valve. (Fig. 14-9) The functions of the safety and air tank charging valves were combined into a single unit. The piston was lubricated from oil-filled grooves attached to the bottom of the skirt. A removable cylindrical cavity in the piston crown allowed cavity volume changes. Not only did a water jacket encircle the exhaust passage in the head, but a piece of sheet metal, wrapped around the cast steel cylinder, formed a jacket to cool that also.[15]

Control of fuel injection remained an extremely difficult and frustrating problem. The first attempt using compressed air to assist in the injection process used this method: The fuel charge was metered and pumped into a cavity around a needle valve leading into the combustion chamber. After top dead center a cam lifted the needle off its seat, at the same time admitting air from a small accumulator into the valve cavity. The fuel, driven by the air, was blasted into the cylinder through small spray-forming holes; partial mixing of the fuel and blast air aided in the atomizing. The net driving force of the air obviously depended on a pressure differential between the cylinder and the accumulator. This created a problem because the accumulator was charged from the cylinder itself. As a consequence, injection had to be delayed until cylinder pressure had dropped from its maximum. Even then the injection characteristics were

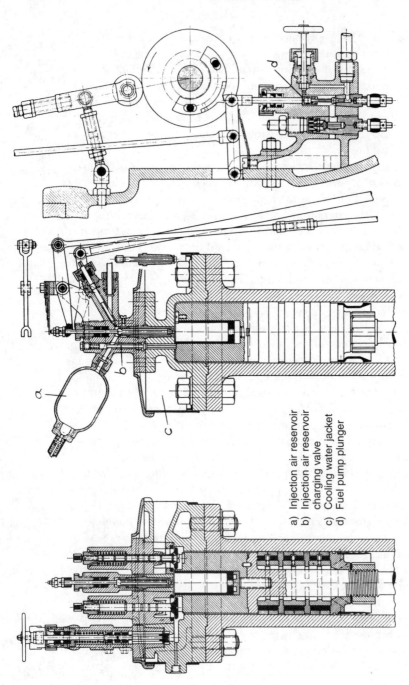

Fig. 14-9   Cylinder and fuel pump section views of engine after first modification, 1894. (Diesel, *Entstehung* ...)

a) Injection air reservoir
b) Injection air reservoir charging valve
c) Cooling water jacket
d) Fuel pump plunger

poor and in turn caused late and only partial combustion. Diesel realized a separate compressor ultimately had to be added which would greatly increase the engine's cost. The test series was completed with an auxiliary air compressor driven by another source of power.

Another momentous date in the engine's early development occurred during this second test series. On February 17, 1894, it ran for a whole minute at 88 rpm under its own power. The maximum output achieved during this period ending in April was 13.2 indicated horsepower.

Precise fuel injection by high pressure air continued to elude an increasingly frustrated Diesel; accurate control over the air was proving extremely difficult. As a result, the injection of gaseous fuels was explored as an alternate possibility. Beginning in April, and for almost a year, hardware was made to inject heated and carbureted kerosene, coal gas and, using dual injectors, both liquid kerosene and coal gas. At that time coal gas held a great attraction in Germany because of the prohibitive cost of oil as set by the cartels and a high import duty. Krupp in particular hoped that Diesel could perfect a gas-fueled version.

Auxiliary electric ignition systems were also tried in order to improve combustion. Even Robert Bosch came to Augsburg at Diesel's invitation to see what kind of spark plug he might be able to devise that could live in Diesel's high pressure cylinder.

The engine went through its third redesign in early 1895. Onto the original A-frame base was added a larger iron cylinder with a cast-in water jacket. (Fig. 14-10) The piston stroke remained at 400 mm, but the bore diameter increased to 220 mm. An overhead camshaft directly actuated the various valves through rocker levers.

The cylinder head had a variety of features to give more test flexibility. A concentric intake and exhaust valve cage construction allowed air and exhaust passages to open into the cylinder independently of each other. All of the combustion chamber clearance volume was in a deep cylindrical cavity in the head itself. A spark plug was screwed into the base of the head with its electrodes protruding horizontally into the cavity.

A housing containing needle valves to admit either oil, gas, or a combination of both formed a cover over the clearance volume cavity. Extending from the fuel valve housing down into the cavity was Diesel's patented, new "double star burner"[16] hopefully to promote better combustion. Fuel passed through a tube into two discs spaced along the tube, each having radially drilled small holes to spray the fuel horizontally into the cavity. (This would be only the first only of a myriad of "injection" configurations tried.)

321

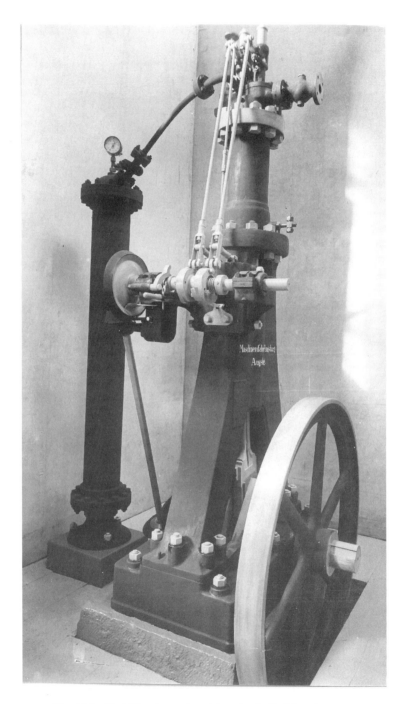

FIg. 14-6   First Diesel experimental engine built at Augsburg,
1893. (M.A.N. Historische Archiv)

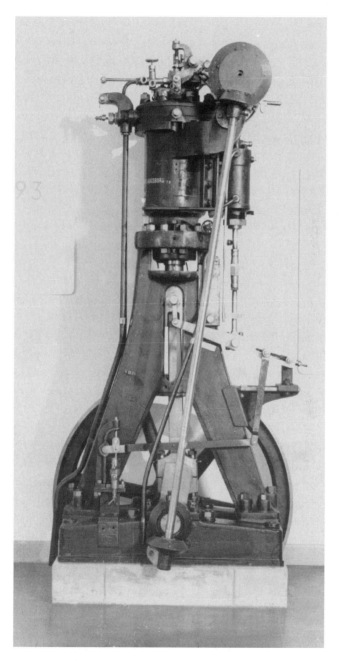

Fig. 14-12   Experimental Diesel engine of 1895-96 in the
collection of the M.A.N. Museum, Augsburg.
(M.A.N. Historische Archiv)

Fig. 14-13   The officially demonstrated diesel engine on test at
M.A.N., February 1897. Its twin is on exhibit at the
Deutsches Museum in Munich. Note the Prony brake
dynamometer and the cooling water hoses going to
and from the cylinder water jacket to cool the piston.
(M.A.N. Historische Archiv)

No power figure was stated, but earlier tests in April yielded 23 ihp at 200 rpm and 34 ihp at 300 rpm.

Testing proceeded with many modifications made to the "star burner": a single, shower head-like disc; four evenly spaced discs; a tube with radially drilled holes, etc. All worked to a more or lesser degree, but the rapid hole carboning could not be eliminated. Diesel next tried a "button" needle valve seat having various spray hole combinations. (Fig. 14-11) These gave the most promise and the protruding "burner" was abandoned.

The addition of an integral air compressor comprised the last major revision to the engine. (Fig. 14-12, Plate) A complex linkage actuated the compressor piston. Overheating of this piston would cause the lubricating oil to catch fire, a problem overcome by water cooling the compressor cylinder.

An exhaust gas analysis by a Krupp chemist confirmed the M.A.N. engineers' surmise that the cylinder did not receive a full charge of air through the restricted intake valve cage. This intake arrangement had been a calculated gamble by Diesel because the cylinder head lacked sufficient area over the piston to add another valve.

The Acceptance Tests of 1897

It was time at last to design a new engine from a clean sheet of paper. All of what had been learned during the painful experimentation of the previous two and a half years could be incorporated in it. Both Buz and

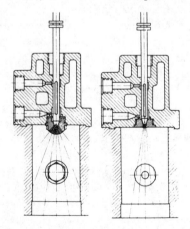

Fig. 14-11 Fuel injector nozzle design, 1896. (Diesel, *Entstehung . . .*)

the Krupp management were encouraged enough to commit funds for an all-out effort, and their confidence proved to be justified. Design work began in January of 1896 and by October a completed engine stood ready.

The external configuration had several distinguishable differences from its predecessors. (Fig. 14-13, Plate) The water-cooled piston operated through a crosshead whose guide was attached to a massive cast pedestal forming one-half of an A-frame. A canted, tubular column provided the other support for the cylinder. An air compressor housing also assembled onto the pedestal. (Fig. 14-14)

The cylinder bore was increased again to 250 mm while the stroke remained at 400 mm. A flat piston crown and cylinder head formed a simple, cylindrical-shaped combustion chamber. Grooved extensions beneath the piston skirt dipped into an annulus-shaped sump at the bottom of the stroke to pick up oil for cylinder wall and piston lubrication. A safety valve was inserted horizontally through the cylinder wall and into the clearance space. (Fig. 14-15)

During the design phase a sudden fear arose that air breathing would be deficient, even with the intake valve separate from the exhaust. This caused the addition of an under-piston charging system. An "automatic" suction and a mechanically actuated discharge valve at the closed off base of the cylinder acted to supercharge the combustion chamber. (Fig. 14-15) When engine tests began it was discovered that the air charging cost more in pumping losses than it helped to improve volumetric efficiency, and the system was removed before the official tests.

A plunger pump with a bypass metering valve for throttling forced a measured fuel charge into the axially located injector. Air for injection entered above the fuel, and as before, when the cam lifted the needle valve the fuel was blasted into the cylinder. The separate air compressor allowed a much greater pressure differential over compression pressure so that adequate force could finally be put behind the fuel to sufficiently atomize the injected fuel and air mixture. The resultant spray combination not only offered good penetration but made for a very "soft" combustion, i.e. a slower rate of pressure rise after injection started. (Diesel "knock" was not heard on these early air-injected engines.) .

Diesel's day of triumph neared. By February of 1897 the new engine's performance had been observed by Krupp, Deutz and Sulzer Bros. The development partners decided that an official test, witnessed by a disinterested observer, would be used as verification of the engine's capabilities. Prof. Schröter came to Augsburg and supervised tests on February 17th having these results:[17]

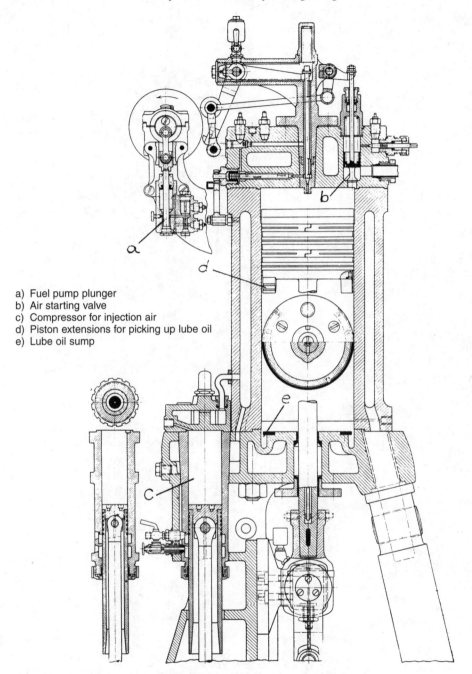

a) Fuel pump plunger
b) Air starting valve
c) Compressor for injection air
d) Piston extensions for picking up lube oil
e) Lube oil sump

Fig. 14-14   Section views of this 1896-97 experimental engine. (Diesel, *Entstehung . . .*)

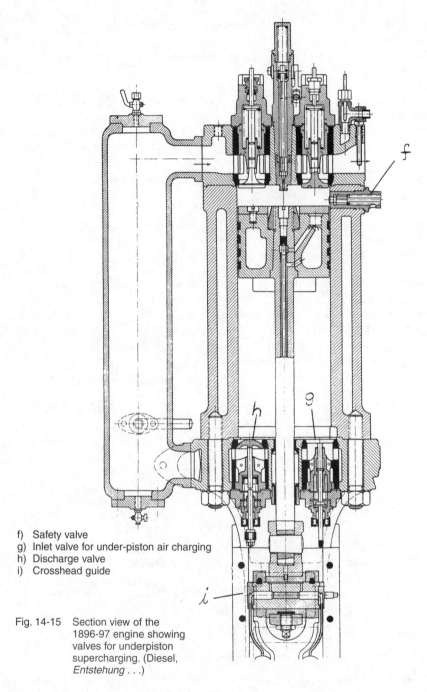

f) Safety valve
g) Inlet valve for under-piston air charging
h) Discharge valve
i) Crosshead guide

Fig. 14-15   Section view of the
1896-97 engine showing
valves for underpiston
supercharging. (Diesel,
Entstehung . . .)

326

Brake horsepower 17.8
Engine speed, rpm 154
Indicated thermal efficiency, %
    Full load 34.7
    Half load 38.9
Brake thermal efficiency, %
    Full load 26.2
    Half load 22.5
Brake specific fuel consumption, g/bhp hr
    Full load 238

A full load p-v diagram taken during the test (Fig. 14-16) shows a "fat" loop and an almost rounded beginning of combustion at the peak pressure point. It is a curve bearing little resemblance to the isothermal combustion curve proposed five years earlier.

Diesel proved to the world that his was the most efficient heat engine ever built. Its efficiency almost doubled that of the average oil engine then available. The figures attested to by Schröter were not the highest attained by the engine. A subsequent test on October 10th yielded a full load brake efficiency of 30.2 percent. While this engine ran reliably and consistently, often for days, it still has to be considered an advanced prototype and not a production design. (A duplicate to the engine, later placed in the Deutsches Museum at Munich, is driven by an electric motor so that the external mechanism may be observed in motion.)

Others shared in the trials and triumphs of the engine's early days at M.A.N. They supported Diesel and gave him that extra effort, without

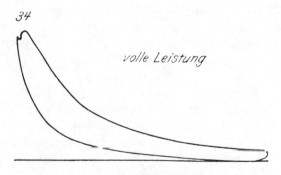

Fig. 14-16 Full-load indicator diagram taken during tests of
                February 1897. Peak pressure was 34 atmospheres
                or 500 psi. (Diesel, *Entstehung . . .*)

which failure would have been a surety. His friend Lucien Vogel, also Buz' son-in-law, worked on the entire early development program. Imanuel Lauster (1873-1948) came to M.A.N. in 1896 to begin on the design of the "acceptance" engine. Lauster's many contributions helped to make the diesel a commercial success for M.A.N. He became chief engineer at Augsburg and finally director of diesel activities for all of M.A.N. Fritz Reichenbach, Hans Linder and Franz Schmucker were other dedicated assistants. They formed part of a trouble-shooting team who managed to keep the first engines running, and placating customers, as these engines suffered through their introductory problems.

Above all, Diesel owed to Heinrich von Buz a debt of gratitude for his steadfastness in the project through the more than four years since the project began. A letter Diesel wrote to his sustainer on February 10, 1897, expressed both a prideful sense of achievement and humility:[18]

> Highly respected *Herr Commerzienrath!*
>
> Although I am far from entertaining an opinion that with my new motor I have now obtained the objectives which I set before me, I am warranted in saying that the results so far obtained go far beyond what has heretofore been done, and that the principles I have followed signify a new era in engine construction.
>
> I realize that I could not have advanced thus far without the kind, competent and generous assistance you gave me and I also know that you must have placed great trust in me and my cause to promote it as you did, never losing patience, even in the dark moments when no real progress became apparent, but always steering toward the goal with superior wisdom and experience.
>
> To your good wife also I wish to express my gratitude for the hospitality I enjoyed in your home and the often repeated words of encouragement and appeals to patience which went right to my heart and helped me to make my way through the many adversities with which I was confronted during the times of the test period.
>
> Most Gratefully,
> Diesel

The Licensees

Prospective licensees were arriving in Augsburg even before the official tests of February 1897 as the word spread about the encouraging test work. Diesel's earlier book had not been forgotten, and there were those who took it upon themselves to stay informed of the progress, or lack of it, on the engine.

Diesel held license agreements with M.A.N. and Krupp giving them rights to manufacture and sell in Germany, but the rest of the world remained free for him to exploit. Gebrüder Sulzer were interested in the engine from the outset, and they had signed an option agreement in May 1893 in which they were to pay Diesel 20,000 marks per year until deciding to build engines themselves. This was finally done in 1903 and began Sulzer's entry into a field that soon saw it become one of the leaders.

Two early licensees from 1894 carried on development work concurrent with that at Augsburg: F. Dyckhoff Fils, Bar-le-Duc, France (Frédéric Dyckhoff, one of the brothers, was an engineer friend of Diesel's), and Carels Frères in Ghent, Belgium. Both Dyckhoff and Carels had operable engines prior to 1897, and the latter was one of the first to construct larger size diesels after 1900.

Gasmotoren-Fabrik Deutz took a sub-license from M.A.N. (still Maschinenfabrik Augsburg) and Krupp in 1897. Diesel licensed Mirrlees, Watson & Yaryan Co. Ltd. of Glasgow who built the first British diesel also in 1897. Adolphus Busch (1839-1913) acquired rights for the United States and Canada in 1897 and the following year had made the first U.S. diesel for his St. Louis brewery. He founded also in 1898 the Diesel Motor Company of America, New York City, a firm that fought for years to survive before the right designs and proper manufacturing gave the engine a chance.[19] In all, there were fifty-one options, licenses and sublicenses granted by Diesel and his assigns before 1900, with a total of eighty-one by the time the basic patent expired.

Diesel was at the pinnacle of his success, having acquired both fame and fortune. Sadly, even though the outer man retained a look of confidence and pride, the soul went through stormy seas. His health, undermined by the mental frustration of the trying years in the test lab at Augsburg, forced him to take more time away from work. Always subject to severe headaches since a boy, he had for years fought off painful and more frequent attacks striking his nervous system. (There was no decisive medical diagnosis of his occasional infirmity, but the evidence now points to him being manic-depressive.) Rest seemed to be the only remedy. Aggravating his strained nerves was a declining state of his finances. He had few peers as an engineer, but as a businessman he fared poorly. Extravagant living, bestowed not so much on himself as on his wife and children, ate into his resources. The later demise of a patent holding and development company (Allgemeine Gesellschaft für Dieselmotoren A.G., Augsburg), set up in 1898 and to which all of his millions on paper had been pledged, gradually eroded his net worth to a dangerously low point.

Some harsh critics claimed his productive work ended shortly after the success of the Augsburg tests, but the record disproves this. One of his contributions was the tireless promotion of the engine's potential.

Finally, beset by failing health, financial adversity and a new round of vicious criticism, Diesel disappeared from a boat crossing the English Channel on a calm moonlight night in September 1913.

The diesel made its public debut in Munich at an exposition of power plants held during June 1898 where engines built by M.A.N., Krupp and Deutz operated side by side in a show of solidarity. Three of Germany's most prestigious manufacturers of internal and external combustion prime movers were announcing that they believed in this newest heat engine. Nevertheless, acceptance came slowly, and years passed before the ponderous, slow-speed machine found its way from a stationary power producer into other applications.

NOTES

1. Rudolf Diesel, *Theorie und Construction eines rationellen Wärmemotors,* p. 64 of a manuscript completed at the beginning of 1892. Translation by Kurt Schnauffer, *The invention of the Diesel Engine – the triumph of a theory,* (Augsburg, 1958), p. 6.

2. Johannes Lehmann, *Rudolf Diesel and Burmeister & Wain,* (Copenhagen, 1938), p. 13.

3. Diesel, *op. cit.*

4. Rudolf Diesel, *Eines rationellen Wärmemotors,* (Berlin, 1892). Translation by Bryan Donkin: *Theory and Construction of a Rational Heat Motor,* (London, 1894), 85 p.

5. German patent No. 67,207 of December 23, 1892, (Filing date February 28, 1892) followed by British No. 7,241 of April 14, 1892, and U.S. No. 542,846 of July 16, 1895. Diesel received a patent, based on the German, from all the European industrial countries.

6. For a more complete story of Diesel and his Carnot engine see: Lyle Cummins, *Diesel's Engine,* (Wilsonville, 1993).

7. Rudolf Diesel, Donkin translation, *op. cit.,* p. 47.

8. British patent No. 7,241 of 1892, p. 4.

9. Schnauffer, *op. cit.,* p. 9. Fig. 2, p. 9 is a photo of the handwritten draft claims.

10. British patent No. 7,241 of 1892, p. 13.

11. Schnauffer, *op. cit.,* p. 14.

12. Rudolf Diesel, *Die Entstehung des Dieselmotors,* (Berlin, 1913), p. 8ff.

13. *Ibid.,* p. 13.

14. *Ibid.,* p. 15ff.

15. Friedrich Sass, *Geschichte des deutschen Verbrennungsmotorenbaues von 1860 bis 1918,* (Berlin, 1962), p. 442.

16. German patent No. 86,633 of March 30, 1895. Similar patents for the newly incorporated improvement were British No. 4,243 of February 27, 1895, and U.S. No. 608,845 of August 9, 1898. The U. S. patent was reissued on April 2, 1901, (No. 11,900) with four additional claims. Diesel was granted several other improvement patents, which like the above, were granted in numerous industrialized countries.

17. Diesel, *Die Entstehung, op. cit.,* pp. 84-85, and Sass, *op. cit.,* p. 440.

18. John W. Anderson, "Diesel, Fifty Years of Progress," *Diesel and Gas Engine Progress,* May 1948, p. 27, and Schnauffer, *op. cit.,* p. 16, with slight translation changes by the author.

19. See: Cummins, *op. cit.,* for the story of the diesel engine's introduction into America.

Epilogue

By 1900 the spectrum of reciprocating internal-combustion engines was virtually complete. Gas, gasoline and the less volatile oil fuels, spark and compression ignition, four-stroke and two-stroke cycles all offered a variety of choices for designers. Creative minds of the nineteenth century, filled with an internal fire of their own genius left a legacy for the new "century of power" to follow.

As that now past century has also closed, a differing set of conditions raises questions about these machines that have been with us since the Ottos, the Clerks and the Diesels brought them into being. A concern for the quality of our environment and the conservation of resources has caused a penetrating look to be taken at these long time companions. Fortunately, newly discovered understanding of the fire burning within their cylinders and the technology developing from that knowledge will help to restore our engine friends' reputations.

How interesting are the means by which that reputation will be redeemed: a stratified-charge engine, proposed one hundred years ago by Otto, and an ultra-light, clean burning, high-speed diesel engine for personal transportation vehicles. The Stirling engine remains a question mark although it burns cleanly and efficiently on almost any fuel. We see combinations of spark ignition or diesel combined with electric power to form "hybrid" combinations that may only be interim solutions until fuel cells penetrate the market in significant numbers.

With our anxiety over the life of resource reserves and their effective management, it is well for us to heed the lessons taught through the successes and failures of earlier engine pioneers. Because of limited technology, they at times, too, faced apparent energy shortages, but as the need arose they developed or adapted new fuels to engine use. Working on the engine itself, they increased thermal efficiencies by six-fold from Watt to Diesel.

Our generation faces a similar challenge in a real liquid fuel energy shortage that may come within the lifetime of many now living. As we plunge into the seeking of solutions to our dilemma, we must never must never forget that *an engine and the fuel it consumes are inseparable partners;* the one cannot progress without the full cooperation of the other. This precept is vital to the planning of future I-C powerplants, since an engine's design, whatever the source that lights the fire, determines its fuel and binds us to those future resource requirements.

INTERNAL FIRE

The future of the I-C engine is exciting to anticipate because with new technology, still only in the mind's eye of some creative soul, it is too early to predict that the demise of the internal combustion engine is at hand.

BIBLIOGRAPHY

As chapter notes include most of the sources drawn upon, it would seem redundant to list them all in a bibliography. The following, therefore, are distilled sources, including those already cited, to offer a general background.

Anderson, John W., "Diesel, Fifty Years of Progress," *Diesel and Gas Engine Progress,* May, 1948.

Cardwell, D.S.L., *From Watt to Clausius.* Ithaca: Cornell University Press, 1971.

Carnot, Nicolas Leonard Sadi, *Reflections on the Motive Power of Fire; and Other Papers on the Second Law of Thermodynamics, by E. Clapeyron and Clausius.* Edited. and intro. by E. Mendoza. New York: Dover Publications, 1960.

Clerk, Dugald, *The Gas and Oil Engine,* 6th ed. New York: John Wiley & Sons, 1896.

Cummins, Lyle, *Diesel's Engine: From Conception to 1918.* Wilsonville, Oregon: Carnot Press, 1993.

Dickinson, H.W., *A Short History of the Steam Engine.* London: Frank Cass, 1963.

Diesel, Eugen, Gustav Goldbeck and Friedrich Schildberger, *From Engines to Autos,* trans. by Peter White. Chicago: Henry Regnery, 1960.

Diesel, Rudolf, *Die Entstehung des Dieselmotors.* Berlin: Verlag von Julius Springer, 1913.

Diesel, Rudolf, *Theory and Construction of a Rational Heat Motor,* trans. by Bryan Donkin. New York: Spon & Chamberlain, 1894.

Donkin, Bryan, *Gas, Oil and Air Engines,* 2nd ed. London: Charles Griffin, 1896.

Emmerson, George S., *Engineering Education — A Social History.* Newton Abbot, England: David & Charles Ltd., 1973.

Evans, A. F., *The History of the Oil Engine.* London: Sampson Low, ca. 1930.

Goldbeck, Gustav, *Gebändigte Kraft-Die Geschichte der Erfindung des Otto-Motors.* Munich: Heinz Moos Verlag, 1965.

Güldner, Hugo, *Das Entwerfen und Berechnen der Verbrennungs-kraftmaschinen und Kraftgas-Anlagen.* Berlin: Verlag von Julius Springer, 1921.

Hardenberg, Horst O., *The Middle Ages of the Internal-Combustion Engine 1794-1886.* Warrendale: SAE, 1999.

Hiscox, Gardner D., *Gas, Gasoline and Oil Vapor Engines,* 3rd ed. New York: Munn & Co., 1900.

Klemm, Friedrich, *A History of Western Technology.* Cambridge, Mass.: MIT Press, 1964.

Lieckfeld, Georg, *Oil Motors, Their Development, Construction, and Management.* London: Charles Griffin, 1908.

Obert, Edward F., *Internal Combustion Engines,* 3rd ed. Scranton: International Textbook Co., 1968.

Redwood, Boverton and George T. Holloway, *Petroleum and its Products,* 2 vols. London: Charles Griffin, 1896.

Ricardo, Sir Harry and J. G. G. Hempson, *The High-Speed Internal Combustion Engine,* 5th ed. London: Blackie & Son, 1968.

Robinson, Wm., *Gas and Petroleum Engines.* London: E. & F.N. Spon, 1890.

Roller, Duane, *The Early Development of the Concepts of Temperature and Heat — The Rise and Decline of the Caloric Theory.* Cambridge, Mass.: Harvard University Press, 1950.

Rolt, L.T.C., *Victorian Engineering.* Middlesex: Penguin Books, 1970.

Sass, Friedrich, *Geschichte des deutschen Verbrennungsmotorenbaues von 1860 bis 1918.* Berlin: Springer-Verlag, 1962.

Singer, Charles, E.J. Holmyard, A.R. Hall and Trevor I. Williams, eds., *A History of Technology,* Vol. IV. Clarendon, England: Oxford University Press, 1958.

Tuska, C. D., *An Introduction to Patents for Inventors and Engineers.* New York: Dover Publications, 1964.

INTERNAL FIRE

Appendix

ABSTRACT TRANSLATION OF BEAU DE ROCHAS' CYCLE.*
(French Patent, 1862.)

CONCERNING COMPRESSION IN A GAS ENGINE.

..... The conditions for perfectly utilising the elastic force of gas in an engine are four in number:-

I. The largest possible cylinder volume with the minimum boundary surface.
11. The greatest possible working speed.
III. The greatest possible number of expansions.
IV. The greatest possible pressure at the beginning of expansion.

The characteristic of gases to disperse over a given area can be turned to excellent account in pipes, but is, on the contrary, evidently an obstacle to the utilisation of the elastic force developed in the gaseous mass. It has been shown [in a former part of the patent] that in pipes the utilisation — that is, the heat transmitted — is in proportion to the diameter of the pipe. In cylinders, therefore, the loss would be in inverse ratio to the diameter, but this only applies to cylinders of very small diameter, and the loss really diminishes more rapidly in proportion to the increase in diameter. Thus the typical design, which, for a given expenditure of gas, assigns a cylinder of the largest diameter, will in this respect utilise the most heat. We may also conclude that, as far as possible, only one gas cylinder should be used in each separate engine.

But the loss of heat in the gas depends also on the time. Other things being equal, the cooling will be greater the slower the speed. Now greater speed seems to entail a cylinder of small volume; but this apparent contradiction disappears if we remember that, for a given consumption of gas, the stroke is not necessarily and invariably limited to the volume of the cylinder.

In utilising the elastic force of gas it is necessary, as with steam, that expansion should be prolonged as much as possible. In the typical design described above, there is a maximum of expansion for each par-

*From:Bryan Donkin, *Gas, Oil and Air Engines,* 2nd ed., (London, 1896), pp. 432-34.

ticular case, although the effect is necessarily limited. The arrangement will, therefore, give the best result, which restores to the motor what may be called its liberty of expansion, that is to say, the power of expanding as much as may be thought desirable, within practical working limits.

Lastly, the utilisation of the elastic force of the gas depends upon a function closely allied to prolonged expansion and its advantages. This is the pressure, which should be as great as possible, to produce the maximum effect. Here the question clearly is to obtain expansion of the gases when they are hot, after compressing them while cold. This is to a certain extent an inverse method of prolonging expansion to that employed when a vacuum is formed. The latter process is not at all suited to gases, because all such compression necessitates an equivalent condensation, and even supposing the gases were combustible, it would be impossible to heat them instantaneously.

Theoretically, therefore, it is possible to utilise the elastic force of the gases without limit, by compressing them indefinitely before heating, just as the elastic force of steam may be utilised without limit, by prolonging expansion indefinitely. Practically an impassable limit is attained, as soon as the elevation of temperature due to previous compression causes spontaneous combustion. If compression be then continued, the work done by it would be represented by expansion prolonged to the same point, less the loss caused by all useless work. The natural limit is here reached, and the arrangement which best attains it will utilise to the most advantage the heat supplied.

The question of heat utilisation being thus stated, the only really practical arrangement is to use a single cylinder, first that the volume may be as large as possible, and next to reduce the resistance of the gas to a minimum. The following operations must then take place on one side of the cylinder, during one period of four consecutive strokes:

I.   Drawing in the charge during one whole piston stroke.
II. Compression during the following stroke.
III. Inflammation at the dead point, and expansion during the third stroke.
IV. Discharge of the burnt gases from the cylinder during the fourth and last stroke.

The same operations being afterwards repeated on the other side of the cylinder in the same number of piston strokes, the result will be a particular type of single-acting, or half-acting engine, so to speak, which will evidently afford the largest possible cylinder, and what is still more important, previous compression. The piston speed will also be greatest in proportion to the diameter, because of the work which is performed in one single stroke, which would otherwise occupy two. Clearly it is impossible to do more.

As the temperature of the gases coming from a furnace is practically constant, and that of the external atmosphere varies relatively only within narrow limits, the initial temperature of the mixture at the moment of admission into the cylinder will also be practically constant. It will, therefore, be possible to determine the limit of compression at which combustion is produced, and to make the design of the engine conform to it. Thus the maximum effect will always be obtained, for each proportional dilution of the combustible. At the same time there will be no necessity to use electricity, because the starting of the engine being determined by the action of the steam [*sic*], the gases might be admitted only when the speed has become great enough to produce spontaneous inflammation. In any case compression, by helping to mix the charge thoroughly and by raising its temperature, would be favourable to instantaneous combustion. If the initial temperature in the generator corresponded to a pressure of 5 or 6 atmospheres, inflammation would be spontaneously produced if the gases were compressed to about a quarter of the original volume, the effect of loss of heat being neglected. After complete inflammation the pressure would be hardly 30 atmospheres, and as combustion would be effected without excess of air, the pressure would in any other case (i.e., where an excess of air was admitted) be necessarily less. Probably, therefore, in many cases, the absolute limit of utilisation of the heat may be attained.

We may sum up the question by saying that, although the typical arrangement here described can be most completely and perfectly adapted to the utilisation of the elastic force developed by combustion at constant volume in the gaseous mass, it is quite simple. It is perhaps rather a convenience than a necessity to use lift-valve distribution. This is generally the best method, and nothing proves that it may not be applied to the four-cycle type of engine.

INTERNAL FIRE

Index